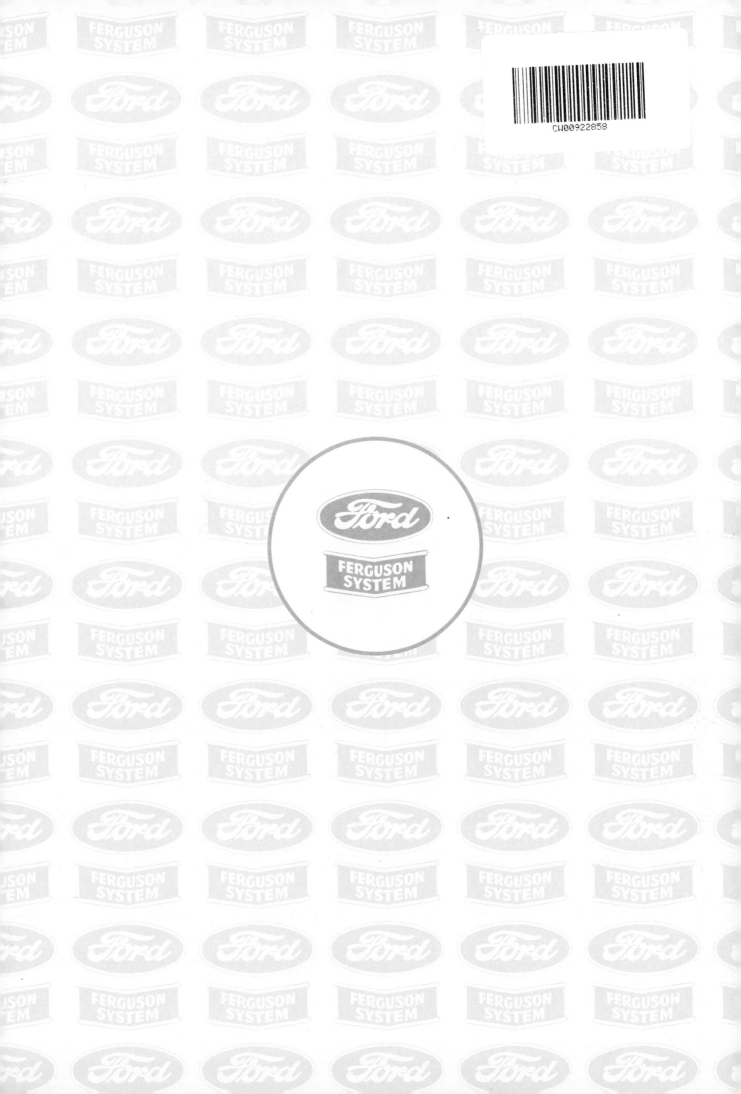

FERGUSONS
THE HUNDAY EXPERIENCE

John Moffitt and John Farnworth

First Published 2000

ISBN 09533737 5 4

A catalogue record of this book is
available from the British Library

Published by

Japonica Press
Low Green Farm, Hutton, Driffield,
East Yorkshire YO25 9PX

Design and page layout by Banks Design

Contents

Acknowledgements

Agco, holders of the brand name Massey Ferguson are thanked for their permission to reproduce old advertising material and spare parts diagrams.

Antique Power and David Lory are thanked for their kind permission to reproduce articles written by David in *The Antique Powers* of September/October 1995, November/December 1995, January/February 1996 And March/April 1996. These are in Chapter 5.

The three actors at The June 1999 Pageant – Alex Albone, Jerry White and Bill Martin are thanked for their permission to reproduce their speeches and their imaginative and enthusiastic participation in the event.

Nigel Liney, Peter Warren, Sir Jeremy Chance, Bt., Alexander Von Behr, Mrs Margaret Sansom, Frank Davey, Rob North and Tony Sheldon, J P A Maitre, Aubrey Burgess, Gus Macleod-Henderson,Mack Shone, Alex Patterson and Roy Harriman are thanked for their wonderful recollections which are presentedin Chapter 12. Dennis Griffith was kind enough to provide the contact with Mrs Sansom.

Trystan Farnworth loaned his Ford Ferguson Brochure which comprises Chapter 7 and this adds immeasurably to our story. Thanks also to Roger Wyerman for the last page of the book "Excellence Lives On".

Many other people have helped with the creation of the collection. It would be impossible to list all but special thanks go to George Potts who has toiled relentlessly over several years on the restoration of the collection.

Sincere thanks go to all those people too numerous to mention who have helped me in many different ways along the road to assembling this collection, and without whom the whole project would not have been possible. Thanks also go to The Museum of English Rural Life at Reading University who have over the years assisted in sourcing information on Fergusons.

Finally thanks to my co-author John Farnworth who selected the material from my archives and then compiled the book. Thanks to him also for the loan of the Ferguson Brochure which comprises Chapter 2 and which provides such an insight into Harry Ferguson's global objectives and worldly thinking.

Collector John Moffitt to left, and faithful restorer George Potts

Preface

by John Moffitt CBE

It was in 1963 that I first became interested in collecting old farm tractors and equipment. That interest ranged across the whole spectrum of agricultural development during the twentieth century. This resulted in my setting up the "Hunday Countryside Museum" which was opened to the public in 1979 by our most gracious lady, the Queen Mother.

A great deal of hard work by a lot of people and friends resulted in the museum winning the coveted award of "Museum of the Year" in 1981 and the following year, "Reserve in the Museum Award of Europe for new Museums".

At that stage I was no expert on any one manufacturer as I had chosen to collect historic machines from every maker and did not begin to seriously address one manufacturer until the mid 1980s. Harry Ferguson intrigued me, not just because of his ingenious hydraulically operated three point linkage, but also because of the vast range of mounted attachments to do virtually every job on the farm.

After ten years the lack of visitors in the North of England resulted in the Hunday Collection moving almost in its entirety to Wimbourne in Dorset initially as a joint venture, but now established as a trust by Mr Pat Ridgewell. The success in this new location has seen over 100,000 people visiting the collection, gardens and craft centre each year since opening in 1990.

I retained only my Ivel tractor and three Gyrotillers and began to concentrate on trying to collect every piece of Ferguson equipment that was made from the 1936 Ferguson Brown tractor through to 1960. This collection now includes over 40 different tractors and over 100 different attachments sourced from the UK, the USA and France. I am somewhat resigned to the fact that I will probably never find all the attachments made by the great man, but as of today it is probably the most comprehensive collection of Ferguson equipment in the world and they are now generally known as the "Hunday Fergusons."

The experience of setting up the first Hunday museum, disposing of it, and then setting up this private Ferguson museum, has brought me into contact with a very diverse range of vintage enthusiasts from around the world. Through this I have made a great many friends and acquaintances. I have witnessed the growth of the vintage farm machinery movement and an ever increasing thirst for knowledge by collectors and observers alike. I have also come to realise that a dynamic approach to the presentation and recording of vintage equipment is vital if interest in the movement is to be sustained and that interest actively passed down to future generations.

Once the Ferguson collection was well underway I began to think how I could present and make available to a wider audience all the inherent information it contains. Having been the first president of the "Friends of Ferguson Heritage Club", I offered to open up the collection to club members and the public for an open day. This was in June 1999. Besides presenting the collection, we made a one and a half hour pageant of "living history" to show how Ferguson represented the culmination of mass produced, small tractor development which had in effect started with the Ivel tractor in Bedfordshire – and I conveniently had one of the only two surviving examples in the UK! Ford was the classic early mass producer of small tractors and he had ultimately linked up with Ferguson for the Ford Ferguson tractor venture.

So it was that the Ivel, Fordson and Ferguson tractors came to be the key themes of our pageant, with actors narrating the triumphs and tribulations of Dan Albone (the inventor of the Ivel), Henry Ford and Harry Ferguson. We have reproduced their narrations in this book as they were a most effective and possibly first ever stage interpretation of tractor development.

Following on from the open day and pageant I decided to try and somehow document my collection in an informative manner. The idea started as a simple brochure, but I soon realised that I, together with John Farnworth, could in fact bring together some hitherto unpublished and/or previously uncollated information which would surely be of interest to the vintage tractor movement generally and Ferguson enthusiasts in particular around the world. It is our hope that this "Ferguson" book will address the many aspects of vintage machinery enthusiasts' interests. It now seems to involve not just simply the collection of equipment, but also literature, memorabilia, models, company and personnel history, restoration and preservation. Additionally it has become a truly international activity, with vintage equipment moving freely across the oceans between buyers aided and abetted to an ever increasing degree by use of the internet. We have also witnessed the emergence of a small industry of spare parts suppliers and reconditioning services, an ever growing interest in company history, production of vintage equipment books like this – and magazines, the establishment of single and multi marque clubs, the staging of rallies and events, interest in the recollections of old company employees, and the reproduction of equipment in model and scale forms. But perhaps the most fascinating aspect of the vintage equipment movement is the friendships which are made and visits to the most unlikely places in search of our treasures.

I had originally thought of listing the specifications of the equipment, but realising that this in the main part had been done by my co-author, decided to illustrate my collection by way of photos and a selection of parts diagrams. On reflection this has begun to seem logical because so many collectors need to know (and query me frequently!) the precise nature of missing parts when undertaking restoration projects to original specifications. Parts diagrams are in themselves an art form and Ferguson's are a splendid example of clarity of presentation. The presentation of parts diagrams in such number is probably a unique part of a book of this type – it may raise a few eyebrows but I am certain that it will prove useful to restorers.

I believe that the reproduction of Harry Ferguson's speech to the International Food Conference in 1943 is the first time that the substantial part of this speech has been published for wide scale circulation. It is a marvellous summary of his global dreams for both farm mechanisation and world economic development.

Several people have thought of producing a book on the Ferguson Brown tractor, but have apparently fought shy of such a venture probably because of the limited data available and perhaps limited market. Because I have been fortunate enough to obtain some hitherto unpublished photographs of this tractor at work it seemed appropriate to devote a specific chapter to this unique tractor. We also reproduce the brochure on the introduction of the Ford Ferguson to the UK as this tractor was a definitive landmark in the mass production of Ferguson System tractors.

David Lory is the leading collector of Ferguson equipment in North America and has given me great help in assembling the Hunday collection. His interpretation of Ferguson tractor development offers an original and so far not widely circulated North American perspective.

We have also pulled together some previously unpublished letters and documents by Harry Ferguson and others. Two chapters on Ferguson models and memorabilia, and literature will be of interest to these growing sectors of the vintage movement.

The book closes with a chapter which relates the very varied experiences of a selection of Ferguson employees around the world.

Disclaimer. The authors have made every endeavour to ensure the accuracy of technical data provided in the text but neither they nor the publishers can accept responsibility for its absolute accuracy and how readers may choose to apply the information in practice. Anyone restoring or operating a machine should always consult original manufacturers' specifications and recommendations.

Foreword

This book is about John Moffitt's dedication to the engineering genius of Harry Ferguson, and his putting together of what is considered to be the most comprehensive collection of Ferguson equipment and related items anywhere in the world today.

John is perhaps best known as a cattle breeder and in particular for his famous Hunday* Herd of Holstein Friesians. He has exported cattle to places all over the world including Russia, South Africa and Japan, as well as winning championships at all the leading UK agricultural shows, and is himself an international judge.

John's pioneering work in the cattle AI and Embryo Transfer field, and setting up of eight satellite transfer units in the UK, as well as the new concept "MOET" testing scheme will not be forgotten. In addition he built up the firm Hunday Electronics which pioneered electronic identification for dairy cows and pigs, and whose products were exported to many countries throughout the world before being bought out by the American firm Osborne Industries.

John established the Hunday Countryside Museum which was opened by the Queen Mother in 1979. This is now relocated on a new site at Wimbourne in Dorset where it continues to attract large attendances. In many ways this new collection of "Hunday Fergusons" is a follow up collection to this and created in his retirement for more relaxed and personal enjoyment.

As a Ferguson user myself I have fond memories of my first TE 20 tractor and I share John's enthusiasm for this great pioneering inventor.

In my capacity as Patron of "The Friends of Ferguson Heritage" I was privileged to attend their AGM and open the pageant which John had created for them at Westside in Northumberland in 1999. I was astonished by the scope of the collection and the amazing turnout of some 1,200 enthusiasts for this first full public viewing . The pageant showed how the Ferguson tractor came to be the culmination of small tractor development. I am told the idea for this book arose out of this pageant.

John's remarkable collection is recorded in this book, but the book is about much more than that. As well as being a record of one man's collection, it also provides a wealth of hitherto unpublished archive material, and creates a wonderful exposé of the many dimensions of the vintage agricultural machinery movement. I believe that it is the first time that one man's collection has been recorded in such a way. The book contains hundreds of photos of his collection as well as letters, period photographs, sales brochures and recollections of Ferguson employees' experiences. The reproduction of Harry Ferguson's speeches brings to light the global ambitions which he had for his now immortalized "Ferguson System".

John Farnworth who has already written several books on the whole century and a half of Massey Ferguson history, which have set new standards for reference books on vintage agricultural machinery, is to be congratulated in pulling together all this material into such a concise and readable format. I can only describe the final result as a great credit to the "two Johns" as I believe that they have created one of the most fascinating books to date which is a must for anyone interested in farm mechanization and the development of the agricultural tractor.

Henry Plumb.

The Lord Plumb of Coleshill DL, MEP, FRAgS
(formerly President of the European Parliament, the NFU and the Royal Agricultural Society of England)

* Hunday was the name of John Moffitt's father's first farm. The prefix Hunday was subsequently applied to their herds of dairy cattle and the electronics company as well as John's first Countryside Museum

AN INTRODUCTION TO MY COLLECTING HABIT
by John Moffitt CBE

My first tractor

My interest in vintage tractors began in 1963. An Oliver rowcrop standing by the roadside on a regular journey which I had to make between two farms caught my eye and I decided one day to see what the owner was going to do with it. After some haggling and an hour later, I became the proud owner for the sum of £8. The tractor was well shod on rubber tyres with a high speed six cylinder engine which apparently had never been abused. It was an old lease lend machine of 1942. We soon had her running and there began my enthusiasm for anything old in agricultural machinery, and although not a dealer myself, I subsequently became the owner of over 200 tractors.

ABOVE John Moffitt with the first tractor he collected in 1979 – an Oliver 70 rowcrop

My first Ferguson

Shortly after the purchase of the Oliver 70, I was told of a Ferguson Brown nestling in the hills above the market town of Hexham in Northumberland. Mr Dodd of Town Farm, Allendale, a small dairy farmer, was retiring and the tractor was for sale. Hot foot one evening I called to see him and he proudly started the "Fergi Brown" and drove it around the yard. I could see in the corner of the same building two halves of another Ferguson Brown, and to cut a long story short, and an hour or so later, I became the owner of the two of them for the sum of £70. Since

that date several Ferguson Browns have come my way but not, I might add, at the same price. The highest figure I have heard of was £15,000 in 1998 for an early serial number tractor in good restored condition.

And so I came away the proud owner of my first Ferguson Brown – at that time few were known to exist but it is surprising how many have appeared from the woodwork during the past thirty years and who knows how many may still be in hiding awaiting discovery. It is worth noting here that only about 1270 Ferguson Browns were made between 1936-1938 but there are probably about 100 known to be surviving.

My enthusiasm began to grow and obviously I had no difficulty in picking up redundant TE 20s, but it was the rare, unusual and strange adaptations and accessories, and different models, that came to be my objective.

The disease

Today, bargains in the vintage tractor world are difficult to find, but involvement in agriculture is a definite advantage. Being nosy and observant in old farm stockyards and buildings will often turn something up even if it is only an old cast iron seat. Of course the local scrap dealer is a good source of knowledge even if you have to double the figure you first thought of when trying to do a deal.

Now my only interest these days is in Harry Ferguson and trying to find the remaining rare pieces of equipment that were made in small numbers.

The decade of TE 20 Ferguson tractor production from the Banner Lane factory in Coventry, from 1946 when over 500,000 were produced, has ensured that many thousands of these wonderful little tractors still survive in remarkable condition. The "Fergi" is the ideal beginner's tractor for the young and old enthusiast alike and you can be sure of plenty of spare parts from the dozen or so dealers in Ferguson equipment. The Ferguson is the last of the simple internal combustion engine tractors – no complicated electronics and generally easy to start by the handle if the battery is low. Of course with the simple two furrow plough you will be welcome at the dozens of local ploughing matches throughout the country. At these you can test your skill and there are always people to help the novice or beginner.

The dedicated collector is looking for the rare and unusual models that were made in much smaller numbers. Early models with their correct serial number plates and registration numbers will always make a premium. The orchard, vineyard and industrial models when in good condition command high prices. I recently heard of a TE 20 fitted with a Selene four wheel drive unit making over £9,000, but they are rare and I am still looking for one!

Doing a deal

It is often more than a bit tricky dealing with a farmer who believes the tractor he is selling is years older than it actually is – especially when he has been assured by a so called "expert" that it is worth a fortune. But the buyer is always right so you can easily walk away. This is of course hard to do if it is something you really want and you know it is rare, and that if you walk away you may never get another opportunity. All of us, as collectors, have had a mean turn and left what was considered an expensive item only to find the next week that it has been snapped up by someone else. On the other hand, the price can just as easily come down in your favour so patience can be a virtue.

The "Reekie" tractor

The Reekie tractor brings back a story I heard from the man himself – John Reekie - whom I had the good fortune to meet in 1994. He was then in his mid 80s but still active and with a clear mind. He told me of his early days with Harry Ferguson. John Reekie came out of the forces after the Second World War and set up a business as a blacksmith. He quickly recognised the need to get involved in tractor distribution and became Scotland's leading Ferguson agent supplying tractors to the raspberry growing area around Dundee in the east of Scotland.

I pick up the story as told by John Reekie. Mr Smedley of Smedley Fruit fame came to John one day and said he wanted a tractor to go between the rows of raspberry canes in order that he could dispense with horses. John, the ever inventive engineer, said he would think about it and during the ensuing week decided that it would be possible to reduce the width of Harry Ferguson's TE 20 by chopping down the half shafts and their housings to create a tractor of not more than 3ft. 6in. wide to suit the rows of raspberry canes.

He discussed the ideas with Mr Smedley who gave him the order to progress. Within a week John had produced a prototype for evaluation which not only worked well but brought orders pouring in from other growers in the area. Smedley was delighted and ordered six more conversions for himself as well as a further six for his French fruit farms.

Now all this was happening without Harry Ferguson's knowledge of the abuse to the famous little Ferguson – that was until a request came to the Ferguson spares stores in Coventry for a short half shaft! The half shafts occasionally broke through the weld as they were not case-hardened after the shortening modification. The request was treated with disbelief and a response issued that no such part existed. The reply was treated with indignation and it was not long before the story of the "Reekie" conversion became public knowledge. Harry Ferguson's outrage at the abuse of his famous tractor had him set off immediately for Scotland to see the Reekie conversion. However, John was the best Ferguson dealer in Scotland and neither party wanted litigation, not least because John could not afford to fight a legal case and could not afford to lose the Ferguson agency.

BELOW The "Reekie" Tractor

Harry Ferguson said that he must stop the production of what he believed was a very unstable adaptation and that if John continued then he would cease further business with him.

This actually resulted in Ferguson designing and producing the Ferguson narrow version of the TE 20 some two years later and thereby allowing Reekie to fulfil his outstanding order book. (Some correspondence between Reekie and Ferguson is reproduced in Chapter 4. Also see letters from J. Reekie and Harry Ferguson pages 90 to 98).

Ferguson implements

I have been surprised by how long it has taken for the vintage movement to become interested in Ferguson implements as the Ferguson tractor is nothing without its proper tackle attached. In my eyes it is naked without an implement attached.

One of the troubles which one comes across is how many of a certain implement were actually made. We see ploughs, cultivators, ridgers etc, frequently going for a song, but who knows how many game flushers were made? Was it 5-10 or 100? I only know of three in preservation. They were made for the more wealthy landowners who wished to ensure that their precious game birds were safe from the hay reaper by flushing them out before the hay was cut. This allowed the eggs to be collected and the chicks reared artificially. The game flusher which I have was, I am told, never sold and was found in a coal merchant's yard in Scotland where it had remained for many years in the open, catching every drop of rain that cascaded off the old iron roof. The owner very generously gave it to me and since then it has been painstakingly restored.

ABOVE The Game Flusher as found in a coal merchant's yard in Ayrshire

The days of finding a set of Ferguson implements at a farm sale where the auctioneer has not appreciated their value are all but over. The spies are generally out everywhere and they have usually been informed by someone who wants to ensure that the dealer doesn't get a bargain. Finding a good buckrake for example, complete with serial number plate, is extremely rare as most have been abused, left outside to rot or are filling a gap in a hedgerow somewhere.

The ever diligent collector or dealer, of which there are a growing number, visit farm sales every week and do manage to pick up the occasional bargain. The ever popular 30 cwt. Ferguson trailers normally found with a rotting main frame and sides are fetching exorbitant prices despite the fact that a good restoration can cost up to £1,000. The one I have came from a local water board (fortunately stored under cover) for my opening offer of £15! – but then you have to be lucky at times.

Some 25 years ago I brought two container loads of tractors from Australia including a Case cross-mount type tractor that only cost 8 Australian dollars (£3) but that is unlikely to happen again!

The Find............

Collecting Ferguson implements is not unlike a detective story. Someone somewhere will remember a neighbour developing or trying an adaptation for a specific purpose using the three point linkage to carry the implement. But can he remember where that implement is now or what precisely it was? The tracking down of Ferguson implements is made more confusing by the fact that other manufacturers made implements to fit the tractor, but many of these were not badged Ferguson.

It would be fair to say that many of Ferguson's different implements were farmer designed before being built by different manufacturers. For instance, my neighbouring agricultural engineers, Fewsters of Stocksfield, made the fork lift and dump skip under licence, and Steels of Sunderland turned out many thousands of ploughs and cultivators for Ferguson.

Implements, unlike tractors, are inclined to be left in the stackyard and are eventually swallowed up by the undergrowth. I have personally dug out fork lifts, half tracks, a front weight carrying tray, an earth moving blade, cranes etc. that had literally disappeared with the one time owner saying "well it had to be about here somewhere". In my opinion, collection is like fishing – you cast the line out, anticipate the bite as the adrenalin builds and then one senses success as some rare hitherto undiscovered machine is dragged out of the bushes.

It is of course more interesting to find these lost treasures oneself rather than buying from a dealer who has had all the fun as well as adding to his investment.

FERGUSONS FROM THE USA

Few people in the UK, from where we write this book, appreciate that Harry Ferguson had factories in the USA which produced a range of implements for such specific crops as cotton and maize. I became fascinated by the Ferguson activities in the late 1940s and early 50s, particularly in the USA and before the merger with Massey-Harris. After Ferguson's merger with Massey-Harris, some implements were also made at the by then Massey-Harris-Ferguson plants in Toronto.

In trying to complete my Ferguson collection I felt I should try to find some of the more rare machines that were made only for the North American market such as corn planters, corn pickers, side mounted forage harvesters etc., but I was soon to find that they are difficult to come by and long distances have to be covered in the search. I was surprised how rare they are and how high the cost of getting implements to a central point for shipment. On my numerous business trips to North America I have chased up a side mounted baler and other implements in Columbus Ohio, Louisville Kentucky, Northfield Minnesota, Platteville Wisconsin, Illinois, Montana, Nebraska, Iowa, and Kansas.

Of course in this vast continent one needs other enthusiasts who are prepared to cover vast areas, sometimes on fruitless journeys, and not least who have the time. Dealers and collectors the world over are the same so you never really know what is going on until you actually arrive on site!

Perhaps one of the most interesting scrap yards I have ever visited was 15 miles north of Madison in Wisconsin where every implement and tractor has a price tag affixed and there is no haggling. There were acres of machines in long straight rows – combines, balers, reapers, ploughs, tractors etc. etc. and equally well displayed row upon row of spare parts of every description sheltering under large pine trees that inhibit the undergrowth from taking over and hiding that illusive part.

ABOVE AND NEXT PAGE Near Madison in Wisconsin is to be found the scrap yard of scrap yards!

Visits to vintage shows in North America are fascinating. Collectors the world over are a great source of knowledge, one is always learning something new and picking up memorabilia at the various trade and publication stands.

One finds a great number of John Deere, International, Case and Oliver collections but I have been disappointed at the small number of Ferguson equipment enthusiasts, with many items being rare and attracting high prices. The Fergusons are also usually poorly represented at vintage gatherings in North America. I can only put this down to the fact that the Ferguson was too small for larger arable farms and only to be found on the smaller farms.

I travelled some 500 miles north from my base in north Minnesota to see my first Ferguson side mounted forage harvester, one of only three currently known to exist. One has to remember that probably less than 50 were made and technically they were all supposed to have been recalled at the time of the Ferguson and Massey-Harris merger. The farmers were compensated, or in most cases given M-H equipment thus avoiding the difficulty of maintaining spares for a small number of machines.

I also managed to purchase two Ferguson 40 tractors, one a high clearance with an inter-row cultivator for maize, and the other a

standard model. Again I was surprised at the scarcity of these models. Even the Ferguson TO 30, similar to the TE 20 but somewhat more powerful, are not very plentiful.

Collecting is great fun. As I said earlier, it is a bit like fishing. First the anticipation of the fish taking the bait, then the chase before landing it on the bank, then ready for the next one. Of course we are always after that illusive big fish and there are always the ones that get away. As a last resort, if you can't find what you want you can always make a full scale replica .... see Chapter 8!

A Ferguson Book

The logical extension of my collecting habit has been this book. The purpose of this, by use of my Ferguson collection as a focal point, is to look at the many dimensions of the vintage machinery collecting habit. I hope that besides providing new information on Ferguson, the book will show how the "collecting hobby" has come to be much more than this.

CHAPTER 1

A Brief Chronology of the life of Harry Ferguson

To set the scene for this book, a simple chronology of the life of Harry Ferguson is presented, followed by a listing of the Ferguson patents.

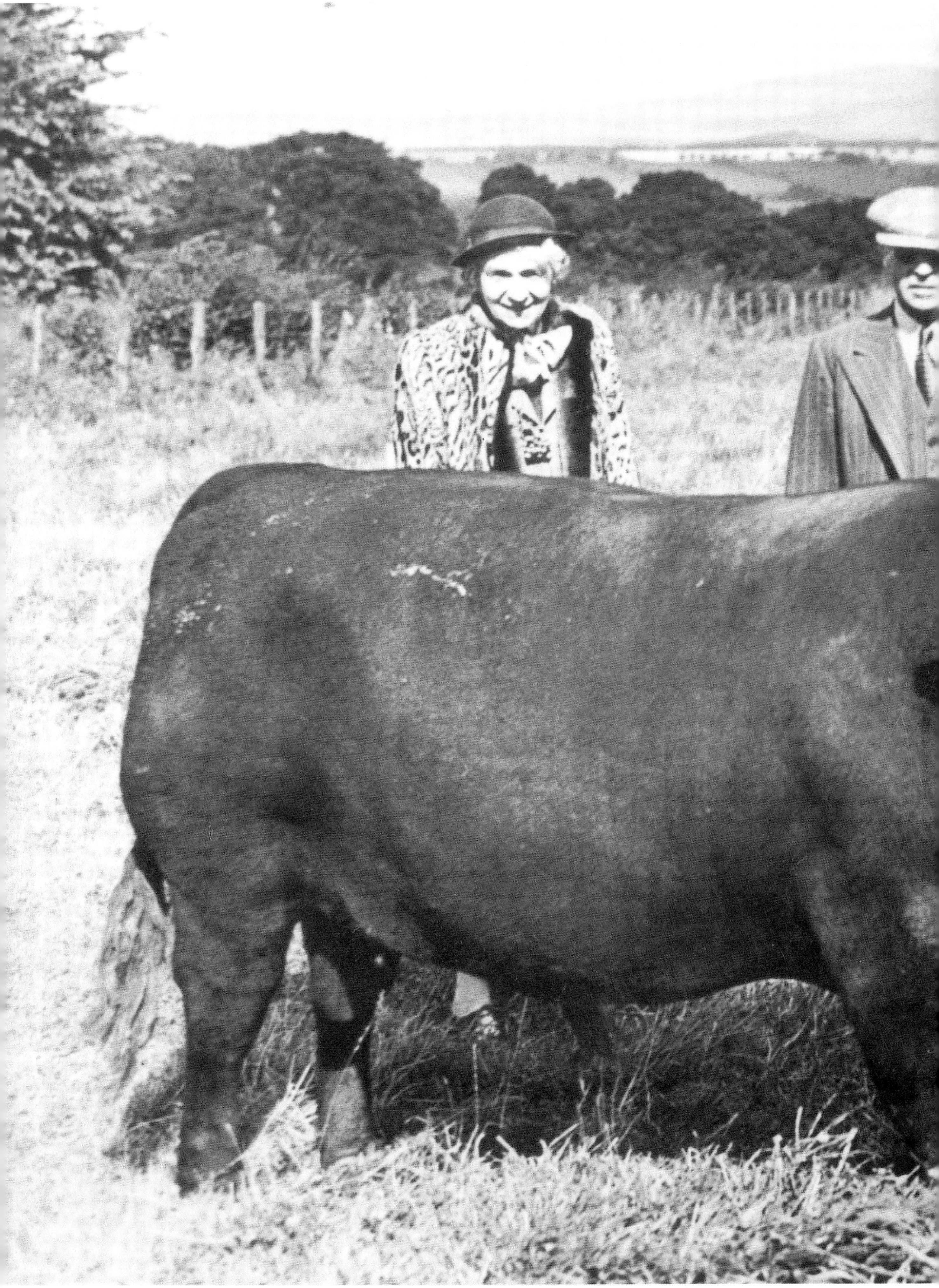

Mr and Mrs Harry Ferguson visiting the farm of the famous Aberdeen Angus breeder Bob Adams who used Ferguson tractors

Harry Ferguson 1884 - 1960

Harry Ferguson at the wheel of one of his famous tractors

1884 November 4th, born Henry George at Lake House, Growell, Dromore, Co. Down. He was the fourth of eleven children. Showed mechanical aptitude at an early age.

1898 Aged 14 years. Leaves school to work on his father's farm where he came to hate the toil of farm work.

1902 Aged 18 years. Harry Ferguson goes to Belfast to serve an apprenticeship in the motor business at his brother Joe's workshop on the Shankill Road.

1903-5 Attends classes at Belfast Technical College and there meets John Lloyd Williams who is to become the only intimate friend he had and in fact retained.

1903-5 While working in brother Joe's workshop he meets T McGregor Greer from Tullylagan between Cookstown and Dungannon and becomes a family friend.

1904 Harry Ferguson competes in motor-cycle events to obtain publicity for the Ferguson car and motor-cycle business.

1908 Harry Ferguson goes with John Williams to air meetings at Rheims and Blackpool where he becomes interested in the aviation industry.

1909 (December) Ferguson takes a plane built by himself to Lord Downshire's estate at Hillsborough and on flying a distance of 130 yards becomes the first Briton to build and fly his own aircraft.

1910 (April) Ferguson takes his plane to Massereene Park, Co. Antrim and after a few attempts manages a flight of just over one mile. Later in the year made a three mile flight to win an aviation prize.

1911 Harry Ferguson forms his own business known as May Street Motors and employs John Williams and Willie Sands who had served his apprenticeship in the maintenance of machinery in the linen industry.

1912 May Street Motors becomes Harry Ferguson Ltd. Ferguson takes a great interest in and competes in motor races.

1913 Harry Ferguson marries Maureen Watson whose family own a grocery shop in Dromore. 1913 is the year in which Harry Ferguson really started inventing by trying to improve carburettors – two ideas were patented.

1913-4 Harry becomes involved in UVF activities and helps distribute arms brought into Larne Harbour on the arms ship Mountjoy II.

John Williams joins Royal Flying Corps on the outbreak of war.

Ferguson starts to sell Overtime tractors brought in from America.

1914-7 Ferguson and Sands get the reputation of being expert ploughmen after giving countless demonstrations of the Overtime tractor pulling a Cockshutt plough.

1917 (March 19) Ferguson and Sands by direction of the Irish Board of Agriculture are given the job of travelling all over Ireland to improve the efficiency of tractors and ploughs so that more acres of land can be used to increase food production during the war.

(December) Under Ferguson's guidance Sands makes a plough which fits a Ford Eros Tractor and gives a public demonstration near Coleraine.

Hugh Reid joins Harry Ferguson Ltd. as a journeyman draughtsman.

Fordson tractors tested in Cheshire, England for suitability for British agriculture by British Board of Agriculture and found to be satisfactory. Ford grants patent rights free to UK for manufacture of tractors in Cork. 6,000 tractors imported from USA prior to factory starting.

1918 Sands develops a plough to fit a Fordson tractor using a Duplex hitch.

1920 Willie Sands leaves Harry Ferguson to set up business on his own account at Lisburn Road.

Archie Greer becomes Harry Ferguson's chief helper.

1921 Ferguson and Greer go to Ford Tractor plant at Cork to carry out tests using a Fordson tractor. Patrick Hennesy who was later to become chairman of Ford of Britain was the man sent to assist them.

1922 (May) Ferguson and John Williams

go to Bucyrus, Ohio and agree with a John Shunk that he should produce 50,000 ploughs for use with Fordson tractors.

(June) The job for Shunk is so great that he decides not to go ahead and Ferguson gets Roderick Lean to make his ploughs in Mansfield, Ohio.

1923 Willie Sands returns to Harry Ferguson and immediately starts to develop the plough further.

1924 Ferguson develops further his interests in motor-racing.

Lean goes bankrupt.

1925 A company called Ferguson-Sherman Incorporated is set up to manufacture ploughs in Evansville, New York State.

The patent known as draft control is applied for on February 12th.

1926 The patent is approved in June.

1928 Sands leaves Ferguson and purchases a Bean bus for use in public transport.

Fordson tractor goes out of production.

Ferguson establishes a major road race in Ulster.

Discussions with Allis Chalmers, Rover and Ransomes about the possibility of building a tractor incorporating his principles come to nothing.

1929 Ferguson decides to build a tractor incorporating his linkage patent and plough.

1931 John Chambers and Trevor Knox join the design side of Ferguson's activities.

1932 Ferguson, Sands and Greer start making sketches of their ideas for a tractor.

1933 The Black Tractor is built and ready for testing. Parts for it had been made by the David Brown Co.

1934 Ferguson persuades David Brown to manufacture the Black tractor.

1935 Ferguson changes Harry Ferguson Ltd. in Belfast to Harry Ferguson (Motors) Ltd and forms Harry Ferguson Ltd with McGregor Greer and John Williams to market the Brown-Ferguson tractor.

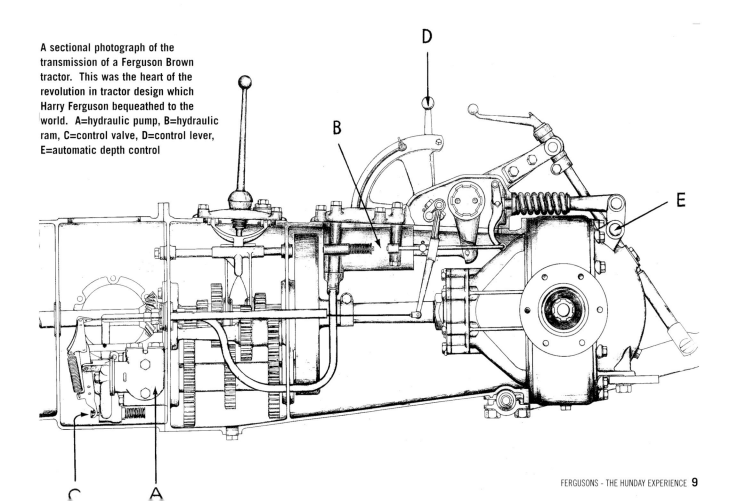

A sectional photograph of the transmission of a Ferguson Brown tractor. This was the heart of the revolution in tractor design which Harry Ferguson bequeathed to the world. A=hydraulic pump, B=hydraulic ram, C=control valve, D=control lever, E=automatic depth control

The famous engineer's hand on the control lever which brought implement control to the tractor seat – Harry Ferguson on a Ferguson Brown tractor

1936 (May) The Brown-Ferguson as it was first known is shown to the public.

(June) The first tractor (No 12) is sold to John Chambers' father.

Bob Annet, a farmer's son, is employed to set up a training school.

1937 (June) Ferguson Brown Ltd as a company is formed. Ferguson Brown tractors well received in the hilly stony lands of Scotland and Norway.

1938 (October) Harry Ferguson and John Williams go to America and take a Ferguson-Brown tractor and implements to show to Henry Ford. An agreement (known as the handshake agreement) is reached whereby Ford agreed to manufacture a tractor for Ferguson and it became known as the Ford-Ferguson.

Central PTO patent granted.

1939 (January) 1,200 tractors had been made by David Brown for Ferguson and sold.

(April 1st) The Ford-Ferguson prototype is ready and tested.

(June) The first mass produced Ford-Fergusons are ready for marketing.

(July) David Brown has made and is ready to market his own tractor to be known as the VAK1.

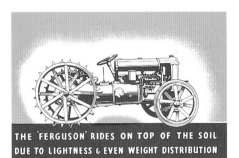

THE 'FERGUSON' RIDES ON TOP OF THE SOIL DUE TO LIGHTNESS & EVEN WEIGHT DISTRIBUTION

FERGUSON POWER IS AVAILABLE FOR USE

ONE of the reasons why the Ferguson uses less than half the fuel of any other tractor of similar capacity.

HEAVIER TRACTORS SINK AND OFTEN REQUIRE 50% OF THEIR POWER TO OVERCOME THIS SINKAGE...

From the start Harry Ferguson laid great emphasis on the fact that a lightweight tractor could perform the same duties as a heavier tractor

Henry Ford in the driving seat receiving a briefing from Harry Ferguson following the launch of the Ford Ferguson tractor in the USA

A pair of Ferguson Brown tractors painted by J H Appleyard for John Moffitt

(October 12th) Ferguson having just returned from America and having brought with him a Ford-Ferguson and implements gives a demonstration at Greenmount Agricultural College to Ministry officials including Sir Basil Brooke, the then Minister of Agriculture.

1940 John Williams who had joined the Royal Air Force on the outbreak of war is killed in a car crash with a stationary lorry. Ford Ferguson demonstrated in Bedfordshire, UK.

1942 Steel shortage threatens production of Ford Ferguson tractors.

1939-45 Ford-Ferguson tractors are manufactured and sold from America.

1945 Ferguson gets Trevor Knox to return to Britain to explore the possibilities of Ferguson tractors being manufactured there.

(July) Ferguson has a meeting with the Ministry of Finance at Stormont with a view that his tractors be mass produced in Northern Ireland.

(September) Ferguson has a meeting with Sir John Black, Chairman of the Standard Motor Company and they agree that the old Standard Motor Company premises at Banner Lane, Coventry, which had been used as an ammunition factory during the war, be used for production of the Ferguson tractor which was known as the TE 20.

1946 Production of Ferguson TE tractors starts at Coventry, England. Engineering department gives priority to development of a big Ferguson tractor known as the LTX which was built and tested by the time of the merger with Massey-Harris.

1946 Ford established new company called Dearborn Motor Corporation in place of Harry Ferguson Incorporated and severed the link with Ferguson.

1947 (July) Ford announces the introduction of a new tractor, the Ford 8N (known in Ireland as the Ford Minor) incorporating Ferguson System hydraulics.

1947 (November) Harry Ferguson goes to America to see for himself what is happening and decides on December 11th to take legal action against Ford for dishonouring their agreement and producing a tractor of his own fitted

A Ferguson TEA 20 painted by J H Appleyard for John Moffitt

The badge that made an empire after the merger of Ferguson and Massey-Harris

Harry Ferguson driving one of his tractors on his estate

with Ferguson system hydraulics and linkage.

End of Ford Ferguson tractor production.

1948 (January) The legal battle between Ford and Ferguson which was to last for four years and cost millions begins.

Ferguson TO tractor production starts at Detroit, USA.

1950 Ferguson has lunch with Winston Churchill. Churchill described him as a remarkable man.

1952 (April) Ferguson settles with Ford and received damages totalling 9.2 million dollars with certain other conditions. Negotiations with James Duncan, the chairman of Massey-Harris start regarding a possible merger.

1953 (August 4th) Ferguson merges with Massey-Haris and forms Massey-Harris-Ferguson which becomes the world's largest manufacturer of agricultural tractors and machinery.

1954 Ferguson sells his interest in the company to the other directors for approximately 3.75 million pounds.

Production of Ferguson TO 35 tractor starts in USA.

1956 End of TE Ferguson tractor production at Coventry.

Massey-Harris-Ferguson introduce a new British tractor designed in America called the Ferguson 35 in preference to the British designed Ferguson TE 60.

Ferguson TO 40 tractor introduced in USA.

1958 Massey-Harris-Ferguson becomes known world-wide as Massey Ferguson - the name it still retains.

Production of the MF 65 tractor starts in Coventry, UK.

1959-60 Ferguson involved in racing car design and considers a return to tractor design.

1960 (October 25th) Harry Ferguson is found dead at his home Abbotswood. He was aged 76 years.

LET US BEGIN AT THE BEGINNING...THE FARM

Our purpose in developing the entirely new system of land cultivation which is embodied in the new Ford Tractor with Ferguson System was to give effect to four principles which we take to be fundamental.

1. To so cut the cost of farm products that farming can be made prosperous *without increasing the cost to the consumer.*

2. To make farming attractive to youth and largely solve the unemployment problem by stopping the drift from the land.

3. To assist all other industries through a prosperous agriculture, and to *stimulate greater industrial use of farm products by cutting costs, thus increasing the total farm market.*

4. To lay the foundation for a greater National Security.

To achieve these four great objects, we should *not* aim at producing *more* foodstuffs. *We should aim at a lower cost of production of all farm products.*

The one basic cost of all costs is that of farm production. It is the prime item in the cost of living of all the people. In the final analysis it determines the cost of all our commodities, services, and comforts.

The present high cost of farm production rests on the fact that, in the main, the nation's farms are still being operated with animal power, as they were generations ago.

That the most basic industry of all has not heretofore been able to adopt the principles of mechanization which have made other industries prosperous, is a challenge to everyone, whether he thinks in terms of the single farm or the whole agricultural community, whether he be economist, humanist, or statesman.

Harry Ferguson

Harry Ferguson's objectives for agriculture

I have long held the conviction that something should be done about farming. In too many cases, farming has not only ceased to be profitable; it has also ceased to be interesting.

The land itself has not collapsed or shrunk either in expanse or productivity. But means have not been at hand whereby the family unit, on which the well-being of the land must depend, could produce at a profit and at the same time have the leisure to enjoy the fruits of their labor.

When Mr. Ferguson approached the problem of mechanization in terms of fundamental principles, and solved it in terms of the average farm family, our purposes became as one. We both believe farming can be made profitable, without increasing the cost of farm products to the consumer.

That is why we introduced the new Ford Tractor with Ferguson System just a few brief months ago.

Henry Ford

Henry Ford's commitment to agriculture

The Steel's factory where implements for Fergus borers, potato spinner seen under constructi

I made many in the UK – post hole and ridging ploughs are here

Ferguson System Patents

Patents granted to Harry George Ferguson, Donegal Square East, Belfast, Northern Ireland

Application date	Patent number	Feature
12th Sept 1917	119883	Arrangement for direct hitching and controlling plough including the first top link
1st Feb 1918	122703	Improvements to the above. Now known as the "Belfast" plough hitch. Transfers tractor weight to plough to ensure depth
15th Dec 1919	160248	Two point linkage or "Duplex" hitch by way of both upper and lower links set to converge to effect line of draft forward of rear axle, depth controlled by varying length of upper link. The first "virtual hitch point" system plus partial overload release by weight transfer
28th June 1921	186172	As 160248 but with depth wheel
3rd Nov 1921	195421	Modified 160248 allowing draft to balance penetration via spring mechanism
11th Dec 1923	226033	The ultimate version of 160248 "Duplex" hitch employing automatic mechanical depth control via slipper in furrow bottom linked to linkage. Achieved full weight transfer while retaining safety features of 160248
12th Feb 1925	253566	"Master Patent" incorporates the principle of "draft" control whereby the depth of a ground engaging implement is automatically controlled by reference to the effort or draft needed to pull it. Means of linkage movement to be effected by electric, mechanical or hydraulic device. Also covers draft control by means of tractor's transmission torque
3rd July 1928	320084	Converging three point linkage plus front furrow width control via cranked cross shaft. The second dimension to 160248
3rd July 1933	421983	Improved efficiency tractor transmission using internally toothed ring gear reduction (as used on Black and type A tractors) plus power take off driven from final drive (ground speed PTO) placed centrally over drawbar plate plus belt pulley drive plus internally mounted dual ram draft control using 253566
5th Feb 1936	470069	Hydraulic draft control by placing the control valve on suction side of an oil immersed pump to avoid aeration and heating of oil. Simple "flow on demand" system
5th Feb 1937	470087	Development of 253566 and 470069 incorporates automatic release of hydraulic pressure to protect implement on hitting obstruction
5th Feb 1936	471515	Check chains/anti-sway blocks for three point linkage that allows lateral movement in work but limits sway when raised
30th Nov 1937	510352	Major transmission improvements by incorporating a constant running lay shaft in gearbox thus allowing PTO and hydraulic pump to be driven whenever clutch is engaged whether in gear or not, plus pump driven before or after dog clutch, plus restatement of PTO shaft position as per 421983 rearwards within the three point linkage
8th July 1939	541220	Adjustable row crop front axle that allows track width to be varied from 48" to 76" without altering the front wheel alignment

Source: Harry Ferguson. A brief history of his life and tractors.
Other Ferguson patents relate to ploughs, cultivators, farm transport etc.

CHAPTER 2

Harry Ferguson's global objectives for farm mechanisation

This chapter comprises excerpts from the address by Harry Ferguson delivered to the delegates of the International Food Conference at Bethesda, Maryland, USA on June 5th 1943. It also includes excerpts from addresses by Harry Ferguson delivered at Washington, D.C., USA between May 17 and May 27th 1944. This text is reproduced directly with photographs from an obviously official printed and bound record of his speeches with photographs, and includes a foreword by him dated 1947. It is uncertain which organisation prepared this compilation of his speeches, though it was printed in the USA and bears the Ferguson System logo on the rear cover thus suggesting that it was produced by Ferguson in the USA.

The speeches are a most valuable summary of Harry Ferguson's philosophies on world economic development in general, including how the development of farm mechanisation could relieve poverty in the post war years.

HARRY FERGUSON'S FOREWORD OF 1947

My whole economic philosophy and all my efforts are guided by the knowledge that the best way to improve the total economy will be through *cutting the costs of production of agricultural products*, which *control the cost of living*.

There must be implements of an altogether new type which will produce, for the first time in history, enough food to feed all the people of the world. And, also, produce from the land—the source from which all wealth comes—a new wealth to enrich the world.

Our Plan for prosperity, security, and peace can be stated in two simple propositions:

1. Make the good earth produce *more than enough* to keep its whole population in comfort and contentment.

2. And, what is equally vital, produce that "more than enough" at prices which the people of the world can afford to pay.

That is our ambition. That is the course to which I am wholly dedicated.

HARRY FERGUSON

DETROIT, MICHIGAN
December 1, 1947

EXCERPTS FROM THE SPEECH OF JUNE 5TH 1943

A NEW HOPE FOR MANKIND

Gentlemen: *We have not asked you to come here primarily to see a Tractor and a new System of Implements. That is a secondary reason for the invitation we sent you. Before I go any further, I want to impress most deeply upon you that it is the *Plan*, the idea behind this new System, which is of primary importance.

I suppose you know that only one invention in ten thousand succeeds. The reason is that there is no plan behind the failures. The one that succeeds has a plan behind it.

If we had no plan behind our machinery, it also would fail. Not one line was put on paper, not one thought was expressed on this machinery in any form, until we had worked out, in Northern Ireland, a Plan for a revolution in the production costs of the necessities of life.

You would not come here and take back to your respective countries any possible story or report of the worth of this new machinery unless I gave you a background upon which to judge it. Therefore, I am going to tell you the Plan on which we work. When you know what that Plan is, I know you are going to approve of it. I know you are going to say it is the most far-reaching Plan that man has devised. If you agree, then your task of judging the worth of the machinery is simplified, because you will have a standard by which to judge it. The machinery is of secondary importance, but without it the Plan could not be carried out.

First, there is the Plan. To put that Plan into effect, machinery must be designed fitted to that Plan. Your task today, in the interest of all your own countries, is to judge whether the machinery we are going to show you will fit the Plan. If the Plan be good and the machinery be good, then we have the greatest and best news that you have ever heard. We have a new hope for mankind.

Never for a moment, during the twenty-six years I have been working with some

---

*The excerpts which follow, through page 26, are taken from the address by Mr. Harry Ferguson delivered to the Delegates to the International Food Conference, at Bethesda, Maryland, June 5, 1943.

3

of my friends in Ireland and over here, have we devoted our attention to any form of localized machine; that is to say, we took into consideration every world condition that exists. No country has been left unconsidered.

I made up my mind all those years ago that unless we could make a machine for the whole world, which would revolutionize agricultural production all over the world, we would fail in our task in just the same way as many big companies have failed in the past. All the companies making tractors today are scarcely touching the fringe of the possible world tractor business. In other words, the farm mechanization industry is hardly born yet. You can judge, today, this Plan and this equipment, from the standpoint of world conditions.

THE ABOLITION OF POVERTY

Abolition of poverty is our first problem. Let us first understand what poverty is.

What is poverty? What is want? Poverty and want can best be described as the inability to purchase the bare necessities of life. Any man who can not obtain the necessities of life is definitely in poverty. Any man who can purchase them is not in poverty. He may be poor, but he is not in poverty.

Many plans have been presented for meeting the problem of poverty and destitution. But none of them can possibly succeed unless something be done to create the wealth with which to put those plans into effect.

I think my own British countryman, Sir William Beveridge, has suggested a very human plan. It has many excellent qualities, and it is one which I personally support up to the hilt and which I believe the great majority of the people in our country would support. It is stalled at the moment, however, and will remain stalled until the British Government can see some way of financing that plan. You people in your own countries will be faced with exactly the same problem. You want to do for your destitute people what Sir William is thinking of doing, but he can do it, and you can do it, only if the

4

wealth exists with which to do it. The problem is to find that wealth.

Sir William proposes something like two pounds per week to meet the problem of poverty—approximately ten dollars. Very good! But, what good will the proposal alone do?

Will that money keep people out of poverty? What do two pounds or ten dollars per week mean?

Two pounds or ten dollars per week will keep a man out of poverty provided it will purchase for him the necessities of life. But he will still be in poverty if it won't. One pound, or five dollars, will keep a man out of poverty provided the necessities of life are cheap enough and he can buy them for that price. You may keep that man out of poverty for just the exact length of time that it takes for the prices of everything to go up, and then he is in poverty again.

We can not and never will solve the problem of poverty until we solve the problem of stabilizing prices, and until we solve the problem of creating wealth to a far greater extent than we have ever done in this world before.

Now we can do that. We have the means. We are going to show you that today.

THE DISASTER OF THE PRICE INCREASING SYSTEM

When this war is finished, there will be two ways in which we can run the world. We must either progress or go backwards. We can not stand still. One way to run it is the way we have been running it. No country is exempt. And the way we have been running it is on the basis of ever-increasing wages, salaries, and profits to meet the ever-increasing cost of living. In every country we continually are raising wages; shortly following these raises, up goes the cost of living again on all the things that we buy, and then wages must go up again.

That can only lead to disaster and further wars. There can be no peace in this world, no security, no real solution of the problems of want and poverty, until we stop

5

this ever-increasing cost of living and ever-increasing rise in wages and salaries. You do not make a man any richer by giving him an increase in wages except as a purely temporary expedient. In a little while that increase in wages has put up the cost of living and he is just as badly off as he was.

Take, for example, the very serious coal strike which we have had in this country [U.S.A.]. The miners wanted two dollars a day more than they were getting, because the cost of living had gone up. We will assume that they get their two dollars per day. Who benefits? Half a million miners and their families. Bear in mind that coal is in direct or indirect use everywhere, every day, all the time, and has a direct bearing on the cost of everything we eat, wear and use. Yet, it is no more fundamental than wood or steel or any other material. You can not give a rise in wages, you can not increase the cost of anything, regardless of how simple or unimportant it may be, without affecting the cost of living.

Half a million miners and their families, some two or three million people, get a temporary benefit by this increase in wages. For how long? For a brief period since it is only a temporary expedient. Two or three million people are benefited for a short time, and then they are just as badly off as ever. But there are another 130,000,000 people who are immediately and definitely worse off.

It is a terrible situation when a country must be run in that way. You gentlemen are all faced with exactly the same problem. In another few months, the miners will be shouting for another rise. War or peace, it is always the same. They will have to get it, and the cost of living will go up again. Everything we buy, which requires the use of coal, will be increased in price, and we will have to pay it. Thus the cost of living will go up. That is the system on which we have been running the world for many years; and it is the system with which we will have to continue, unless someone does something to make a change.

We propose to make that change in a very practical form. We propose to sub-

6

stitute for the "Price Increasing System" the universal benefits of the "Price Reducing System".

Under the present system of ever-increasing prices we are heading for inflation. We are heading for endless bickering and friction between the people of every country. Why? Because there can be nothing but bickering so long as strikes go on and people feel they must strike to get more money to meet the increased cost of living. Up go the wages . . . up goes the cost of living . . . up go the wages . . . and the vicious circle goes on. The result of that can only be more wars, because so long as people are kept in a ferment there will be war. There will be people trying to better themselves through war if they can't do it in any other way.

I say to you, deliberately, that unless we can solve this problem of the "Price Increasing System," we are headed for another disaster of the same kind that we have today.

THE PRICE REDUCING SYSTEM

Our new "Price Reducing System" is a complete revolution. It alters the whole outlook for mankind. Let's apply it to the coal miners. Suppose President Roosevelt could say to us today, "Go out and make new machines that will bring down the cost of living by $2 a day," and suppose we did. What would happen? The miners would be perfectly satisfied. They don't care whether they get $2 a day more, or whether they can buy the equivalent of $2 more with their present wages. The miners would get what they want with a price reduction the equivalent of $2 per day, and there would be an *immediate and welcome benefit to the other 130,000,000 people in the country*. Then, instead of having nearly the whole of the population worse off when any one section or group receives a rise in wages, *you would have the whole population immediately benefiting*.

Gentlemen, this is the way to Peace. This is the way to prosperity and the future of the world.

But there is only one place to start. *It is the farm which is the basic cause of the*

7

"Price Increasing System". The whole trouble is definitely in agriculture.

That is not the farmer's fault, as we will see shortly. He must be given the opportunity of producing the necessities of life at a cost so low that we can cut the vicious circle of ever-increasing prices and wages.

We are going to show you how to cut that vicious circle and bring about the benefits of the "Price Reducing System". We have made **a complete revolution in the application of mechanics to the land.**

The Ferguson Tractor which—with its integrated implements—has brought a revolution in the application of mechanics to the land.

Before we can bring about the benefits of price reduction we must revolutionize the methods on the farm, because it is what happens on the farm—to the cost of production of the necessities of life—that is at the base of all the trouble.

The methods of production on the farms of the world today are hopelessly antiquated.

Look at the equipment with which farmers are trying to make a living. You will be shocked to see the machinery with which the farmer is working his farm. You will see why the cost of living is always going up.

In the past fifty years the world has progressed more than it did in the 50,000 years previously! Why? Because the inventive genius of the world turned its attention to

8

industry for producing automobiles, radios, etc., etc., and devoted its time to making equipment for factories to produce at ever-reducing cost.

While all this genius has been devoted to the manufacturing industry, it has not been applied to the farm, and the farmer's equipment today is substantially as it was hundreds of years ago. There really has been very little advance.

Some of you may say that we have in America, England or Russia quite a number of tractors. Such tractors do not solve the problem, because you can use tractors and yet increase your costs of production. Again, you can use them under certain ideal conditions of operation—large farms, good farming land, level fields, and so forth— and reduce your costs of production. But the main point is this: farm mechanization, up to this time, has been so limited in its general application to the whole of agriculture throughout the world, that it has been adopted only in a very restricted way.

There are, I suppose, only two or three million tractors in the whole of the world, but there still are many millions of horses, mules and other draft animals. Why? Not

This picture shows the compact, light weight of the Ferguson. Implements are instantly attachable. Adjustable wheel tread makes the unit adaptable to all crop conditions.

9

because the farmer is a "mossback" or because he is slow, it is because the machinery, the mechanization offered to him, will not suit his conditions. If we are going to bring about the benefits of the Price Reducing System, we must give the farmer something which will cut his costs, cut them in pieces,—not on a beautiful, level field or in one particular crop, like wheat, but everywhere, under all conditions, all over the world.

I believe that the world could absorb something approaching 100 million tractors for agriculture and industry.

Probably 99 percent of the farms in the world are operated by hand or by animal power. Only a mere fraction are mechanized in the sense that a factory is mechanized. Why do factories use electricity and steam or oil engines to drive their machinery? Why don't they drive their machinery with horses or bullocks or mules? The reason is simple. The cost to the factory owner would be so excessive that he would be bankrupt in a few months. So animal power is not used in factories. Man has known from the earliest days of history that animal power is the most costly kind of power. For example, a few thousand years ago in Egypt man turned to water power, and later in other countries developed steam, and electricity—in fact anything which would get him away from the animal as a means of supplying power.

Why has agriculture had to continue the use of animal power?

Agriculture is more important to mankind than all the other industries in the world put together—yet it is about the only industry left in the world that is still being conducted by antiquated methods. Why, gentlemen? *Because until now no one has come along with machinery which will do, on all the farms of the world, everything which animals now do—and do it at a fraction of the cost.*

It is that machinery you are going to see today. We are going to show you that we can go to any country in the world, no matter what the farming conditions, and cultivate and produce its crops at *half the cost* at which they are now being produced.

If the Government of each country will help to inform their farmers of what this

10

machinery will do, and if it be established on their farms, the cost of living can be brought down by half.

By doing this we can eliminate the "Price Increasing System" and substitute instead the "Price Reducing System". We thereby solve the problems of poverty, ever-increasing friction, insecurity, and take the first practical step toward the elimination of war.

THE OLD SYSTEM AND THE NEW

Until recently, all attempts to mechanize farming started with a combination of a tractor and separate implements—that is, a tractor, either four-wheeled, three-wheeled

Through this unique linkage the tractor and implements are integrated so that implement and tractor work together through the hydraulic system built into the tractor.

or crawler, as one unit, and the implement as another—two separate and distinct units. There are, of course, a few tractors today made with *unit implements*. However, the time required to attach them and the breakages in use are so great they can be used only

11

under conditions so limited that they cannot be considered as a solution of the agricultural problem.

When we come to cutting the cost of production on the farm, it is not only the question of a saving in time that we have to think about. If we could save a farmer fifty percent of the time he now spends doing his job, he might not be any better off, because time isn't money unless he can make money with it.

This implement—the tiller—will stir the soil deeply without inverting it, leaving the soil loose and open to air and water. Its special construction permits this machine to work without damage in soil that is full of large stones or other obstructions.

Time saving is not the only consideration. We cannot reduce the cost of production on the farm 50% by saving time alone. We have to consider a great many other things. One is that the farmer will get a much greater yield from his land. If, for the same number of working hours, we can give him twice the yield from his land there is a 50% reduction of cost right away.

We are told that we must have weight to get traction. That is true in relation to

12

tractors of the ordinary type, but our new System of combining the tractor and implement in one unit solves that problem.

The conventional tractor had to be heavy to get traction, and also to make it safe for the operator. This weight was disastrous to the land. With the Ferguson System the need for excess weight has been eliminated, and so also has the danger to the operator.

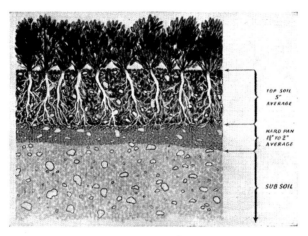

Cross-Section of Soil on President Roosevelt's Farm

This picture illustrates conditions found on President Roosevelt's farm at Hyde Park. That farm had been cultivated for years with animal power, and more recently with a heavy tractor. The soil is a sandy loam. Here the plants were growing in five or six inches of loose soil. Underneath this there was a pan which had been packed by horses and the weight of the heavy tractor.

When it rained, the water lay on top of the land, making it difficult to get the work done because the top soil would not dry quickly.

Eventually the water dried off, without getting through the pan into the subsoil. This was bad, because, when droughts came, there was no moisture in the subsoil to nourish the plants. As a result, the farm would grow practically nothing.

13

Those years of packing that pan meant the farm was practically destroyed.

The pan could not be broken up with horses, because horses hadn't the power. There wasn't any point in breaking it up with a heavy tractor because a heavy tractor would pack it down again.

We broke that pan with our light tractor and it is now growing record crops. We have worked a revolution on that farm at practically no cost by merely breaking the pan so that the moisture can seep through and allow the plants to get the nourishment they need.

But there is another thing. It costs a lot of money to buy a heavy machine and a lot to drive it over the land. Weight is not so bad on rails or on a road, but when you take weight on the land it costs heavily in gas or oil to move it because it sinks.

For instance, you can push a bicycle with the greatest of ease on a hard road, but take it into a soft field and you can't ride it at all. Why? Because it sinks. If you dismount, you can push it with your little finger, because it doesn't sink.

THE DISASTER OF DAMAGE TO THE IMPLEMENT

You know that the vast majority of the land in the world has rocks or roots in it. A horse-drawn implement, generally speaking, will not break when it strikes an obstruction, because the horse has no flywheel or momentum. He comes to a dead stop. When the plow strikes an obstruction, it is hard work for the farmer to pull the horses back and lift the implement over the obstruction. That means it takes a strong man to work horses all day long. With cattle the work is even more difficult.

See what happens in the case of the heavy tractor, when you strike an obstruction. There is tremendous energy stored in the flywheel. The wheels are locked by the obstruction, and the energy in the flywheel tends to lift the front of the tractor. The result is that you get too much weight on the rear wheels of the machine. This weight is increased by a tremendous downward thrust from the implement. In the case of an ordinary

14

tractor there may be as much as three tons weight on the rear wheels. This momentarily gears the wheels to the ground and something is likely to break or bend.

We spent a fortune in solving that one problem, because it is far more serious to damage a farm implement than it is to damage any other piece of equipment in the

Illustrating the indestructibility of the implement. When the implement strikes an obstruction, the *rear* end of the tractor is raised, thus reducing the traction and preventing damage to the implement. The connection between tractor and implement holds down the front end of the tractor so that there is no danger to the operator.

world. If a man's automobile breaks down, he takes it to a garage. If a farmer breaks an implement, it is not the cost of the new part that upsets him so much as the fact that he can't get on with his job. *Farm machinery should be fool-proof.* The farmer must be able to catch the weather—to do the job when the soil conditions are exactly right. If an implement be damaged in the critical days of spring, it may be a disaster for the farmer.

So the question of breakage is a deadly serious one for the farmer. We will show you how we solved it.

*(Here Mr. Ferguson demonstrated with his model,
and later in the field, how this was done.)*

15

PROBLEM OF THE SMALL FIELD AND THE SMALL FARM

I know that many of you represent countries where the farms are very small. **The smaller the farm, the more urgent the need for mechanization.** There is not sufficient land to maintain the animals supplying power and also to provide adequately for the farmer and his family. The small farmer has a life of slavery and poverty, and his purchasing power is so low that he is of little value to other industries.

Finger-tip control of the hydraulic mechanism for raising and lowering the implement, and easy steering of the tractor, make it possible for anyone, young or old, to work close to fences and in awkward corners—a feature particularly valuable on small farms.

Horses can work in small fields where the combination of a heavy tractor and a wheeled implement won't work. You can take horses into quite small fields, but it is hard work because you have to carry the implement into the awkward corners.

So today, we have the case of the farmer, who is the most important citizen in the whole world, still conducting his business by slavery and manual work, whereas in the factory it is done by "finger-tip control".

16

This is all wrong. Agriculture should have been the first industry to be modernized and not the last.

The Ferguson System can be operated by a child in small fields and awkward corners, and makes the horse look as foolish in a field as he would now look in a factory.

(Here Mr. Ferguson demonstrated with the model, and later in the field, how the new System completely eclipses the power animal on the small farm.)

LABOR-SAVING MACHINERY CREATES EMPLOYMENT

There is a theory that labor-saving machinery creates unemployment. That is entirely erroneous. Labor-saving machinery does the opposite. Take as an example a country where, with this light tractor, you can do as much in one hour as can be done in 100 or 200 hours by hand labor. You say that it is going to create a great deal of unemployment. No; the very reverse is true because the first great thing that happens when you save time and labor is that you reduce the cost of your product. The lower the price, the more you can sell. The more you sell, the more employment you can give.

Some of your countries may wish to import your machines; others may be large enough to manufacture your own. If you manufacture your own tractors, you will require thousands, hundreds of thousands, or millions, as the case may be, depending on the size of your country. The moment you start manufacturing you create employment from mining right through manufacturing to transportation and distribution.

To equip your factories to make this machinery will create great employment in other industries, since you must have all the machine tools, must build all the factories, etc., etc.

There are a multitude of new jobs that will arise when you start to manufacture on a big scale. Taking it by and large, you create employment with labor-saving machinery. You don't reduce it. That is a very important thing to remember, because you will have to face it often when you are telling the story of what you are going to do with labor-saving machinery on the farm.

17

PLOW

CORN PLANTER

CULTIVATOR

MIDDLEBUSTER

SPRING TOOTH HARROW

RIDGER

TILLER

ONE-WAY DISC TILLER

A Few of the Implements

Most of these implements, and others not shown here, are integrated with the tractor to a degree not previously attained in farm machinery.

CORDWOOD SAW

UTILITY TRAILER

ENSILAGE CUTTER

LOADER

DISC RIDGER

3-TON TRAILER

DRILL

LAND LEVELER

MOWER

SPIKE TOOTH HARROW

WEEDER

TANDEM DISC HARROW

the Ferguson Tractor Operates

Through designing and engineering developments underway, more and more implements will be brought into the Ferguson System.

GRADER

COMBINE

CRANE

SCOOP

SUBSOILER

TRANSPORT BOX

OFFSET DISC HARROW

STALK CUTTER

The moment you equip your farms with labor-saving machinery to the extent that your farmers can produce for half the cost, the cost of living can be brought down. Men won't need such high wages because they will be able to buy more for less. Companies won't need to pay their managers so much and they won't need so much profit because they will be able to buy more for less. The result will be that if the cost of living is lower, the cost of all manufactured goods will come down. The lower the cost for manufactured goods, the more you will sell. The more you can sell, the cheaper you can make them. The cheaper you can make them, the more you can sell.

So, instead of having a vicious circle of ever-increasing prices, reducing markets and ever-reducing employment, you get the circle working the other way. You get more employment and cheaper goods; cheaper goods, and more employment. This leads to the manufacture of other goods, because the people will have the money to buy them.

In other words, the Ferguson System of agricultural production is primarily a Wealth Producing System. You start with something that isn't a luxury, it is wealth-producing machinery. The more economically you cultivate your land, the more wealth you create.

WORLD MANUFACTURE

I plead guilty to the fact that my own country—the British Isles—has not given as much to some countries as it has taken from those countries. The United States has done the same thing to a certain extent. For example, we had special privileges in China and India and other countries, and we manufactured there and we took more out of those countries than we should have taken. I think it would have been better for ourselves and better for the people of those countries if we had left more there and taken less.

I do not believe in a policy of taking this new equipment to any country, establishing large factories, making colossal profits and getting all we can out of the country. That is not our idea. I hope we have got away from that kind of imperialism and that we are going to see a new world in this respect.

20

Let us take China, for example. Our hearts go out to that heroic country. Many people should be taken from the land in a country like China, where there are not sufficient industries. China ought to have a better balance in her economy, with fewer people on the land. China can use, in agriculture and in industry, 10,000,000 of these little tractors.

The great Banner Lane Works of Standard Motor Co., Ltd., Coventry, England,
devoted exclusively, since 1946, to the manufacture of Ferguson Tractors.

But don't think for a minute that the tractor is the main proposition. The tractor is only a small thing compared with the equipment. Our tractor will operate about 160 different pieces of equipment for industry and agriculture.

When China is fully equipped and mechanized, she will average at least ten pieces

21

of equipment for every agricultural tractor and two or three for every industrial tractor. That would be close to 100,000,000 pieces of equipment.

Just think what a vast industry that will be. We do not propose to China or any other country that it can just jump into production on this machinery the moment the war is over. It can't be done. Realizing that you have to build up to it, we have laid our plans to collaborate with you. We will have your experts come to Detroit or London, as the case may be, and we will train them in this new System of agricultural production.

The building and maintenance of graded, well-drained roads both on farms and from farms to improved highways is an important element in farm mechanization—efficient haulage is just as necessary as efficient tillage.

Then we will work out something like a five- or ten-year plan. You will import from us, say for one year, all the tractors and all the implements that you need. You will use these to establish your dealerships, your service, and your education, and to teach your farmers how to use them.

The next year you will want a great many more, and the following year you can begin to do a little assembling. You can buy, say, the main body of the tractor from either London or Detroit, and assemble parts of it.

[22

The next year you could begin to make some parts, and by the fifth year you might be in full production yourselves.

If you have a very small country, and no hope of exporting the machinery, do not start manufacture. You may do your farmers and your whole country an injury. If your population is small, you can't manufacture without very heavy cost to the farmer, and that will defeat the objective we have in view. Better buy from some other country and sell cheaply to your farmers, thus keeping the cost of living low. Consider making other things that you can make at lower cost in your country for home consumption and export.

This machinery is wealth-creating machinery. It will create the wealth with which your populations can buy other manufactured goods, the necessities and comforts of life—and thus enormously increase employment. It will lay the foundation for the complete recovery and reconstruction of the whole world after the war, if it is properly applied and properly used.

I want you to get that vision and I want you to understand that, if your country wishes to share in this manufacture, we are not going to block the way and refuse to collaborate. We are going to assist you to do it, because we believe that the more wealth we create in your countries the more goods you can buy from the United States and Britain.

Who is the United States' best customer? It is not the poorest country in the world; it is one of the richest—Great Britain. Great Britain, one of the biggest manufacturing countries in the world, is the best customer the United States has. Let's make China a rich country. Let's make India a rich country. Let's make all your countries rich. Then, you will buy more from us. In Britain and the United States we have great inventive ability. It is up to us to continue improving our machinery, equipment and products of all kinds in order to make things which you will buy from us, and which will keep us rich also. We will collaborate with you to the utmost of our capacity.

23

THE GREATEST EMPLOYMENT-GIVING, WEALTH-CREATING OPPORTUNITY IN HISTORY IS UPON US

I urge that each of you insist on having appointed in your country a brilliant Minister of Agriculture, a man with vision, a man with foresight and driving energy. He should be a man competent to stir up your farming communities; to show them that they are on the wrong lines; to inspire them with the idea of running their farms on modern lines; to help them become educated on how to get the best from their land; and to help them with marketing plans which will keep down the cost of living.

The biggest job in any country after the war—after that of the President or Prime Minister—will be that of Minister of Agriculture. If you get an incompetent Minister of Agriculture, and an incompetent Department of Agriculture, you will pay a heavy price for it. You will have to *inspire* your farmers if you are to solve the terrible problems with which you will be faced.

One thing I beg of you. Don't subsidize your farmers. You may want to lend them money or you may want to help the finance companies to lend them money for the purchase of new equipment. That is all right. But don't subsidize them. That will defeat every objective you have in view.

What do subsidies do? By increasing taxation they raise the cost of living and keep us in the vicious circle of the "Wages and Price Increasing System". Subsidies destroy initiative, and you know that the average farmer has not been thinking and using his initiative. Has he been planning how he could save an hour on this job and a day on that job? Certainly not! He has been doing much the same old things his grandfather did before him. In the factory we pay men fabulous salaries to plan and to think, and inspire them to do so, so that costs can be cut. In the interests of humanity it is infinitely more important that we inspire the farmer to plan and to think, and to think hard, so that he may find new and better ways of saving time and cutting production costs. This, in turn, will bring down the cost of living and raise the standard of life. If you give the farmer a subsidy, why should he think? Don't give him a subsidy

24

New Ferguson Tractor Plant under construction (March, 1948) in Ferguson Park, Detroit, Michigan

—educate and inspire him. Tell him you won't subsidize him. Tell him he has to make a profit by producing at less cost, and that he must equip his farm with modern machinery. If necessary, help him to get a small loan to buy that machinery. When you have done all that, you will have taken the first step on the shining road to success.

What do we seek? We seek Peace, Security, Prosperity and Happiness. With all the sincerity I possess, I tell you that we will attain those splendid things exactly in proportion as we get the farmers of the world to modernize, to mechanize, and to mix their thought with their labor.

EXCERPTS FROM SPEECHES BETWEEN MAY 17TH AND MAY 24TH 1944

The excerpts which follow are taken from addresses by Mr. Ferguson, delivered at Washington, D. C., between May 17 and 27, 1944.

During that period five scheduled demonstrations were held. There were, in addition, several smaller, informal demonstrations and discussions.

Altogether, more than 1000 important and influential men were in attendance, and heard the ideas which are reproduced here as excerpts from what was said on those occasions. These men included commercial and governmental representatives—including Ambassadors—from many countries in Latin America, Europe and Asia; U. S. Senators and Congressmen; representatives of the office of the President of the United States, the U. S. Departments of State and Agriculture, the Soil Conservation Service, and the Farm Security Administration; and top executives from some of America's largest industries.

26

The power animal on the farm is the greatest obstruction on the highway of human progress. The animal was not designed for farm work. He was merely adapted to it.

REORGANIZATION OF FARMS

I want to say this word of warning to you bankers and to you financial people who are now making loans to the farmer to buy this tractor. You will have to join us in one thing. There is no sense in having the farmer buy this tractor and equipment and also keep his horses. He does not need to. But the curious fact is that we can hardly induce him to get rid of his horses. He has, for some reason, the idea that they do not cost him much to keep. Our biggest job is to educate the farmer to get rid of his horses after he gets the tractor.

We need the bankers and financial people to cooperate with us in warning the farmer that he cannot realize the values inherent in this machinery unless he gets rid of all his animal power.

After many years of study and checking and collecting data from every part of the world, we have facts and figures here which are simply staggering in their importance to the whole world. To bring the thing home to us here in America, I have taken three

27

sizes of farms, a 10-acre farm, a 30-acre farm, and a 100-acre farm. We have the figures*
on what their average incomes are all over the country, and the cost of keeping horses.
While these examples deal with American conditions, *the relations are the same all over
the world.*

I am going to take a 30-ACRE FARM as a fair example of what can be done
through mechanization with this new System, which makes possible the complete
elimination of the horse. We will assume that on this 30-acre farm two horses, or two
power animals, have been used, which is common. We know from the averages that we
have that the income would not be over $400 per annum.

Thirty-acre farm with two power animals produces income of only $400.00.

Two horses require, on the average, all the farmer can grow on ten acres.

With that income, that poor farmer is of very little use to industry, because he has
no surplus with which to buy from the local merchant in the local town, and those local
merchants in turn, if they cannot get the orders, cannot pass them on to the cities.
So something must be done to increase his purchasing power.

Now, here is how it goes: On the average, two horses consume all that the farmer
can grow on ten acres of land. In some places you can keep a horse on four acres, in

*The figures used in the examples which follow are based on prewar data. Although current figures for
prices and income are different, the basic relations illustrated here remain the same.*

28

some places on three. On others it will take ten to feed a horse, sometimes even twenty-five or thirty. It depends on how much the land will produce. But five is actually a little low for the whole of America.

Supposing the farmer buys a tractor and keeps his horses. He is no better off; he may be worse off. But the moment he sells those animals he immediately is in the happy position of having the equivalent of a 50% addition to his land available for productive use. Some of the ten acres that fed the horses had to be cultivated and harvested. He had all the labor and toil of planting and harvesting and storing to feed those horses all winter.

Thirty-acre farm with tractor power adds ten productive acres, improves methods and provides extra time. Increases income to $1,000.00.

The moment he gets rid of the horses he gets rid of that labor, and besides, he has ten acres of additional land, and if that land is worth $50 or $100 an acre it is a very valuable gift to him indeed.

Previously he had only twenty acres of land to earn his $400, because ten acres went to feed the horses. Now we have given him his whole thirty acres, less the amount that feeds the tractor. I will come to that in a minute.

If his income was $400 on twenty acres, it must be $600 on thirty acres.

29

With the increased yield due to better cultivation, and cultivation at the right time, and with being able to catch the weather and not lose his crops when bad weather comes, being able to do his work quickly and at the right time, he can easily save another $120 a year. That is a conservative estimate.

Next, we have saved him a tremendous percentage of the time that he now wastes with horses. What is he going to do with that saved time? Obviously saving time will not make him any more money. Time is not money unless it is used for more production.

Assuming he is a good husbandman, he will make use of that time. With the increased production on the farm, and the time we have saved him, he can easily keep four more cows, but I will be conservative and fix the figure at two. That would bring him in at least $90 a year. He can easily keep 300 hens. That will bring him $150. He can raise 300 chickens, which will bring him another $90. These new enterprises will bring in a total of $330.

The total increase in income is an advance from $400 to $1,050, and I am making now no allowance whatever for an improved standard of living, more home-raised food and saving on purchased food.

But he has to run his tractor. He can easily run that tractor for $50 a year for fuel and oil on a 30-acre farm. There is no difficulty in doing that. That $50 he can earn on half an acre of potatoes. That one-half acre will feed the tractor where it formerly took ten acres to feed the horses. That is, indeed, a revolution.

It may be objected that I have not made any allowance for depreciation. On a 30-acre farm the depreciation on the implement is so little that you could not calculate it. You could run the tractor for thirty years, easily, and the implements for nearly one hundred years, because the implements are practically everlasting except the ground-engaging parts which are replaceable as needed.

Neither have I made any allowance for depreciation on the horses. So, if we let the one balance the other, which is the best way to handle that problem, what do we get?

30

We get a 150% increase in that farmer's income annually by the use of this System, and complete dispensing with all animal power.

SUMMARY: INCREASED PRODUCTIVITY THROUGH MECHANIZATION

30-Acre Farm—2 Horses

Present Cash Income............................		$ 400
Add 10 Acres—50% Increase.......................		200
Increased Yields—Small Loss from Weather, Etc......		120
Other Increased Yields Made Possible by		
Time Saved—More Livestock		
Example:		
Keep 2 Cows........................	$ 90	
Keep 300 Hens......................	150	
Keep 300 Chickens..................	90	
	$330	330
(No Allowance for Improved Standard of Living		
More Family Food—		
Saving Purchased Food)..................		.....
		$1050
Less Costs Tractor Operation.....................		50
		$1000 (150% increase)

Now let us consider a 100-ACRE FARM. One the same initial basis per acre, this farmer has a $1,600 income, and he raises it to $3,140 by the same process. It takes $80 to run the tractor. His increase in income is 91%.

100-Acre Farm—4 Horses

Present Cash Income............................	$1600
Add 20 Acres—25% Increase.....................	400
Increased Yields—Less Loss	
From Weather, Etc............................	400
Other Increases Made Possible by Time Saved, a More	
Profitable Crop Rotation, and More Livestock.....	740
(No Allowance for Improved Standard of Living by	
Growing More Family Food and Saving on Pur-	
chased Food)................................	.....
	$3140
Less Cash Costs of Tractor Operation..............	80
	$3060 (91% increase)

Now, a 10-ACRE FARM. In this case we are assuming that the man is now running it as a truck farm, and keeping one horse, which would take five acres to feed. From the extra five acres available after turning to the tractor, he would increase his income $375 purely on an acreage basis. But further gains are possible as shown in the

31

following summary, bringing his income up from the original $375 to $1000. His income would be increased, therefore, 153%.

10-Acre Truck Farm—1 Horse

Present Cash Income	$ 375
Add 5 Acres—100% Increase	375
Increased Yields—Less Loss From Weather, Etc.	250
(No Allowance for Improved Standard of Living by Growing More Family Food and Saving on Purchased Food)	.....
	$1000
Less Cash Costs of Tractor Operation	50
	$ 950 (153% increase)

(The preceding tables are *examples only* of many ways in which the farmer's income can be increased.)

Any one who has ever handled animal powered equipment will appreciate this practical demonstration of the compactness and ease of handling of the Ferguson Tractor and Ferguson Implements. Every inch within the 16-foot enclosure is tilled without leaving a tire mark. This is just one of many examples which show why it is no longer necessary to keep power animals on the farm.

What of smaller holdings? There are many small holdings of less than 10 acres. In this case, what we have done very successfully is to get these men to club together.

32

Maybe four, five, or six of them combine and buy the equipment, and they make a complete success of it. By this method it is possible to solve the whole problem of world mechanization.

The old idea that only big farms should be mechanized is wrong. **The smaller the farm, the greater the need for mechanization, because the power animal eats so much of what that farm produces.**

ECONOMIC BENEFITS OF INCREASED PRODUCTIVITY

Now we come to the effect on the economics of the country. You will say, of course, that if we increase the productivity of the land of this country by soil conservation, by intensive cultivation, and all of the other things, that we will produce so much that prices will fall.

That is exactly what we are aiming at. That is what I have been working for—for twenty-seven years—to put the farmer in a position where he *could take much less for his crop and still be prosperous.*

I do not suggest that this large reduction in prices will come as a sudden slump. That could not happen. It will take us some years to mechanize all the farms of this country, and still longer for the rest of the world. So there will be a reasonable period during which this fall in prices will take place.

Other things can happen if our Plan be applied fully throughout the whole world. If the farmer eventually gets only half pre-war prices, that, in turn, will bring about a halving of the cost of living, because distribution of the farmers' products is handled on a percentage basis. If the purchasers from the farm can buy at half price, they can sell at half price. Thus, eventually, living costs would be only half.

The farmer, in common with all other citizens, would get the benefit. Everything he would buy would be cheaper. Everything all you manufacturers make would be cheaper. And, because they were cheaper, you would have an enormous market, because more people would buy. The more people who buy, the cheaper you can make, and the cheaper you make, the more you can sell. In other words, the vicious circle we have

33

been living in would be reversed, and we would be heading for security and safety instead of for disaster, as we now are.

WORLD-WIDE NEED FOR MORE FOOD

Finally, the greatest need for the increased farm production, made possible by this System, is in the enormous requirement of more food throughout most of the world. This need was summed up in a statement in 1943 by Mr. Paul H. Appleby, formerly Under Secretary of Agriculture for the United States:

"The starting point for any discussion of food is to be found in this basic fact: *this long after the Industrial Revolution, two-thirds of the people of the world are normally engaged in producing food, and two-thirds of the people of the world do not have enough to eat.*"

Here are some very startling figures, showing what the world can absorb in increased production, if all people are to have an adequate diet. According to a semi-official, preliminary estimate, there is needed a 25% increase in cereals. In all other foods, such as meat, dairy products, fruits and vegetables there should be *well over 100% increase.*

One of the most effective ways to increase food production and guard against the hazards of crop failures in many parts of the world is through the use of mechanical power to provide irrigation to supplement the natural rainfall.

34

Gentlemen, I think that answers any argument against an increase in production. If we do not do these things—increase production, and reduce the cost of living, and provide employment for the people—we are going to have another war within twenty-five years, and nothing can stop it.

Now, for the first time in history, it is possible to mechanize efficiently the operations of farms of every size. The use of Ferguson System equipment will create the wealth necessary to buy manufactured goods of all kinds and so provide maximum employment and bring prosperity to the world.

A PROGRAM FOR ALL GOVERNMENTS

Here is my proposal: Immediately after the war ends, the ablest businessmen in this country, and other countries, should get into an enormous production of this machinery. As quickly as we can develop it, we will give employment to millions of people from mining right through manufacture to distribution. The market is there, waiting for the machinery. We must supply millions of these tractors within a few years after this war, and implements by tens of millions.

We are willing to collaborate with any country which will work with us. We want to help them with manufacture where it will pay them to manufacture. This will depend

35

on the size of their country, and whether they can manufacture economically. We will give them all the facts and figures they want.

Every government should tell its people, and all manufacturers, that this basic idea of eliminating the costly, antiquated power animal and old type tractor from the farm is entirely sound. They should state the fact that the only hope for the future of farming and industry, and to save the country from disaster, is farm mechanization with modern equipment.

We want the governments to help educate farmers on how to get the best crops from their farms. Especially do we want the governments to help in marketing. A situation could arise where the middleman would begin to collect all the benefit of the price reduction on the farm. That is something which we, as a company, cannot handle. That is a government job, and the government should see that the consumer gets the benefit of any reduction in price to the farmer.

Let me emphasize once again that however great the employment-giving benefits of this gigantic industry may be, they are really small compared with the world-wide assets of the *use* of the machinery *on the farm*.

It is the *use* of the machinery on the farm which will create the wealth to buy goods and bring prosperity to the world. The difference between farm machinery and ordinary manufactured products is that farm machinery is by far the most important *wealth-creating* machinery.

Let me quote you from a speech made a few days ago by that brilliant and splendid man—Mr. Bernard Baruch:

> "Since happiness flows more readily from a life that is not embittered by hardship, we must constantly seek to improve our own conditions and help the rest of the world to the same end."

That can be achieved only through agriculture. What we need is energetic and strenuous effort on the part of men of intelligence and good will.

We are really engaged not upon a profit-earning enterprise but upon a great Crusade to save the world from disaster after this war and lay the foundation for peace, prosperity, and happiness throughout the world.

36

PRINTED IN U.S.A.

CHAPTER 3

A Living History Interpretation of Small Tractor Development

On June 5th 1999 the Hunday Fergusons were placed on display in an open day for members of the Friends of Ferguson Heritage club and the general public. The event comprised a pageant to depict the development of the mass produced tractor and a parade of the Hunday Fergusons. Models belonging to the Hunday collection were also on display and several trade stands were in attendance.

ABOVE A semi panoramic shot of some of the 600 people who sat and watched the actors in the marquee as the tractor history paraded before them

The pageant featured three actors who played Dan Albone, Henry Ford and Harry Ferguson who each had primary historical roles in the development of small mass-produced farm tractors. Dan Albone made the Ivel tractor – the world's first effective small tractor to be produced in significant numbers starting in 1902. Henry Ford produced the first truly mass produced small tractor as the Fordson model F and later the Ford Ferguson tractor in conjunction with Harry Ferguson. Harry Ferguson was responsible for the design of the Ferguson hydraulically controlled three point linkage system which was first incorporated in the Ferguson Brown tractors and later the Ford Ferguson and Ferguson tractors. The basic idea of the pageant was to create a "living history" of small tractor development by use of actors to portray these three men who had played such key roles.

These three pioneers were acted by non professional actors who had interests in agriculture and agricultural machinery. They were:

ALEX ALBONE who is the great, great nephew of Dan Albone. He was educated at Oundle School and the Royal Agricultural College, Cirencester after which he went to Cornell University, USA to study agricultural management. After returning to the UK he spent five years in London as a financial futures broker before he returned home in 1989 to help his father and brother in the farming business. He and his brother Dan run the farm and grow wheat, barley, oilseeds, sugar beet, peas and potatoes on 2,500 acres in Lincolnshire. Alex, being a member of the original Albone family, lent true authenticity to the event.

JERRY WHITE is a full-time teacher of farm and horticultural mechanisation at the Kirkley Hall College of Agriculture, Ponteland, Newcastle upon Tyne. He was born in the north east of England in 1960 and after primary education attended the College of Arts and Technology at Newcastle. He worked for a while in agricultural contracting before returning

ABOVE The three famous people portrayed in the pageant. Left Henry Ford, middle Harry Ferguson and right Dan Albone

to education at Newton Rigg College, Cheshire and Rytcotewood College in Oxfordshire. His hobbies include amateur dramatics, restoring vintage cars and motor cycles, and flying at Newcastle Aero Club. Jerry's lifelong interest in vintage machinery, traction engines and education made him ideal for the part of Henry Ford.

BILL MARTIN is a farmer's son from County Down where the fields are small and the hills steep. He graduated from Queen's University, Belfast and joined the Northern Ireland Ministry of Agriculture as a general advisor in the 1950s. In 1961 he was transferred to Greenmount College and given the task of creating a mechanisation department including maintenance and modifications. Harry Ferguson's equipment became a major part of teaching needs and Bill became a lifelong supporter of Harry Ferguson on whom he has lectured to many audiences in Ireland. Bill also set up a small Ferguson museum in the college and wrote a booklet on Harry Ferguson (*Harry Ferguson*, published by the Ulster Folk and Transport Museum). No one could have been better suited to play Harry Ferguson than Bill with his soft Northern Ireland accent.

These three actors were only given a briefing framework of the pageant objectives. This chapter presents their interpretations of the men they portrayed on the day, accompanied by photographs of the pageant.

A comparison of the principal tractor types featured in the pageant

	The Ivel	Fordson F	Ferguson Brown	Ford Ferguson	Ferguson TE 20	Ferguson 35
Year introduced	1902	1917	1934	1939	1946	1956
Wheels	3	4	4	4	4	4
Weight lb*.	2800	2920	1848	2340	2371	2890
Fuel	Petrol	Petrol	Petrol, TVO	Petrol, TVO	Petrol, TVO, Diesel, LO	Petrol, TVO, Diesel, LO
Cylinders						
HP	1	4	4	4	4	4
Gears	12-15	22-30****	20 bhp	23 bhp	28.2 belt hp	35 PTO hp
F'd speed mph	cone clutch only	3F, 1R	3F, 1R	3F, 1R	4F, 1R	6F, 2R
Hydraulic 3pt	1-3	1.53-6.93	1.6-4.9	2.2-6.6	3.4-13.3**	1-10.5***
Hitch	No	No	Yes	Yes	Yes	Yes
PTO	No	Optional	Optional	Yes	Yes	Yes
Belt pulley	Standard	Optional	Optional	Optional	Optional	Optional

*petrol model **at 2000 rpm *** at 1500 rpm ****depends on model

LEFT The Ivel painted by J H Appleyard in 1978 for John Moffitt
ABOVE LEFT The Fordson model F – Harry Ferguson did most of his three point hitch development on this style of Fordson tractors
ABOVE The Ferguson 35 was the last "pure" Ferguson tractor. This British "grey/gold" has a diesel engine – Harry Ferguson had never favoured diesel engines

Alex Albone as Dan Albone (1860-1906)

EARLY LIFE

My name is Daniel Albone, Dan to my friends and I was born in Biggleswade, Bedfordshire on 12th September, 1860, the youngest of a family of eight.

My father, Edward, was a sawyer, but he had many irons in the fire including renting land that he used for market gardening and where I was first introduced to the land.

My parents were also the tenants of the Ongley Arms near the bridge over the River Ivel. The Inn was on the Great North Road and was a regular stopping place for stagecoaches. As children we all witnessed the hustle and bustle of the travellers and in particular the quietness of the town after the thunderous hooves had passed into the distance.

I was only four years old when my father died at only 43 years of age, leaving my mother to bring up her large family. My eldest brother was 12 when the tragedy happened and mother had to take on the additional responsibility of Official Publican, still managing to send us to school at a cost of a penny per week for each of us.

I left school at twelve to become an apprentice to a small engineering firm repairing mill machinery and also learning the trade of a mill-wright.

From an early age I was fascinated by bicycles, Boneshakers and Penny Farthings and when just 13 I invented an improved bicycle and well remember a few years later being interviewed by the "Wheeling" magazine after winning a number of road races on one of my own bicycles.

Our home, the "Ongley Arms" was not a grand place but there were a number of out houses where I was able to work at nights and keep my tools and it was from here that I developed the "Ordinary" bicycle and founded the "Ivel Works" in 1880 at the age of only 20.

It was not my intention to mass produce bicycles but to develop a light-weight machine for which I was gaining a national reputation, supplying machines to the police, army and not least the Nobility, advertising a light "roadster" for £11. My favourite, The "Ivel Racer" was sold for £13.10s.0d.

By the age of 24 my eldest brother had emigrated to Australia and my eldest sister had died, so I was no stranger to tragedy but as well as working all day in my cycle works, I took over the Ongley Arms and my sister, Emma, became housekeeper.

MARRIAGE

In August 1887 I married Elizabeth Moulden of Hitchen and we travelled to Skegness by train for our honeymoon. By this stage in my life I was producing 30 bicycles a week, had established the Ivel Works and changed the name of the Inn to The Ivel Hotel which became the regular meeting place for all the cyclists in the area. I also introduced a Ladies' Bicycle and supplied such notable aristocracy as The Duchess of Bedford.

Time does not permit me to go into further detail of the cycle works but I soon recognised that a motorised bicycle would be attractive and in 1889 I was already producing and selling these machines. A motor car was my next challenge and in the following year we turned out our first car using an Astor engine but the competition in this field was very strong and we decided to concentrate on what I knew best.

RIGHT The Ivel tractor driven by Alex Albone. Note that here the tractor is without its hood to cover the engine

AN AGRICULTURAL MOTOR

Sufficient of Bicycles. In 1896 I woke early one morning and without disturbing my wife, I went to my office to put down on paper my ideas for an agricultural motor. I cannot really recall what motivated me with such a crazy notion but I felt that farming had to become more mechanised and the idea of a large steam engine to do this work was not only very expensive but also damaging to the land.

A year or so later my original thoughts began to take root with the option of a number of proprietary makes of engine that were available on the market. I experimented with an "Astor" developed by an engineering enthusiast, Lord Astor, a well-known Bedfordshire family. My concept of a 3-wheeled farm motor to work on the small field adjoining the works weighing under 30 cwt, and of 12 to 15 HP, that could pull a 2 or 3 furrow plough was the objective and I soon had a prototype machine ready for testing.

The agriculture motor as it was called, - the word "Tractor" had not as yet been conceived - attracted a great deal of attention by local farmers who could see the benefits of such a machine. However a price of around £300 was somewhat expensive and would have to do the work of two or three pairs of horses to be justified.

In 1902 a pre-production version was given extensive public trials that received great attention by the press who were most complimentary. This has been preserved in the London Science Museum. In the following year, with orders already on the books, I exhibited the Ivel No 131 (the one you see here at Hunday - actually number 31 as we started numbering from 100), at twenty major Shows in England including the Royal Show where it gained the first prize in the new machinery classes and went on to win over 28 medals up to my death in 1906.

The necessary capital for development was of prime importance and to raise the money I formed a new company attracting more than adequate finance. Perhaps if I had known that I had only another four years to live, I might have done differently.

There were no implements specifically made for the tractor so I had to develop those necessary for the task by adapting established horse-drawn implements. Those for ploughing, cultivating, sowing and reaping were all important. One of my last inventions early in 1906 was a potato planter that could plough and carry out all the operations in one pass.

During 1904-5 I had many enquiries from overseas and sold machines to Australia, New Zealand, Egypt, Africa, France and Canada. In fact Ivel tractors were sold to twenty-five different countries. I even developed a tractor for the Fire Service and an "Armoured" vehicle for military use in 1904 but it was not taken up by the Army. No records survive of how many tractors were produced it but was probably under 500.

Looking back on my life as I died on 30th October, 1906, I realised that I had crammed a great deal into my 46 years, not forgetting the Motor Bicycle, the Ivel Landaulette and the Ivel Four-Seater Motorcar. However, I take great pride in the fact that I really was the inventor of the first truly versatile small tractor from which my successors, Henry Ford and Harry Ferguson almost two decades later, brought mechanisation to every farm in the land.

Jerry White as Henry Ford (1883-1947)

EARLY LIFE

My name is Henry Ford and I was born at Dearborn in Michigan, USA on 30th July 1863.

My grandparents and my father emigrated from Ireland and I am told, left their native land due to "Too little Food and Too much Law." From a small farm in Cork County, John Ford, my grandfather, who had relatives living near Detroit, not surprisingly chose to take his family there to start a new life where at least they had friends.

In 1848 grandfather was able to buy 80 acres of land for a total of $350 and soon established himself as a farmer with my father, William Ford who continued the farming business after his death.

I was the eldest son and as I grew older was expected to take on an increasing share of the work. I found the work tedious and unrewarding and I well remember walking many weary miles behind the plough.

I thought "what a waste of time behind a slow moving team of horses" but despite these early thoughts I have always maintained a lifelong interest in agriculture.

From my early school days I was always interested in all things mechanical to the detriment of my schoolwork and I only made modest progress with the "Three R's".

As a farm boy I was always tinkering with bits of equipment and in 1879, at the age of 16, I left home to take an apprenticeship in Detroit. I worked for several engineering companies to gain experience, supplementing my meagre wage by doing watch and clock repairs in my spare time.

MARRIAGE

In 1888 I married a farmer's daughter, Claire Bryant, and continued my obsession to build a reliable combustion engine. By 1893 I succeeded and began to experiment by putting it into a frame in my small shed at the bottom of the garden and by 1896 I took it out for its first test run.

The car was so simple and successful that in 1893 I persuaded ten Shareholders to invest a total of $100,000 in issued stocks to set up the Ford Motor Company which proved an immediate success, but not I might add, without being occasionally on the brink of financial disaster.

In 1908, I saw the production of my first Model T Ford car that continued in production until 1927, selling more than 15 million vehicles of what was the world's first, continuous line production.

TRACTOR DEVELOPMENT

With my Agricultural background and with the Model T now safely in production, I turned my attention to the development of a cheap tractor that could be available to every farmer and in 1907 set up a small team to develop my ideas, resulting in a prototype which I have retained and it is now on display in my Museum. For convenience and cost effectiveness, it used many parts from the Model T car and only weighed 1,500 lbs. My predecessor, Dan Albone, whom I greatly admired, was the only other manufacturer at that time to produce a small lightweight tractor. Dan's view was that size and weight were not important, particularly for the small farmer.

To manufacture this tractor, I formed a

new company in 1915 called Henry Ford and Company, which was only formally registered in 1917.

My determination to deliver a cheap purpose-built tractor for even the smallest farmer was drawing nearer and resulted in the Model F that entered production in 1916 and selling at the low price of only £256 changed the face of world agriculture. Up until 1925 over 500,000 Model F's were produced and during 1924 they were selling for only £150.

The war with Germany was taking its toll in Europe, and England in particular, and resulted in a visit from the young Winston Churchill, a junior minister in the government. He persuaded me to release the first 6,000 tractors from the production line to help in the war effort and to feed the British people.

At home, for the thousands of farmers in the USA who wanted a cheap tractor, they could also use the Model T car by converting the rear axle using one of a number of manufacturer's conversion kits and thousands of these were sold.

For political and social reasons, as well as my Irish roots, I set up a Production Plant in Cork, Ireland during 1929 which was intended to be the main export centre for world trade. The new Model N to be produced, although similar to the Model F, did not reach the production output forecast, which was also influenced by the depression hitting world farming.

Manufacturing stopped in 1932 with only 7,000 tractors being made and the plant was moved to London, Dagenham, to produce an uprated model for the UK and European markets.

NEW DESIGN

I had for some time been working on a completely new design of light tractor at home in the US and had been watching the progress of Harry Ferguson's patent attachment for mounting the implement directly onto the tractor and indeed much of his pioneering work was done using Fordson tractors.

It was perhaps fortuitous that due to production difficulties with David Brown, who were producing the Ferguson Brown tractor, that Harry secretly shipped a tractor and implements to Dearborn in 1938 for me to see and to demonstrate the versatility of this revolutionary lightweight tractor.

I found the demonstration held on land near my home very interesting and impressive and before Harry Ferguson returned to the UK we had a handshake agreement for all to see, but no contract. Harry cancelled his contract with David Brown immediately on his return.

The Ford engineers began work immediately and within a year, the Ford Ferguson Tractor was ready for production with the design and manufacture involving a massive investment necessary for me to incorporate Ferguson's patent. Harry and I had agreed, with the handshake agreement, to work together in a spirit of mutual trust.

Our immensely successful tractor entered the market in 1939 and soon caught the imagination of the world's press, but the lack of legal paperwork over the patenting was causing great confusion among senior directors of both of our companies. I was to be in control of the manufacture of

the tractor and Harry was responsible for the marketing – something that had been proved he was good at. Despite all the difficulties, Harry and I were determined to maintain the spirit of the agreement.

Difficulties continued to arise, not least with the name. My son and others in the Company were against Ferguson's name being displayed on the front jointly with Ford. The tractor was to be known as the 9N and was demonstrated widely by an 8-year old from our local school.

We launched the tractor at $585 which included rubber tyres, PTO and self starting system but the war years intervened and production fell from 43,000 units in 1941 to less than 1,600 units in 1942.

In England, however, the successful Fordson N continued to be produced and with the uprated E27N coming on stream after the war. The British directors of Ford were very reluctant to become involved with Harry Ferguson - the new company preferring to stick to their own designs.

My son, Edsel, died suddenly in 1943 and at the age of 80 years I again took over the reins as President until my grandson, Henry Ford II was able to take control of the business, which he did two years later.

At the age of 82, I passed out of this world leaving my grandson, Henry, to make some tough decisions. The 8N had come on stream with a 4-speed gearbox and improved performance much to the annoyance of Harry Ferguson who had not been consulted. Perhaps the lawsuit that followed is best told by the man himself, Harry Ferguson.

Bill Martin as Harry Ferguson (1884-1960)

EARLY LIFE

I was born on 4th November 1884 at Dromore, Co Down, in Northern Ireland and was christened Henry George Ferguson.

I was the fourth born of eleven children to an austere Ulster small farmer with a deeply religious upbringing. I was known from birth as Harry and memories of my childhood are of an unhappy home life, which I prefer not to dwell on as we were a poor family, with not infrequently little or no food of any substance.

Some years later in my life, speaking at a conference in the USA during the summer of 1943, I was asked about my childhood

and the poverty in Ireland during my youth. I replied,

"What is poverty; what is want; poverty and want can best be described as the inability to purchase the bare necessities of life. Any man that can purchase them is not in poverty. He may be poor, but he is not in poverty."

As a family we endured a life of hard labour day after day with a father who enforced upon us unremitting tyranny in a culture that allowed no books other than the Bible. On more than one occasion I was forced to walk for eight miles while my father rode in the trap and when we got home I had to feed, water and rub down the horses before going to bed.

I think my father treated me more harshly than the rest of the family because I was more independent and perhaps stubborn to those in authority both at home and at school, and not surprisingly it was the deeply religious upbringing that turned me to atheism.

I left school at 13 years to work on the family farm but left a few years later to work with my brother, Joe in Belfast as an apprentice to his now expanding motor business, attending classes at Belfast Technical College in the evenings.

This was the happiest time of my life and I made a number of friends for the first time, John Williams and Tom McGregor Greer in particular, and with their help

I competed successfully in motor cycle events.

Brother Joe's business was prosperous and I turned my attention to building a car while also taking great interest in the new exciting business of aviation, so much so that I set my heart on building an aircraft which I did in 1910 when I was only 26. I managed to fly my aircraft for just over a measured mile – the first flight ever to be recorded in Ireland.

The following year I formed my own business known as "May Street Motors" and John Williams and Willie Sands, who had also served apprenticeships at the same time joined me. I changed the name of the business to "Harry Ferguson Ltd." and began to compete in numerous motor races.

MARRIAGE

The following year, 1913, I married Maureen Watson, whose family owned a grocer's shop in Dromore. The outbreak of war in 1914 saw my loyal and talented engineering colleague leave to join the Royal Flying Corps so I began to turn my attention to the land and managed to secure the agency to sell the imported Overtime tractor from the United States.

Doubling the arable acreage in the war effort to feed the people of Ireland meant the ploughing of many old pastures for which the Overtime was ideally suited and I became an accomplished ploughman giving countless demonstrations with the Overtime pulling a Cockshutt plough. On 17th March 1917 my old colleague Sands and I were given the job by the Irish Board of Agriculture to travel throughout Ireland to help improve efficiency of ploughing to allow more acres to be utilised.

DRAFT IDEAS BEGAN TO TAKE ROOT

This is where I began to realise that the conventional way of pulling a plough was far from ideal as it required a heavy tractor such as the Overtime to avoid wheel slip which led Sands I and to develop a plough to fit the Fordson Tractor in 1918 using a Duplex hitch. We went to the Ford Plant in Cork in 1921 to show the directors and carried out a working demonstration.

The idea was so simple and impressive that I took out a patent before going to Ohio and signing an agreement with Roderick Lean to make 50,000 ploughs to fit the Fordson Tractor, but unfortunately Lean went into liquidation and the deal fell through.

In 1925 I formed a joint company with Sherman to be called the Ferguson Sherman Plough Co. to manufacture ploughs in the USA and successfully patented the Draft Control Mechanism to fit the tractor and plough. This was to become an essential part of every tractor being manufactured but also caused me a life of continuous legal battles.

I freely admit that it may be my Irish nature and childhood upbringing that caused many of my problems and in particular to retaining employees. I lost Sands, my lifelong talented and dedicated engineer who left to set up a bus transport business.

I realised early in the development of the plough that the Fordson tractor was not ideally suited for the plough lift arrangement and I turned my attention to a completely new design of a lightweight tractor specifically for the task. In 1931 John Chambers and Trevor Knox joined the design team of our Ferguson business.

FERGUSON BLACK AND FERGUSON BROWN TRACTORS

By 1933 we had completed the prototype known affectionately as the "Black Tractor" now in the Science Museum, and the following year we persuaded David Brown to manufacture the tractor at their works in Huddersfield, forming a separate company to market the new "Ferguson Brown" that began to roll off the production line in 1936.

It was necessary with this new revolutionary design to set up training schools not only for the service engineers but also for the enthusiastic buyers, which was undertaken by Bob Annet in the same year.

Soon differences of opinions between David Brown and myself over the manufacture of the tractor began to emerge. I always seemed to want something difficult to manufacture and I could see bigger opportunities in America by association with Henry Ford.

So unknown to David Brown I took a tractor and implements to America in 1938 to show Henry Ford and demonstrate to him and his senior engineers the flexibility of this lightweight tractor and the three-point linkage arrangement of the implements.

I also took with me a working scale model to explain exactly how the linkage mechanism works and the extra traction given to the rear wheels. We sat face to face at the table over the model on the table outside in the field where the demonstration was taking place. Henry

Ford and I got on well together and he was obviously very impressed with the demonstration, so much so, that we shook hands on a deal that was to seal the fate of my patents, but much to the distrust and concern of Henry Ford's son, Edsel and other directors.

On my return I terminated the contract with David Brown with only 1,270 Brown Fergusons being completed.

FORD FERGUSON TRACTOR

By April of 1939 the Ford engineers had made tremendous progress with a new design incorporating both Ford's streamlining and uprated engine, and my all important three-point linkage.

By the end of the year I was able to bring a completed production model of the newly named "Ford Ferguson" back to Greenmount Agricultural College to demonstrate to Ministry officials including the Minister himself.

Although in the handshake agreement we had arranged that Ford would manufacture and I would be responsible for the marketing, I fully expected to be consulted over the design, especially the linkage mechanism. When this failed to transpire, my frustration boiled over and I sent Trevor Knox to explore the possibility of manufacturing in Britain and arranged meetings with the Ministry of Finance at Stormont with a view to the manufacture in Northern Ireland in 1945.

I also had a high level meeting with the Chairman of the Standard Motor Company, Sir John Black, who agreed that the old car premises at Banner Lane which had been used as an ammunition factory during the war, could be used to produce the Tractor to be known as the now famous TE 20.

LAWSUIT

The following year my links with Henry Ford terminated acrimoniously and we began production at Banner Lane. In 1947 Henry Ford announced a new tractor, the 8N, incorporating my hydraulic system. I quickly visited America to see for myself and immediately took out legal procedures against them for dishonouring their agreement and filing a $251,100,000 lawsuit against the Ford Motor Co.

A long drawn out battle over the next four years took a great deal out of me as I always feared that I might lose the battle and everything I had. However, I was successful in not only winning but also being awarded damages of 9.2 million dollars. Although the award was far from what I felt was adequate it was at least a moral victory.

The production of the TE 20 was in full swing at Banner Lane and during the ten years of manufacture that started in 1946, over 500,000 were produced.

The success of this tractor brought world-wide interest which prompted Massey-Harris, one of the world's largest tractor-machinery manufacturers, to try to buy the Ferguson business. However I was not then ready to sell but finally agreed to a merger of the two companies in 1953.

I was approaching my 70th birthday and although happily living at Abbotswood in the Cotswolds, business pressures began to tell and I decided to retire and sell my interest in Massey-Harris-Ferguson for 3.75 million pounds.

The story of Massey Ferguson lives on and I can look back with pride and pleasure in the knowledge that virtually every modern tractor, both large and small, incorporates my draft control principle.

I ended my 76 years on this planet neither a happy nor contented man. Life had taken its toll and I was found dead in my home at Abbotswood on 25th October 1960.

The Billy Smith model collection displayed in the museum. Lord and Lady Plumb (left and centre right) with the late Billy Smith's wife (right) and daughter (left)

Tractor artist Mr Oliver chats to Lord and Lady Plumb

Lord and Lady Plumb chat with the raffle ladies who had pitched their stand in front of the static display of equipment in the museum

AFTER THE PAGEANT

Some of the 1,200 people who attended the pageant

Parading and enjoying Ferguson equipment at the open day after the pageant

Virtually the whole of the Hunday Ferguson collection was paraded around a ring after the pageant. Here are a few shots to recall the day.

CHAPTER 4

Some Ferguson letters

In this chapter are reproduced eight Ferguson Brown era letters, the Ferguson Brown tractor warranty of the modeller Billy Smith (see Chapter 10) and six letters from Ferguson to Reekie Engineering relating to the development of the narrow track Ferguson Reekie "Universal Raspberry Tractor". This tractor was first a matter of concern to Ferguson but later accepted. The chapter finishes with a personal letter from Harry Ferguson to John Reekie after his obviously wrenching break from Massey-Harris-Ferguson and his continuing concerns about the menace of world communism.

The letters are self-explanatory and contain some fascinating points of interest about the development of Ferguson tractors and implements.

Harry Ferguson Ltd.
Huddersfield
Telephone:
Huddersfield 2685.
Telegrams:
"Farming" Huddersfield.
Manufacturers: David Brown Tractors Ltd.

Telephone:
Huddersfield 2685.

Telegrams:
"Farming" Huddersfield.

Manufacturers: David Brown Tractors Ltd.

Dear Sir,

<u>PROFITABLE FARMING.</u>

The great purpose behind our efforts in the past 20 years has been to simplify and cheapen agricultural production to such an extent that every farmer can substantially increase his profits.

Many farmers and distributors are asking our opinion as to the use of paraffin fuels. We have decided to answer these queries very fully and frankly and to send to every Ferguson owner and distributor this letter dealing with the subject.

Many farmers who have not owned tractors previously are paying very little attention to the warnings issued about the use of paraffin fuels. This makes it all the more urgent that they should understand the risks they are running.

We are quite open-minded and can speak without prejudice as the Ferguson tractor is equipped for the use of paraffin. The great plan behind our efforts is to make farming profitable to the utmost, and after 20 years experience of all makes of tractors, we are of the opinion that over an extended period it is much cheaper to operate any make of tractor on petrol only.

<u>EXTRA CARE AND ATTENTION</u>
<u>REQUIRED WHEN USING PARAFFIN.</u>

The following, taken from a number of tractor Instruction Booklets emphasise that the greatest possible care must be taken when using paraffin.

1. When the engine has reached a certain temperature (which is not always easy to guess) turn over to paraffin.

2. When the engine is idling, or the tractor doing
    light work, it is recommended to run on petrol.
    If damage to the engine is to be avoided, it
    might be necessary in some circumstances, to
    change over from one fuel to the other twenty
    or thirty times per day.

3. The paraffin must be turned off and petrol turned
    on several minutes before stopping the tractor.

4. Skilled attention is needed to sparking plugs and
    ignition. If, for example, a cylinder is misfiring
    the paraffin in that cylinder condenses, gets into
    the crankcase, and so destroys the efficiency of
    the lubricating oil.

5. Some manufacturers recommend a combination of heat
    control valves on the manifold and a radiator
    shutter. To use these fitments correctly is a
    skilled job. You are actually advised to have
    the shutter in one position when the wind is
    behind, and another when it is in front. Only
    the most skilled operators could carry out
    instructions of this kind.

6. Even when the greatest care is taken, you are
    warned by some manufacturers to drain a certain
    amount of oil from the crankcase <u>daily</u> and fill
    up with fresh oil. Thus heavy oil consumption
    adds considerably to operating costs. All this
    clearly admits that <u>despite the greatest care</u>,
    paraffin will get into the crankcase.

Engines run on paraffin must be decarbonised
and the valves ground much more often, which also adds
to the running costs.

There is a great variation in the heat required
to vaporise the different classes of paraffin, and this
in itself is a critical point. A variable jet carburetter
is sometimes provided. Nine times out of ten it is
wrongly adjusted, thus increasing the oil dilution and
engine wear.

CONTRAST WHEN PETROL ONLY IS USED.

All the above complications, risks, and delays
are eliminated, and the farmer gets on with the job.

ACTION OF PARAFFIN ON OIL.

It is impossible to arrange for the complete

combustion of paraffin, at all times with the result that
there is a certain amount of unburnt fuel washing down
the cylinder walls.   Paraffin is most injurious to
the lubricating properties of oil, and damage to the
engine is bound to be caused where this fuel is used.

It is not generally known amongst farmers that
millions of pounds have been spent in endeavouring to
make motor cars and motor lorries use paraffin.   All
these attempts have failed completely because of the
damage caused to engines, despite the utmost precaution.

It would prove a costly business for a farmer
to run his motor car on paraffin; as a tractor engine is
of equivalent design there is not real justification for
running it on paraffin.   The great difficulty is that
damage is not immediately apparent, although it is taking
place all the time.   Sooner or later heavy repair charges
have to be met, thus increasing operating costs considerably.

VITAL NEED TO SIMPLIFY TRACTOR OPERATION.

The big stride forward we have made in simplifying
the Ferguson machinery means that highly skilled, highly
paid operators are not an essential to satisfactory service.
If, however, paraffin be used, skilled and highly paid
operators must be employed.

One farmer advises us that by using petrol only
and unskilled labour, he saves considerably more than he
would be using paraffin.

THE QUESTION OF RELIABILITY.

One outstanding advantage of the horse is his
reliability.   This is something the farmer must have in
his tractor at all costs.

It required 20 years of continuous work to make
our machinery beat the horse in this respect, and to
produce at a fraction of the cost.   Now that we have
accomplished these objects, it is in the farmers' own
interests to take advantage of them, and avoid the risk
of impairing the reliability which has been built into
our machinery.

As a matter of actual fact, a farmer could afford
to pay about 10/- per gallon for fuel for our tractor, and
still produce for much less than horses.

SOME USEFUL FIGURES.

The Ferguson tractor really solves this fuel problem because it requires little more than one third of the fuel needed for most tractors. It costs less to run the Ferguson tractor on petrol than any other on paraffin.

The additional expense per annum, on small or average farms, when using petrol only in a Ferguson tractor is from £5 to £12. This is of no consequence when compared with the saving in repair bills, lubricating oil, time and trouble, and the cost of skilled operators. Nor is it comparable with the very much greater profits a farmer can make annually when using our machinery.

STORAGE TANK.

By having a storage tank, every farmer could have petrol available for all his requirements at the lowest cost.

WHY HAS NO REAL PROGRESS BEEN MADE IN MECHANIZED FARMING?

Motor cars, for example, have developed rapidly and their sales can now be counted in millions. Tractor sales are still counted in hundreds. The motor car has been developed along modern lines. It has been made lighter, simpler, and more economical to operate. We were convinced that tractor designs must follow in the same way, and the rapid development of our machinery proves that we were correct. The use of paraffin, however, introduces complications into tractor operation. It calls for a skilled attention which the average farmer cannot supply, and a high upkeep cost which he cannot afford.

The more this subject is studied, the more apparent it becomes that the use of paraffin, in any make of tractor, is not an economy but an expense.

Yours faithfully,

for HARRY FERGUSON LTD.

Harry Ferguson

The following extracts are quoted from an article on tractor performance and maintenance prepared by the outstanding independent authority in this country - The Institute for Research in Agricultural Engineering, University of Oxford:-

1. "The primary cause of rapid engine wear and heavy tractor depreciation is bad combustion of paraffin."

2. "The primary cause of this rapid deterioration is what is called crankcase dilution."

3. "It may as well be said here that it is impossible to avoid dilution completely."

4. The opinion of a number of prominent repair Agents was summed up by one of them as follows:- "If it were not for the jobs which arise from faulty lubrication in one form or another, we might as well close down the tractor repair side of our business altogether."

5. Following up these repairs..........we found that..........."the vast majority occurred in the engine itself and were due not to actual lack of oil but to the use of poor thin oil.........Very frequently an expensive high grade oil had been used..........,but the tractor owner or driver had not realised how quickly the oil was deteriorating in the engine so as to become useless as a lubricant."

IF YOU HAVE NOW ANY DOUBTS ABOUT THE HIGH UPKEEP COST OF USING PARAFFIN IN ANY MAKE OF TRACTOR, WE STRONGLY URGE YOU TO GET FROM OXFORD A COPY OF THE ARTICLE "TRACTOR PERFORMANCE IN THEORY AND PRACTICE" DATED JANUARY 5th 1937.

Harry Ferguson Ltd.
Huddersfield

Telephone:
Huddersfield 2685.

Telegrams:
"Farming" Huddersfield.

Manufacturers: David Brown Tractors Ltd.

W A R N I N G.

For the reasons clearly set forth in the enclosed copy letter, confirmed by extracts from a report issued by the Institute of Agricultural Engineering, Oxford, we strongly recommend the use of petrol only in all tractors.

We specifically warn the farmer that he will seriously damage his engine unless our instructions for the care of the Air Cleaner are carried out.

Pay strict attention to instructions on cleaning the engine breather.

We seriously warn the farmer against using any lubricating oils other than those prepared for us by The Shell Company, and labelled as follows:-

"Special oil for Ferguson hydraulic mechanism and engine."

also

"Special lubricant for Ferguson rear axle and grease gun."

We take no responsibility whatever under our Warranty unless the oils and fuel which we recommend are used exclusively.

Tighten all drain plugs carefully after refilling with oil.

Under no circumstances must the tractor be used in top gear for land cultivation. The implements are designed to stand any stress up to a speed of 3 m.p.h. If the tractor is driven above that speed, they may not stand the strain.

Do not carry anything on the implements.

Do not reverse the tractor with the implement in the ground. Pull the Control Lever to the lift position before putting in the reverse gear.

Do not keep foot on clutch pedal when operating.
Use steering connection.
Do not hold clutch pedal in disengaged position
when engine is running.

Do not lubricate any part of the tractor or implements
where no provision is made for lubrication. For example,
if the Ball Sockets are lubricated, they will collect grit
and wear out rapidly.

When storing tractor or implements, smear such parts
as the Ball Sockets with oil. This should be wiped off
before commencing operations.

When tractor and implements have been in operation
for about a week, check all nuts and tighten up securely.
Fuel tank nuts to be tightened gently.

See that there is always a little free end play in
clutch rod.

A new tractor should be kept on light work for about
3 days, so as to allow the bearings to get well run in.

High speed cultivation of land is a mistake, and
enormously increases upkeep costs, including a much
heavier consumption of fuel and oil.   The best and
most economical speed at which to operate is from $2\frac{1}{2}$
to 3 m.p.h.

Do not use bottom links for pulling anything other
than "Ferguson" implements.

Under no circumstances should anything be pulled
from the top link connection on the tractor. Attaching
anything to this connection other than the top link
is highly dangerous.

Do not turn the Steering Wheel unless the tractor
is in motion.

Do not keep the engine running when the tractor
is stopped. This will avoid fuel wastage and sooting
of spark plugs.

When filling tanks, filter fuel carefully.

YOU HAVE BEEN WARNED ! !

READ ABOVE AGAIN - AND AGAIN.

2

L U B R I C A T I O N

TRACTOR.

1. Tests were extended over many years to
   find an oil suitable for the Hydraulic
   Mechanism which would ensure perfect
   operation in Summer and Winter.
   When this oil was obtained, it was of
   such an unusually high quality that it
   was suitable for both Hydraulic Mechanism
   and Engine.

2. The engine dipstick should be examined
   DAILY, and the oil kept up to the
   correct level. In hilly land examine
   dipstick twice daily.
   See that the tractor is quite level
   when this is being done, or dipstick
   will give a false reading.

3. When using petrol only the engine   Days   Hours
   should be drained and filled with
   fresh oil every............................6 or   54

4. Warning - Drain engine when hot.
   Do not wash out the engine with
   paraffin or T.V.O.

MAGNETO

1. Lubricate with 12 drops of sperm, or
   cream separator oil every...................6 or   54

2. If the Impulse Starter ceases to "click"
   when the engine is being turned slowly,
   this will make starting more difficult.

3. To make the Impulse Starter work
   correctly, remove the small screw in
   coupling, and squirt in a little sperm
   or cream separator oil.

4. Two inches lead on the flywheel is the
   correct magneto setting.

ENGINE BREATHER.

In dusty conditions, hold the breather filter
upside down and pour in some T.V.O. Shake
until T.V.O. flows freely through the filter,
every...6 or   54

Fit a new breather element every 12 months.

3.

```
              WARNING RE HEAVY FUEL IN
                FERGUSON TRACTOR.
    _____


          Our strong recommendation is to use
    petrol only.  If this recommendation is not
    taken, the following must be  done:-

        1. Drain ONE QUART of oil from
           engine EVERY WORKING DAY and
           refill with fresh oil.  Keep
           oil up to high mark on dipstick
           but not above it.

        2. Drain ALL oil from engine and
           refill with fresh oil EVERY 3
           WORKING DAYS.

        3. In ordinary conditions examine
           dipstick every working day, but
           in hilly conditions examine
           dipstick twice daily.  See
           that tractor is quite level for
           this examination.

        4. T.V.O. is the only heavy fuel
           we recommend, and do not use it
           until engine is very hot.

        5. Use petrol only when tractor
           is doing light work.


          This care is absolutely essential to
    safeguarding your engine.


                       4.
```

<u>AIR CLEANER</u>.

We cannot too seriously warn farmers
against the danger of dust getting into the engines
of their tractors. Dust has been known to ruin
an engine in 6 days.

The utmost care must be taken at all
times to see that not the slightest leak of air
can take place anywhere between the air cleaner
and the engine. For example, if the carburetter
should be dismantled, the <u>utmost</u> precaution
must be taken to see that all joints are carefully
made on reassembly.

Inspect bowl every working day and fill
up to high level mark with engine oil.

<u>WARNING</u> - In dusty conditions, the
bowl must be cleaned out and refilled with
fresh oil <u>every working day</u>. In exceptionally
bad conditions it may be necessary to clean
the bowl <u>several</u> times daily.

Oil that has been drained from the engine
or transmission can be used for filling the bowl.

5.

TAPPET CLEARANCE.

This should be .006" for the inlet valves,
and .008" for the exhaust valves.

HYDRAULIC MECHANISM & TRANSMISSION.

		Days	Hours

1. Remove Drain Plugs under Gearbox and
   Bell Housing, and drain out all oil
   after a new tractor has completed...............18 or 162

2. This oil should be drained when the
   tractor is warm, and the Drain Plugs
   should be left out overnight. Refill
   with fresh oil.

3. 3 gallons of oil put into the Gearbox
   will bring the oil up to the correct
   level. The oil will filter through
   slowly to the Bell Housing.

4. After the first refill, the Gearbox
   and Bell Housing should be drained
   every..54 or 486
   and refilled with fresh oil.

5. The Transmission Dipstick should be
   inspected every 6 days, and the oil
   kept up to the correct level.

FRONT WHEEL HUBS.

The Front Wheel Hubs should be lubricated until
the oil is oozing out at the end of the
bearings every....................................54 or 486

REAR AXLE.

The rear axle should be drained and
refilled to the High Level Plug after
every...54 or 486

GREASE GUN.

The principle of the grease gun is that it
will force lubricant into the bearings at a
pressure of 2000-lbs. and force out all grit
and dirty oil.

-4-

To obtain these results, the grease gun should
be kept going until the lubricant begins to
ooze out of the bearings.

After each full working day of either tractor
or plough, the grease gun should be used on
each nipple, and a small amount of lubricant
inserted at the following points:-

<u>Tractor</u>.

Swivel pins.
Track rod sockets.
Pull-and-push rod sockets.
Levelling Lever thread and ball bearing.

<u>Plough</u>.

Coulter hubs.
Wheel bearing.
Wheel bracket.
(This is the bracket which is
bolted to the landside, <u>and if
the bearing is allowed to become
stiff, it will put the plough
out of operation.</u>)

-5-

HOW TO ATTACH AN IMPLEMENT.

1. Back up the tractor so that it is central with the implement.

2. Attach nearside bottom link first.

3. Attach offside bottom link, using levelling lever to bring the link to the correct position.

4. Attach top link from the seat.

HOW TO DETACH AN IMPLEMENT.

1. Drop the implement on level ground and central.

2. Detach top link first.

3. Adjust levelling lever to take all strain off ball sockets.

4. Detach offside bottom link.

5. Detach nearside bottom link.

6. Be careful to put linch pins in their proper clips on the bottom links to prevent chains from being damaged.

7. When top link is removed from tractor, be careful to put the front pin through rocker and rocker yoke without altering adjustment on control spring.

HOW TO ADJUST WIDTH OF FRONT FURROW.

1. To make the front furrow wider, slacken the cross shaft U bolts, and turn the shaft forward at the top.

2. To make the furrow narrower, turn the shaft rearwards at the top. Before slackening the U bolts, put a pencil mark on the shaft and the plough beam. Moving the shaft 1/8" at these marks will alter the width of the front furrow approximately 1".

3. Be sure to clamp the U bolts very tightly after making an adjustment.

4. The correct fixing of the cross shaft on the 10" plough gives a measurement of $12\frac{7}{8}$" from the plough beam to the end of the shaft on the nearside.

8.

PNEUMATIC EQUIPMENT.

All pneumatic wheels are sent out adjusted to give the standard tread of 48". This tread should be used for ploughing, general cultivation, and road work.

All wheels should be bolted to their hubs at all times with the wording "PATENT APPLIED FOR" on the outside.

For varying track adjustments see page 9 of "Hydraulics Harnessed" leaflet.

TYRE PRESSURES - Rear Wheels.

For agricultural work	-	7 lbs.
For haulage work	-	20 lbs.

Front wheels.

Under all conditions	-	20 lbs.

A pressure gauge is supplied free with each set of wheels.

WE LAY SPECIAL EMPHASIS ON THE FOLLOWING:-

1) Examine the engine dipstick DAILY.

2) Drain engine and refill with fresh oil after every 6 days or 54 hours work.

3) Use only the oils and fuel we recommend.

4) Keep the wheel bracket on the plough rear landside tight, and well lubricated.

5) Always lubricate threads before tightening a nut.

-9-

L79-2449

Harry Ferguson Ltd.

Huddersfield

Telephone:
Huddersfield 2685.

Telegrams:
"Farming" Huddersfield.

Manufacturers: David Brown Tractors Ltd.

WLH/EW   January 5th 1937

Messrs.Kay & Backhouse Ltd.,
Foss Bridge,
York.

Dear Sirs,

    We have been asked to quote to supply replicas of
the model tractor and implements, by which the line of
draft exclusive to Ferguson Machinery can be demonstrated
by your salesmen.

    Such models complete in well finished carrying case,
and containing all necessary equipment, cost about £5.0.0.
but we are willing to supply these attractive sets at a
special price of £2.10.0. nett to distributors.

    Will you please notify us whether you would like us
to reserve one of these for you.

        Yours faithfully,
for HARRY FERGUSON LTD.

Walter L.Hill

Harry Ferguson Ltd.
Huddersfield

Telephone:
Huddersfield 2685.

Telegrams:
"Farming" Huddersfield.

Manufacturers: David Brown Tractors Ltd.

AAS/BF

18th June, 1937.

Dear Sirs,

<u>An Important Amalgamation.</u>

The immediate success of our machinery, coupled with the difficulty of meeting the demand, has made it necessary for us to consider how we can best increase our output in the near future.

Many offers of finances have been made to us, but we came to the conclusion that the best means of expansion would be to amalgamate the interests of this Company with those of Messrs. David Brown Tractors Ltd. This amalgamation is about to take place, and a new Company will be formed with very great resources behind it.

Mr. Harry Ferguson and Mr. David Brown will be joint Managing Directors of the new Company, and Mr. Walter L. Hill will be General Manager.

Already energetic steps are being taken in the development of additional new buildings and big additions to the manufacturing plant and machinery. What is equally important, additional orders have been placed for materials to complete this year's requirements and for adequate supplies for 1938. We shall do every-thing possible to avoid a repetition of the shortage in tractors and implements experienced during the early part of this year.

This evidence of the necessity for expansion is final proof of the value of our new inventions, and we hope it will encourage you to redouble your efforts in the great work of establishing British Agriculture on a basis that will guarantee security in war, and immensely greater prosperity in times of peace.

Yours faithfully,
for HARRY FERGUSON LTD.

Secretary.

Telephone:
Huddersfield 2685.

Harry Ferguson Ltd.
Huddersfield

Telegrams:
"Farming" Huddersfield.

Manufacturers: David Brown Tractors Ltd.

WLH/BF   20th August, 1937.

Messrs. Kay & Backhouse, Ltd.,
Foss Bridge,
YORK.

Dear Sirs,

4" SPUDS.

Supplies of 4" spuds will shortly be available, and will be offered at 2/6d. per spud complete with bolts, plain and spring washers.

10" wheels require 24 spuds per wheel and 6" wheels require 18 spuds per wheel. Complete sets retail therefore at £6 per set for 10" wheels, and £4. 10. 0. per set for 6" wheels.

Should any Ferguson owner in your area require these spuds, it will be necessary for the wheels on his Tractor to be re-drilled.

In order to assist you in dealing with such cases, we are prepared to supply you with a pair of 10" wheels and a pair of 6" wheels drilled for 4" spuds, at list less 50%. We will also supply a small drilling template.

The suggested procedure would be to supply the stock set of wheels to the first purchaser of 4" spuds, in exchange for his own wheels, when you would repaint and drill the wheels taken in exchange, so that you would always have in stock a pair of wheels suitable for 4" spuds.

HARRY FERGUSON LTD.

CONTINUATION SHEET......................

Other parts of the machinery will be
affected by fitting 4" spuds, and should be dealt
with as follows:-

1. <u>PLOUGH</u>. The heel of the skimmer may foul the
   4" spuds when in the lifted position if the
   plough swings to the limit of the check chain.
   Skimmers therefore on existing ploughs will
   require shortening at the heel 3". This can
   readily be accomplished by nicking the blade
   on both sides, and breaking off the heel.

   As the shorter skimmer gives better results,
   all ploughs in the near future will be
   delivered with short skimmers.

2. <u>ROW CROP CULTIVATOR</u>. The outside front tines
   require to be set back a sufficient amount to
   clear the 4" spuds, and for this purpose, a
   pair of plates will be supplied free of
   charge to all owners of Row Crop Cultivators
   requiring 4" spuds.

3. <u>ROAD BANDS</u>. The present roadband is not
   suitable for use with 4" spuds. In the near
   future a roadband will be available, which
   can be used either with 3" or 4" spuds.

   We would advise you to fit your
Demonstration Tractor with 4" spuds, as you may
encounter conditions where the additional
adhesion provided by these spuds would make a
noticeable difference in the performance of the
machinery.

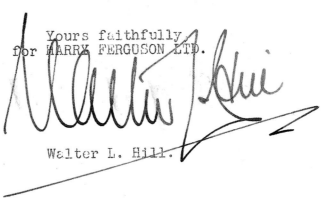

Yours faithfully,
for HARRY FERGUSON LTD.

Walter L. Hill.

FERGUSON - BROWN LTD

HUDDERSFIELD

TELEPHONE
HUDDERSFIELD 4011

TELEGRAMS
"FARMING"
HUDDERSFIELD

WEK/JH

31st March, 1938.

Messrs. Kay & Backhouse Ltd.,
Foss Bridge,
Y O R K.

Dear Sirs,

RE WHEEL SPACERS.

While our standard alternative wheel
tracks meet the majority of requirements for row crop
work, we have found that there are certain districts
in the country where further variations are necessary,
in order that the wheels may travel down the centre of
the rows.

We now have pleasure in announcing that
we are manufacturing wheel spacers in two alternative
sizes, to meet these additional requirements, and that
they are now available for delivery.

To fit these, all that is necessary is
to remove the wheels and screw on the spacers to the
existing wheel studs, and then place the wheels on the
spacers, securing them in position by the existing wheel
nuts.

These spacers are provided in lengths
of 3" and 4½", which give the various track measurements
as follows:-

Standard track with 6" rear wheels, 46½" or 52½".
      "   "   " 3" spacers. 52½" or 58½".
      "   "   " 4½" spacers. 55½" or 61½".

Standard track with 10" rear wheels, 48" or 51".
      "   "   " 3" spacers. 54" or 57".
      "   "   " 4½" spacers. 57" or 60"

FERGUSON-BROWN LTD.

Continuation to

Sheet No.

31st March, 1938.

Messrs. Kay & Backhouse Ltd.

Standard track with pneumatic wheels. 45" or 48".
                                        51" or 54".
    "   "   "   3" spacers.   51" or 54".
                                        57" or 60".
    "   "   "   4½" spacers. 54" or 57".
                                        60" or 63".

    The following are the number of spacers required, together with part numbers and prices.

EX31. Rear Wheel Spacer, 3" - 12 required. 3/-d. each.
EX32. Front Wheel Spacer, 3" - 10 required. 3/-d. each.
EX33. Rear Wheel Spacer, 4½" - 12 required. 3/6d. each.
EX34. Front Wheel Spacer, 4½" - 10 required. 3/6d. each.

    A complete set of 3" spacers will therefore retail at £3.6.0d., and the 4½" at £3.17.0d.

    These prices will be subject to a discount of 15%.

    We shall be glad, therefore, if you will let us have your requirements as soon as possible.

Yours faithfully,
for FERGUSON-BROWN LTD.

SERVICE DEPT.

FERGUSON - BROWN LTD

HUDDERSFIELD

TELEPHONE
HUDDERSFIELD 4011

TELEGRAMS
"FARMING"
HUDDERSFIELD

WHK/JH   12th May, 1938.

W.R. Smith Esq.,
Elm Grove,
Stanwich,
Aldborough St. John,
YORKSHIRE.

Dear Sir,

         We thank you for forwarding the completed
Warranty Form relating to the FERGUSON FARM MACHINERY
which you have recently purchased, and have pleasure
in returning this to you duly signed, together with a copy
of our Spare Parts List and Price List.

         May we take this opportunity of expressing
our appreciation of your patronage.

         You will have received a copy of our
Instruction Booklet. This has not been designed with
the object of explaining how our machinery works, as
we have found that the average owner is only interested
in keeping his outfit in first-class running order,
and if you will have the points set out in this booklet
attended to at the stated intervals, using our recommended
lubricants, we are confident that you can look forward
to more pleasant and profitable farming than you have
ever experienced in the past.

         The dealer from whom you purchased your
equipment will have instructed you in all the essential
points of operation, but should any small doubts arise
from time to time, we trust that you will not hesitate
to make the fullest use of our Service organisation,
which exists solely to give you trouble-free farming.

         In an exactly similar manner to a new
car, a new tractor should not be overworked or overdriven
during the first 30 hours of its service, by which time

FERGUSON-BROWN LTD.

Continuation to

the moving parts will have "bedded in", and you will
be obtaining maximum performance and economy.

By careful thought and design we have
succeeded in giving the farmer what has long been due
to him - machinery with which he can do more and better
work at a lower cost than with any other available
means, and when you have had an opportunity of proving
this we should be very happy indeed to hear from you.

Remember, your dealer is a FERGUSON
enthusiast, or he would not be selling our products,
and you will always find him and ourselves eager to
assist you in every possible way.

With best wishes for better farming.

Yours faithfully,
for FERGUSON-BROWN LTD.

SERVICE DEPT.

FERGUSON BROWN LTD., HUDDERSFIELD

Manufacturer's Warranty

FERGUSON Products are supplied by Ferguson Brown Ltd. (hereinafter called "The Company") with the following express Warranty which excludes all warranties conditions and liabilities whatsoever implied by Common Law Statute or otherwise that is to say :—

In the event of any defect being disclosed in any part or parts of the Company's products, and if the part or parts alleged to be defective are returned to the Company's works carriage paid within six months from the date when the goods are delivered new to the retail customer the Company undertakes to examine same and should any fault due to defective material or workmanship be found on examination by the Company it will repair the defective part or supply free of charge a new part in place thereof. This Warranty is limited to the delivery to the purchaser free at the Company's works of the part or parts whether new or repaired in exchange for those acknowledged by the Company to be defective.

The Company desires and expects that customers shall make a thorough examination of the Company's products before purchasing. Persons dealing in the Company's products are in no way the legal Agents of the Company, and have no right or authority to assume any obligation on its behalf express or implied or to bind it in any way.

For the purpose of this Warranty the term "Products" means and includes only new tractors or implements or parts thereof including replacement parts manufactured by or for the Company to the Company's designs and drawings. It does not include tyres or Electrical Equipment or other proprietary articles or goods although supplied by the Company Proprietary articles are covered by the Warranty (if any) given by the separate manufacturers. On second-hand products no warranty is given by the Company or is to be implied.

The Company's responsibility is limited to the terms of this Warranty and it shall not be answerable for personal injuries or consequential or resulting liability damage or loss arising from any defects. This Warranty shall not apply to defects caused by wear and tear, misuse or neglect or to the defects in any Products which have been altered outside the Company's works or which have been let out on hire or the identification marks on which have been altered or removed.

The Company's liability under this Warranty is dependent upon the strict observance by the Purchaser of the following provisions :—

(a) The Purchaser at the time of purchase shall sign complete and return the form supplied by the Company and attached to this document, and shall obtain from the Company a signed copy of this Warranty. This Warranty shall not be assigned or transferred to anyone unless the Company's consent in writing has first been obtained.

(b) Parts claimed to be defective must be properly packed for transit and clearly marked for identification with the name and full address of the Purchaser and with the Maker's numbers of the tractor or implement from which the said part or parts were taken.

(c) The Purchaser shall post to the Company at its works on or before despatch of such part or parts alleged to be defective a full and complete description of the claim and the reasons therefor.

(d) The Purchaser shall at all times in the operation of any of the Company's products use only those brands of lubricating oil, lubricant or fuel officially approved in writing by the Company.

(e) The judgment of the Company in all cases of claims shall be final and conclusive and the Purchaser agrees to accept its decision on all questions as to defects and to the exchange of part or parts. After the expiration of six days from the despatch of notification of the Company's decision, the part or parts submitted may be scrapped or returned carriage forward by the Company.

This is to Certify that

TRACTOR	No.	616
PLOUGH	No.	581
GENERAL CULTIVATOR	No.	413
RIDGER	No.	319
ROW CROP CULTIVATOR	No.	265

are covered by the provisions of the Warranty as above defined and registered as the property of

WILLIAM R. SMITH, ELM GROVE, STANWICH,

Address ALDBOROUGH ST. JOHN, YORKSHIRE.

For and on behalf of

Ferguson Brown Ltd.

Date 12th May, 1938.

FERGUSON-BROWN LTD

HUDDERSFIELD

TELEPHONE
HUDDERSFIELD 4011

TELEGRAMS
"FARMING"
HUDDERSFIELD
WLH/JH

22nd December, 1938.

Messrs. Kay & Backhouse Ltd.,
Foss Bridge,
Y O R K.

Dear Sirs,

      As you know, this Company - Ferguson-Brown
Ltd. - was formed to amalgamate the activities of two
separate organisations which had, until September 1937,
been separately conducting the manufacturing and marketing .
of our machinery.

      Now that our plans to cater for the export
market are maturing, it has been considered advisable to
segregate the Ferguson and Brown interests so that no
confusion will arise in certain markets.

      To facilitate this, Mr. Ferguson has disposed
of his shareholding in Ferguson-Brown Ltd. to Mr. David Brown,
and the title of this firm will be altered to David Brown
Tractors Ltd.

      Manufacturing and marketing of farm machinery
under a new modified licence granted by Mr. Ferguson will
be continued without interruption, and all engagements entered
into by this Company will be honoured by David Brown Tractors Ltd.

              Yours faithfully,
          for FERGUSON-BROWN LTD.

              David Brown.
              Managing Director.

COVENTRY

TELEGRAMS: FARMING   TELEPHONE: 5533

London Office: 37 Davies Street, London, W.1.

December 31 - 1948

J. M. Reekie, Esq.,
Reekie Engineering Co. Ltd.,
Lochlands Works,
Arbroath,
Scotland.

Dear Mr. Reekie,

<u>Universal Raspberry Tractor</u>

  Following up our previous correspondence and your visit
here the other day, we have been giving careful thought to your proposals
and as I have already advised you we consider that there will be very
little demand for such a tractor, either in the home or export markets.

  Furthermore, we are not at all happy about various points of
the design and our Engineering Department cannot approve this somewhat
major and drastic modification to the tractor.   In the circumstances, we
very much regret that we could not agree to your marketing such a tractor
bearing the Ferguson name.

  I am sorry to be so unhelpful in this matter, but we do
feel very strongly that it would be most unwise to spend further time and
energy on this project.

       Yours sincerely,

LGR/DD.   L. G. REID

Directors: HARRY G. FERGUSON (*Chairman*), A. BOTWOOD (*Managing*), R. A. DAVIS, MAUREEN A. FERGUSON, ELIZABETH M. FERGUSON, L. G. REID E. W. YOUNG

F. 164

Harry Ferguson, Ltd.

COVENTRY

TELEGRAMS: FARMING   TELEPHONE 5533

London Office : 37 *Davies Street, London, W.*1.

May 11 - 1950

PASS TO	DATE	INITIALS
DIRECTOR	13/5	
ACCOUNTS		
SALES		

J. M. Reekie, Esq.,
Reekie Engineering Co. Ltd.,
Lochlands Works,
Arbroath,
Scotland.

Dear Mr. Reekie,

We have been advised by our associated
company in America, Messrs. Harry Ferguson Inc.
that one of their dealers, namely the Neal & Massy
Engineering Co. Ltd., have been in correspondence
with you concerning a Reekie-Ferguson narrow gauge
tractor.

We understand that you have quoted the
Neal & Massy Engineering Co. for the supply of such
tractors and have, in fact, been marketing such a
tractor.

We assume that this Reekie-Ferguson tractor
is similar to the tractor which you sent to us for
our inspection at the end of 1948 and you will remember that we were unable to approve such a major modification to our tractor.

I wrote to you on the 31st December, 1948
and advised you that we were not at all happy about
the design and that our Engineering Department could
not approve the very drastic changes and modifications.
I furthermore advised you that we could not agree to
your marketing such a tractor bearing the Ferguson name.

In these circumstances I am sure you will
understand our consternation to learn that you are
marketing this tractor as a Reekie-Ferguson tractor.
We are extremely concerned about this, particularly
in view of the fact that we consider the major mechanical

Cont'd........

Directors: HARRY G. FERGUSON (*Chairman*), A. BOTWOOD (*Managing*), MAUREEN A. FERGUSON, ELIZABETH M. FERGUSON, L. G. REID, E. W. YOUNG

-2-

alterations you have made to be unsatisfactory and, of course, our warranty will not be applicable to any of our tractors converted in such a way.

Possibly there are circumstances about which I have no knowledge, or possibly we have been misinformed of the actual position, and I would be glad to hear from you with regard to this particular conversion.

Yours sincerely,

L. G. REID

LGR/DD.

F. 164.

Harry Ferguson, Ltd.

COVENTRY

TELEGRAMS: FARMING   TELEPHONE 5533

London Office : 37 Davies Street, London, W.1.

1st. August, 1950.

J. M. Reekie, Esq.
Reekie Engineering Co. Ltd.,
ARBROATH.
Scotland.

PASS TO	DATE	INITIALS
DIRECTOR		
ACCOUNTS		
STORES		
FERGUSON		
ELECTRICAL		
FILE		

Dear John,

I have your letter dated 25th. July,
1950, and note that it has been agreed with
Mr. Young that your narrow tractor can henceforth be named the "Ferguson-Reekie Modified
Tractor".

In these circumstances, I will once
more endeavour to obtain shortened axle shafts
for you, and I am, therefore, contacting our
Production Department accordingly. Immediately
I have advice from them, I will contact you.

Yours sincerely,

C. B. DILLON.

CBD/NG.

P. 164.

Harry Ferguson, Ltd.

COVENTRY

TELEGRAMS: FARMING   TELEPHONE 5533

London Office : 37 Davies Street, London, W.1.

3rd August 1950.

J.M.Reekie Esq.,
Messrs. Reekie Engineering Co, Ltd.,
Arbroath,
SCOTLAND.

Dear John,

For some reason or other the attached catalogue has reached my office and I would like to point out to you that on page 4, showing the tractor working with a 2-furrow plough, that this implement is referred to as a Ferguson 2-furrow plough, but in actual fact, it is a plough which has been modified by someone.

We should, therefore, be glad if you could put this matter right in any further issues.

One further observation which I should like to make and that is on page 7, you show the tractor with a mounted spraying unit attached, and the tractor lying at a very acute angle. I have driven tractors on a good many occasions, but I should certainly be scared to drive the machine at the angle which you have indicated in your photograph, if the tank of the spraying unit was full.

We, at one time, had the option of taking up the distribution of the Patrick & Wilkinson Sprayer, which is very similar to the one shown in the photograph, but we considered it dangerous as one could tip the Tractor over very easily with an ordinary standard Tractor.

Trusting you do not mind us bringing these two points to your attention.

Yours sincerely,

TREVOR V. KNOX.

TVK/MEH.

Directors: HARRY G. FERGUSON (Chairman), A. BOTWOOD (Managing), MAUREEN A. FERGUSON, ELIZABETH M. FERGUSON L. G. REID, E. W. YOUNG

F. 164.

Harry Ferguson, Ltd.

COVENTRY

TELEGRAMS: FARMING   TELEPHONE 5525

London Office : 37 Davies Street, London, W.1.

PASS TO	DATE	INITIALS
DIRECTOR		
ACCOUNTS		
STORES		
FERGUSON		
ELECTRICAL		
FILE		

J.M.Reekie Esq.,
Reekie Engineering Co.Ltd.,
Arbroath,
SCOTLAND.

Your ref PC. JMR/LSC.

September 5-1950.

Dear John,

Sorry for the delay in replying to your letter of August 16th.

I understand that Mr. Reid is taking over all the correspondence regarding the production of a 44" wide tractor and that in due course he will be communicating with you.

With reference to the name plate which you attach to this particular type of tractor. Might I suggest that it would be more in our interest, in fact I have the agreement of Mr. Young and Mr. Reid to this suggestion, if the name plate was placed directly below the Ferguson name and it should read :- MODIFIED by REEKIE. as per the attached.

You have undoubtedly gathered from the conversations you have had with different members of our staff that the most important item as far as we are concerned is to establish that it is a Ferguson tractor and that the modifications are carried out by your goodselves.

Kindest regards.

Yours sincerely,

TREVOR V. KNOX.
Sales Manager.

TVK/BH.

Directors : HARRY G. FERGUSON (*Chairman*), A. BOTWOOD (*Managing*), MAUREEN A. FERGUSON, ELIZABETH M. FERGUSON, L. G. REID, E. W. YOUNG

F 164

Harry Ferguson, Ltd.

COVENTRY

TELEGRAMS FARMING   TELEPHONE 5533

London Office: 37 Davies Street, London, W.1.

John M. Reekie, Esq.,
<u>Arbroath.</u>   September 16, 1952.

Dear John,

PLOUGHS

We have been holding a council of war on this matter
and are now working on a single-bottom plough of our present
type to see whether a bar-point can be developed.   I think
if we could develop it, this plough, as it now is, would cover
the whole of your conditions.   If, in some cases, you used
skimmers only and no discs you would get, occasionally, wear
on the front edge of the mouldboard.   That is why people make
detachable shin pieces.   However, I am convinced that no
plough should be worked without a disc coulter under any
conditions excepting where there are multitudes of loose,
smallish stones as big as your fist and bigger.

If we could make our single-bottom plough work as I
suggest then you would have a universal plough and, of course,
the mouldboard would keep clean in conditions of sticky soil
where a mouldboard with the shin pieces would not.

These shin pieces are a curse from the point of view
of choking up especially after new shin pieces have been fitted.

12" 2-BOTTOM PLOUGH

We are convinced that the best thing we can do at the
moment is to have you send us 2 12" bottoms, a front and a
rear, just as quickly as you can.   We will fit these
accurately to one of our own plough frames and also fit the
wheel and then send the plough back to you to be tested to
the utmost during this ploughing season.   We will not give
you the additional 5" between front and rear bottoms because
I think you can get away without it.

You saw the mess that was made even with this extra
5" when no discs were fitted.   I believe that with discs and
the present fore and aft measurements you will be able to
plough where any plough would work.

Directors HARRY G. FERGUSON *(Chairman)* A. BOTWOOD *(Managing)*, MAUREEN A. FERGUSON, ELIZABETH M. SHELDON, L. G. REID, E. W. YOUNG, I. J. WALLACE

Harry Ferguson, Ltd.
Coventry

F 169A

Continuation Sheet

-2-

NEW DISC COULTER

Manufacturing developments are well advanced. We believe that this disc with the skimmer further forward and no arm to interfere with trash on the inside would be a help to the plough to prevent it from choking up where there is lots of trash. If we are ready in time with this we will equip this plough for you with the discs but, if not, we will send it on without.

A WORD OF WARNING

I most earnestly ask you to make sure beyond all question of doubt that the two bottoms you will send us will be precisely and absolutely bottoms that will be okay for all the future and suit generally all your conditions for a 12" plough.

No matter how long it may take us working together mutually let us get things right at the start and not have to go changing afterwards.

Will you please reply to this to:

Mr. John M. Chambers,
Harry Ferguson Ltd.,
Coventry,

and carry on developments with Mr. Chambers who will be in constant consultation with me.

My sincere and best wishes to you and all of you,

Yours cordially,

Harry Ferguson

HF/TG.

c.c. Mr. Chambers.

Harry Ferguson Holdings Ltd.
Stow - on - the - Wold
Gloucestershire.

Telephones
Office: Stow 190
House: Stow 16

Telegrams
"Holdings"
Stow - on - Wold

John R. Reekie, Esq.,
Arbroath.

July 23rd, 1954.

My dear John,

STRICTLY CONFIDENTIAL.

Thank you very much indeed for your most welcome
letter of July 9th quite unavoidably held over until today
owing to being just about swamped out with events and
correspondence. I need not say how deeply I appreciate
your nice letter. It is more to me than all the millions
I am supposed to have made!

I am sending my reply to you privately because
there is something I want to say to you in confidence.
I can say practically nothing at this time but, be assured,
I am thinking a lot and planning a lot!

I quote from your letter:-

"....to break away from your great interest in
the agricultural world...."

I found it necessary to break away from M-H-F Ltd,
for reasons which will be apparent later on. But that
does not necessarily mean that I have broken away from
the vast agricultural machinery industry. I feel, as I
always did, that Agriculture, Transportation and
Manufacture are the three greatest things in the economic
life of any people and that the solution of those problems
is also the solution of the terrible menace of Communism.

Not only do I appreciate your letter but, also,
the really splendid work you have done to help our Crusade
and your efforts generally. You will be in the forefront
of my mind in whatever the future holds for us. I sincerely
hope that things will so develop that we may be working
together again.

Again thanks and the warmest and best from my family
and myself,

Yours cordially,

Harry Ferguson

Directors: Harry G. Ferguson (Chairman) Maureen A. Ferguson, Elizabeth M. Sheldon, A.T. Sheldon (Managing)
A.T. Sheldon.

CHAPTER 5

History of Ferguson - an interpretation from the USA

David Lory is the biggest collector of Ferguson equipment in the USA, where the enthusiasm for collecting all things Ferguson is at a much less advanced stage then in the UK. David has given great help in the collection of North American equipment for inclusion in the Hunday collection.

Ferguson enthusiasts on both sides of the Atlantic tend to forget that Ferguson was actively producing and inventing on each side of this great divide. Recently David published a series of four short articles on Ferguson in the US magazine *Antique Power*, who have kindly given their permission for reproduction here. It is hoped that this will give some balance to the study and appreciation of Ferguson at an inter-continental level.

Harry Ferguson Builds a Plow

Part 1 of a History of Ferguson Tractors

by David Lory

H. FERGUSON 1884-1960

The agricultural revolution began when Jethro Tull invented the first working seed drill in the 1700s. The 1800s brought the inventions of the grain reaper, thresher, and steam powered tractors. By the early 1900s engineers had designed gasoline-powered tractors with enough horsepower to pull a plow.

In the teens and twenties tractor designs were changed to better meet the needs of farmers. Farmall designed the first general purpose tractor in the early twenties.

By the thirties all that was needed in tractor design was refinement. The greatest of these refinements was probably also the greatest revolution in agricultural engineering. This refinement was a system that not only made tractor use safer, it integrated tractor and implement so that they worked together, and not against each other as before. It also allowed the tractor to become much more flexible, the proof being that hundreds of implements were soon designed for it. This system, consisting of a three-point hitch with draft control, is so widely used that over 85% of the tractors produced in the world since it has been introduced have incorporated it. It is simply called the Ferguson System after Harry Ferguson, who spent most of his life perfecting it.

The best way to appreciate the development of the Ferguson system is to look at the events leading up to its design.

Harry Ferguson was born on November 4, 1884. He was one of eleven children born on a hundred acre farm south of Belfast in what is now Northern Ireland. Farming at the end of the nineteenth century was difficult in Northern Ireland. The soil was poor and the weather was harsh. Harry dis-

liked the drudgery of day-to-day farming, and in 1902 he left the family farm to become an apprentice in his brother Joe's cycle and car repair shop. Harry learned the skills of a mechanic with great enthusiasm and became very good at tuning engines, a skill not very common in those days. With Harry's help, the repair shop became know as the best in Belfast. It was during this time that Harry took evening courses at the Belfast Technical college. This was all the formal training that he had in working with blueprints.

Harry Ferguson also had great skill as a promoter and a salesman, and began building an image for his brother's business by entering motor sports. In 1904 he began riding in motorcycle events in Ireland. With each race and trial he won, he gave more publicity to J.B. Ferguson and Company.

In 1908 he built his own airplane. Other planes had been built in Ireland, but none had been flown. Harry convinced his brother that successes in airplane flying would be good for business. On December 31, 1909, he became the first Briton to build and fly his own airplane. The plane flew 130 yards. In 1910, Harry won a prize for making the first three mile flight,

Tractors built from Ford Model T cars were popular for a short while. One of their biggest drawbacks, as recognized by Harry Ferguson, was that the only small plows available for them to pull were designed for horses.

but after several serious crashes, and his marriage in 1913, he decided to find a safer occupation.

In 1911 Harry Ferguson opened his own business, May Street Motors. The name was later changed to Harry Ferguson, Inc. By 1913 the business was very successful and Harry was working on perfecting carburetors. He soon developed two improvements and was granted patents on them. These were his first. Harry, and later the engineering teams working for him, were granted well over 100 patents.

During World War I, Great Britain lost many of its farm workers and horses to the war effort. To add to the problem, the Germans were cutting off most British food imports. This meant that more land needed to be farmed—with fewer workers. To help meet this need, Ferguson became a dealer for the Waterloo Boy tractor, made in the U.S A. and called the Overtime in Britain. Ferguson promoted the tractor through public demonstrations using a Cockshutt three-bottom plow.

By 1917, Ferguson and his assistant, Willy Sands, had developed great skill as plowmen. These talents were so impressive that the Irish Board of Agriculture asked Ferguson to help improve the efficiency of tractors during the 1917 plowing season. Ferguson and Sands worked with many different makes of tractors and plows. They were concerned that tractors were very heavy, causing compaction of the soil, and that they were not fuel efficient. But what they were most concerned about was plow design.

Plows were still designed to be pulled by horses. They were simply attached to the tractor with a chain or a pin. The wheels of the plow were used to regulate the working depth. Plows were heavy, since they needed their own weight to stay in the ground. But the biggest problem that Ferguson saw was the danger of striking a hidden object in the soil. If the plow was pulled by a team of horses, the horses would simply stop. But tractors had more power, and kept on going until the driver had a chance to react. Often the driver's reaction came too late, as by then the tractor or plow would be damaged, or worse, the tractor would rear backwards and flip over on the driver.

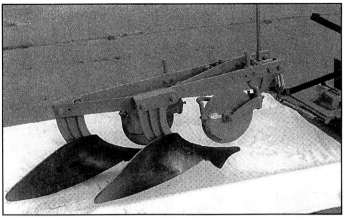

Ferguson's "Belfast" plow of 1917. This is the sole surviving example (probably pre-production). Here it is "hitched" to a demonstration stand. The photo on the right shows a view from the driver's seat when hitching up. Note the plow jaw in line with the drawbar hole in the hitch. The plow and hitch were connected by a shear pin which failed when the plow hit an obstruction. This hitch was designed specifically for the Eros model T conversion. It was later adapted for use with the Fordson.

The main idea that Ferguson kept in mind with all his inventions was to make farming easier. With that in mind, he set out to improve the plow. He soon found that it was impossible to design a plow for all the different makes of tractors. Therefore, he decided to work his designs around the lightweight Ford Eros tractor. This was a kit made by the F.G. Stande Manufacturing Company of Saint Paul, Minnesota, to convert a Ford model T car into a tractor.

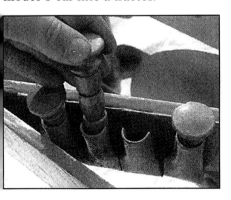

Harry Ferguson's meticulous attention to detail was obvious even in 1917. This special clip was provided to hold four spare shear pins, thereby avoiding delays should one break. The light weight, simplicity, and ease of use that Ferguson products became famous for are implicit in this, his very first plow.

By December 1917, Ferguson demonstrated a 220-pound two-bottom plow for the Eros tractor. This plow was less than one-third the weight and had fewer than one-half the parts of other two-bottom plows. A patent was applied for and approved. This plow was well received by farmers and the press. The main reason it did not become popular was the introduction of the Fordson.

A Fordson factory was to be built in Cork, Ireland, and 6000 Fordsons were to be imported from the U.S. to be sold until the factory was up and running. Though the Fordson was designed to simply pull the implement behind the tractor, it was clearly going to be a force in British agriculture. A number of British farmers were killed in the 1918 plowing season because the Fordson had a tendency to rear up and flip over.

After the stock of Eros plows were sold, Ferguson began working on a plow for the Fordson tractor. It was coupled to the tractor by two links, one above the other. This setup became known as the Duplex hitch, and a patent was applied for in the U.K. December 15, 1919. December 20, 1920, a U.S. patent was granted. This design incorporated the principle of a virtual (or imaginary) hitch point. What this meant was that the line of draft is from a point other than the actual hitch point. This concept is the basis of the Ferguson system linkage used on all modern tractors today. In the case of the Duplex hitch, this point was below and in front of the rear axle. This allowed the plow to stay in the ground without the weight previous plows had needed. The working depth of the plow was controlled by changing the length of the top link. Another feature of his design was that the harder the plow pulled, the more force was applied on the top link, which in turn caused more force on the front wheels, keeping them on the ground. This solved the problem of the Fordson rearing up backwards.

Although the plow was not at the level of perfection Ferguson wanted,

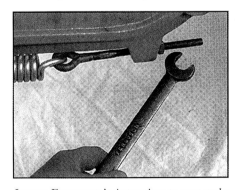

It was Ferguson's intention to use only two sizes of heads for all the nuts and bolts used. Here a very early Ferguson spanner (wrench) is seen with the spring adjuster on the 1917 plow. The spring is the original, but the eye bolt is a replacement. The original having been lost sometime since 1917.

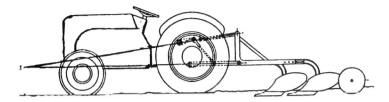

Ferguson's concept of the virtual hitch placed the effective draft point somewhere other than the actual point of attachment to the tractor. In the case of the Duplex hitch shown in this drawing the draft point is at a point (1) in front of the tractor.

he made an arrangement to bring it to Henry Ford, at Dearborn, Michigan, for a demonstration. After seeing the demonstration, Ford was impressed with it and asked if Ferguson would want to work with him, or if his patents were for sale. Ferguson refused both offers, and as they parted, Ford told Ferguson to keep him informed of the plow's progress.

Back in Ireland, Ferguson set out to perfect the plow. The first step was patent #1501651, a depth wheel for maintaining a constant working depth in uneven ground. Before this improvement, the plow's working depth changed as the tractor's wheels went up and down in uneven terrain. This depth wheel was not satisfactory, since it carried some of the weight of the plow and reduced tractor traction. Patent #1501652 used a spring to help control working depth, but this still did not solve the problem in a way that satisfied Ferguson. By 1923, the problem was solved and patented as #1637811. This covers the use of a small skid that ran in the furrow. This design corrected the uneven working depth of the plow in uneven terrain, and carried very little of the plow's weight. This design achieved full weight transfer of the plow to the rear of the tractor, while maintaining the safety feature mentioned above.

In 1925, Ferguson contacted George and Eber Sherman in the U.S.A. They were distributors for the Fordson in New York and had met Ferguson on his earlier trip to the U.S. After comparing the advantages of the plow, they agreed to manufacture it. The Ferguson-Sherman company was set up, and by December 25, 1925, the factory began manufacturing plows. This venture remained successful until 1928, when Fordson production ended in the U.S.A.

The main goal of Ferguson was to have a hitch system for a whole range of implements. The Duplex hitch was not well suited for various implements, because it lacked torsional stability and had slightly adverse steering characteristics. So with plow manufacturing up and running in the U.S., Ferguson went back to Ireland where he, Sands, and Archie Greere began working on this problem. Greere was a pattern maker who had joined Ferguson in 1917. Solving this problem led to patent #1687719, which was filed February 14, 1925, in the U.K. and February 25, 1925, in the U.S.A. This patent is known as the master patent of the Ferguson System. This patent dealt with draft control where the depth of the implement was automatically controlled by reference to the effort or draft needed to pull it. Many different ideas of how this could be achieved were covered by this patent, i.e., electric motors, mechanical clutches and hydraulics. Of these, mechanical lift in combination with hydraulics offered the most advantages. The main problem was designing a constant delivery pump with sensitive adjustments.

In 1928 (in the U.K) and 1929 (in the U.S.A.) Ferguson applied for a patent with the first three-point linkage. It was granted as patent #1916945. This linkage consisted of two top links that raised and lowered the implement with the bottom link, under tension, controlling draft. These links were designed in such a way that the wider end was on the implement and the narrow end on the tractor. This arrangement moved the virtual hitch point up in front of the front axle. This principle allowed the implement to steer in the same direction the front wheels turned. This principle, as well as the previous one in regards to draft control are the basic principles of the Ferguson system linkage even today.

There was still a problem in the hydraulic system. The hydraulic oil was constantly being forced under high pressure through the main valve, either to the lift arms or back to the sump. This resulted in aerating and heating of the oil to such an extent that it sometimes caused the system to become airlocked and stop functioning. There was also a problem of "bobbing" of the implement. This bobbing caused uneven plow depth.

In spite of this problem, Ferguson felt it was time to seek out manufacturers for a tractor incorporating his system. In the experimental stages he had been incorporating his designs in a Fordson. Even though the Fordson was the lightest weight tractor on the market at that time, at about three thousand pounds it was too heavy to be suitable for the design he had in mind.

Next issue: Ferguson Builds a Tractor

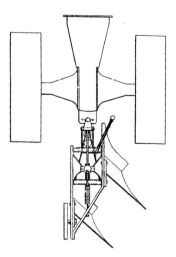

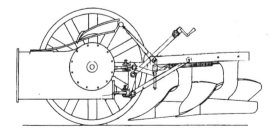

The Duplex hitch designed for the Fordson worked well for a plow, but it did not have the lateral stability required for other implements. Still, it was an important step toward the three point linkage eventually employed.

22 Antique Power

Harry Ferguson Builds a Tractor

Part 2 of a History of Ferguson Tractors

by David Lory

H. FERGUSON 1884-1960

In 1928, after production of the Fordson had ceased in the U.S., Harry Ferguson came to the U.S. to see what could be done with the inventory of plows on hand. On this trip he also planned to meet with tractor manufacturers to discuss producing a tractor with his hydraulic draft control system. Allis-Chalmers showed the most interest and took out a 90-day option on the idea, but they did not follow through.

So Ferguson decided to build a tractor of his own. With the help of

In 1932 and '33, Ferguson built his first tractor, known as the "Black" because of the color it was painted.

Willy Sands, Archie Greer, and John Chambers, work began on the new tractor in 1932. Ferguson used many advanced engineering techniques, many of them learned from his earlier dealings with race cars.

The gears in the transmission and steering were from the David Brown company of Hudderfield, England. The engine was an 18 hp four-cylinder American Hercules. The three-point linkage was changed to one top link with two bottom links. The two bottom links lifted and lowered the implement and transmitted the change of draft to the control. The hydraulic system was driven off of the final drive and was mounted inside the tractor.

Also, a ground speed PTO and a belt/PTO driven from the rear of the gearbox were designed. These ideas were covered in patent #2022767.

The tractor was called the "Black" tractor simply because it was painted black. The design was totally revolutionary. It produced 18 hp and weighed 1600 pounds, making it the first tractor to weigh less than 100 pounds per horsepower. This was made possible by use of the principles in the Ferguson system which allowed the weight of the implement, plus the weight of the soil on it, plus the natural tendency of the Ferguson linkage to pull the implement deeper into the ground, all to be carried on the rear axle. This added up to considerable weight. At the same time, the force on the top link helped keep the tractor's front wheels on the ground. Other advantages of the Ferguson were continuous automatic control of working depth in the soil, and quick and simple attaching and detaching of implements to the tractor. A special plow, ridger,

crop cultivator, and a tiller were designed for the Black tractor.

The problem of the "bobbing" of the implement was solved when the top link, instead of the bottom links, was used to sense changes in draft. The top link sensed the changes under a compression load where the bottom links had used a tension load. The problem of the hydraulic oil overheating was solved in the early part of 1936 when Ferguson placed the hydraulic valve on the suction side of the pump. This cut off the supply of oil to the pump when no oil pressure was required. This arrangement had another advantage: If the implement hit an object hidden in the soil, it caused a drastic increase in draft which allowed the oil in the ram to escape quickly, causing the weight of the implement to be dropped from the tractor. This sudden loss of weight allowed the the tractor's rear wheels to spin before any

The first public demonstration of the hydraulic draft control took place near Belfast, Northern Ireland, on May 15, 1936. Nearly 20 years of invention, construction, setbacks, and achievements had gone into making that day.

The first overseas demonstration took place in Norway in May 1938. John Chambers impressed onlookers by working among stones and boulders. The tractor had the latest 1938 specifications, including 9x22 rear tires and rear fenders.

The steepness of the ground in Norway can be seen here. Many older Fergusons survive in Norway today, where Ferguson tractors of all types are highly regarded.

harm could come to the implement, tractor, or driver. These designs were patented as #2118180 and #2118181.

While Ferguson was still modifying his prototype tractor, he located a manufacturer for it. The firm was David Brown, which had made the Aston Martin cars and gears for the Black tractor. David Brown was the largest gear manufacturer in England. A new company, called David Brown Tractor, agreed to manufacture the tractor, and Harry Ferguson Ltd. was to market the tractor and implements.

The new tractor was called the Ferguson Brown or Ferguson A. It was basically the Black tractor with a few modifications. The first 500 used a Coventry Climax engine developing around 20 hp. David Brown built the last engines themselves. Tractors sold for around $900, while the two-bottom

plow, three-row ridger, seven-tine tiller, and a general purpose cultivator each sold for around $100. Whenever possible, nuts and bolts were one of two sizes and could be adjusted by the Ferguson wrench. This was a ten-inch long, open end wrench, marked in one-inch increments. These markings made it easier to adjust the plow. Harry Ferguson's policy of using two sizes of nuts and bolts continued for the next 30 years.

The new tractor was shown at a public demonstration in May of 1936. Performance was very impressive, especially when compared to much larger tractors. In spite of the excellent response to the tractor, sales were slow. This was partly due to the depressed economy and partly because implements had to be bought with the tractor, making it cost much more than the $560 Fordson.

Because of the slow sales, Brown and Ferguson merged in 1937 to become Ferguson-Brown Ltd. At that time, the Brown name was better known than Ferguson, and it was felt that the new name would increase sales. By 1937, Ferguson had designed many improvements, including a continuously running layshaft in the gearbox. This allowed the PTO and hydraulic pump to be driven whether or not the tractor was in gear. The pump was fitted either to a continuously running layshaft (like the

later TO/FE-35) or fitted behind a "dog" clutch (like the Ford Fergusons or TE/TO 20s and TO 30s). All Ferguson tractors incorporated these improvements right up to today's models. It was not, however, used on Ferguson-Brown tractors. Another design idea was the provision of a power take-off shaft located within the triangle of the converging three-point hitch linkage—exactly where it is found on tractors today.

Sales continued to be slow. Brown felt that a larger tractor would sell better, while Ferguson felt that a lighter, smaller tractor would help. Brown also wanted to increase the price of the tractor, whereas Ferguson wanted to lower the price. These and other problems led to the termination of the agreement between Ferguson and Brown in 1939. Although only around 1250 Ferguson model As were sold, it still was a successful tractor.

Brown decided to have his engineers design a bigger tractor. By July of 1939, David Brown introduced his own line of tractors with a mechanical hitch. Brown stayed in tractor production until he was bought out by Case in the 1970s.

The Ferguson system tractor had passed the experimental stages. Customers in Norway, Sweden, Denmark, and the U.K. were satisfied with the tractor, and companies in the U.S.A. were expressing interest. Harry Ferguson did not wait until the breakup with Brown to look for a new manufacturer.

This late model Ferguson-Brown has remained in one family since it was new. It has worked over 12,500 hours and still has the original Dunlop rear tires.

Harry Ferguson Builds a Tractor

Part 3 of a History of Ferguson Tractors

H. FERGUSON 1884-1960

by David Lory

After the end of production of the Fordson in the United States in 1928, the Sherman brothers, who had manufactured Fordson plows in the United States for Ferguson, set up the Sherman Shephard company to import the British Fordson into the United States. Eber Sherman attended a demonstration of the Ferguson A in Britain in the early part of 1938. When he returned to the United States he reported Ferguson's developments to his friend Henry Ford. Ford had wanted to get back into tractor manufacturing in the U.S. but had not come up with a satisfactory design of his own (see the July/August 1995 *Antique Power* for an account of Ford's tractor experiments). After hearing of the accomplishments of Ferguson he asked Sherman to arrange a demonstration of Ferguson's tractor.

This is what Ferguson had been hoping for. In the fall of 1938 he brought tractor number 722 (a standard production tractor) and a set of implements to Dearborn, Michigan. The demonstration took place in October 1938 at Henry Ford's estate. When the Ferguson tractor had performed, Ford asked that an Allis-Chalmers B and a Fordson be brought in for comparison. Although both tractors pulled the same size plow as the Ferguson A, they both suffered much more wheel slippage when plowing.

The result of the demonstration was the famous "Handshake Agreement" whereby Ferguson would design, engineer, and market the new tractor, and

Ford would manufacture it in the United States. It was also agreed that Ford's tractor plant, which had moved from Cork, Ireland, to Dagenham, England, in 1933, would also manufacture the Ferguson System tractor.

Ferguson returned to England, leaving the Ferguson A in an airport building in Dearborn. While he was away, Ford's engineers took the Ferguson A apart to see how it worked and built two unsuccessful prototypes. By January of 1939 the agreement between Ferguson and Brown was terminated, and Ferguson returned to Dearborn with a small team of engineers. They worked very closely with Ford's engineers in developing a

Though not the first Ferguson System tractor, the 9N built by Ford led the farming revolution spawned by Harry Ferguson's invention. This 1939 9N is owned by the author.

prototype tractor. Ferguson insisted that the new tractor incorporate all of his latest Ferguson System developments. Also included was a design described in Ferguson's 1939 patent for adjusting the width of the front axle without changing the length of the radius or steering linkage.

Ford's engineers concentrated on ways to make the tractor easier and

faster to mass produce. They used many stock items including one half of a Mercury V-8 flathead engine. Ferguson had wanted an overhead valve engine, as it produces more torque, but in order to speed along production, he accepted the flathead engine.

The engine used had a 119 ci gasoline engine producing 23 brake horsepower at 1400 rpm. A vaporizing oil version was later designed for the 9NAN model sold in England during World War II. There were three forward speeds and one reverse.

By April 1, 1939, the prototype was finished and shown to a few special guests. The tractor was know as the 9N Ford tractor with the Ferguson System or just Ford-Ferguson. The shipping weight of the 9N was 2140 pounds. It was painted gray like the Ferguson A and, like the A, used only two sizes of nuts and bolts. The sizes were somewhat smaller, $1\frac{1}{16}$ and $1\frac{1}{16}$, to match standard U.S. sizes. The sizes were used for the next 30 years, both in the United States and the Britain.

Ferguson and Sherman marketed the tractor and implements under the name Ferguson Sherman Manufacturing Corporation. On June 29, 1939, a public demonstration was given. A price of $585 was announced for the tractor, which was much less than the competition. Because the 9N was such a revolutionary design, much time was spent on product training. One or two members of each dealership had to attend a Ferguson school at Dearborn before they were allowed to sell the

Ferguson hoped the Ford Company of England would produce a Ferguson System tractor for the British Empire. Ford did not, and Ferguson arranged to have the Standard Motor Car Company produce the TE-20, known the world over as the "Little Gray Fergie."

tractor. Ferguson personally participated in many public demonstrations. Soon a network of 33 distributors and 2876 dealers was established.

The 9N tractor was well received by farmers. Sales increased rapidly. In 1941 over 42,000 were sold, making the Ford-Ferguson one of the best selling tractors in the world. Production was halted for six months due to wartime prohibitions. When production resumed on September 17, 1942, several detail differences had been incorporated: The tractor was equipped with steel wheels, and the battery and starter had been eliminated, to comply with wartime material restrictions. The war model was called the 2N.

In early 1943, Ford and Ferguson embarked on a project to design and manufacture a larger version of the 2N

called the 4-P. As with the 9N project, the responsibilities of the two parties were not clearly defined.

The war years were a difficult time for Ferguson. The arrangement for manufacturing and selling 9Ns in England was never satisfactory, and Ferguson was growing increasingly unhappy with it. In 1942 the Ferguson-Sherman distribution network broke up. Sales of Ford-Ferguson tractors and implements were taken over by his new company, Harry Ferguson Incorporated. In 1943, Henry Ford's son Edsel died and his son Henry II gained greater influence in the company, exacerbating Ferguson's problems with the English production and the new tractor. In 1944, friction between Henry II and Harry Ferguson resulted in Ford's seizure of the 4-P prototypes and Ferguson embarking on a parallel project of his own. Then, in 1945, Ferguson's friend Henry Sr. passed away and Henry II became president. With Henry Ford II in charge, the agreement with Harry Ferguson was re-examined. At the end of 1946, Ford announced that, by the end of July 1947, production of the 2N would end and Harry Ferguson Inc. would no longer receive any tractors to market.

A new tractor based on the 9N, called the 8N, would be manufactured by Ford and sold through a new organization owned by Ford called Dearborn Motors. Ferguson began losing his distribution network, as many of them switched over to Dearborn Motors. By July 1, 1947, all but two of the remaining distributors had sold their inventories and buildings to Dearborn distributors. Almost all of the 3000

dealers also switched to Dearborn, many with great reluctance. Production ended with over 300,000 9Ns and 2Ns produced. Over 74,000 of these were built in 1946, its last full year of production.

Ford used Harry Ferguson's patents without permission on the new 8N tractor, which led to a huge lawsuit. In 1952 a settlement was finally reached which had Ford paying Ferguson $9.25 million and agreeing not to produce the 8N tractor after 1952. This ended Ferguson's dealings with the Ford Motor Company.

In the early 1940s Ferguson had taken a 9N back to England and demonstrated the tractor and implements. He intended to convince officials of the Ford plant in Dagenham to switch from production of the Fordson to the Ferguson System tractor. The 9N took less raw material to produce and was much more fuel efficient. The Ford plant in England was not under tight control of Henry Ford, and refused to agree to change to the new tractor. Patrick Hennessey, the general manager, had made an agreement with the British Government to purchase 3,000 Fordsons if war started. With this order in hand the officials saw no need or advantage to manufacture the Ferguson System tractor. Once the war was in progress it would be almost impossible to stop production and retool. So for the time being, Ferguson had to be content with British farmers using the 9Ns that were brought in under the American Lease-Lend act. These tractors and implements were performing superbly and had made a great impression on British farmers.

Around 1943, Ferguson had Trevor Knox start locating a manufacturer for his tractor. Additional work was also being done on tractor and implement design. One tractor improvement was a four-speed transmission using helical cut constant running gears, which were much quieter. The brake pedal arrangement was improved with a master pedal as well as individual pedals, the radius rods and center housing were strengthened, and a safety start was incorporated into the gear lever. Other improvements were made to the draft control and an outlet was provided for external hydraulics.

Ferguson is seen here with Sir John Black of Standard seated on a TE-20 shortly after Standard began producing the tractor.

The Ferguson System spawned radical new developments in agricultural engineering around the globe. It brought cost effective machinery to all continents. A disc plow is shown here being used in Africa.

Knox had heard that the Standard Motor Car Company of Coventry, England, was thinking of developing a farm tractor after the war. During World War II, Standard Motor Car had been very busy building airplane engines and other war materiel. Immediately after the war there were extreme shortages of raw materials, and all production had to be sanctioned by the government. This shortage was the main concern of Sir John Black, manager of Standard Motor Car. Harry Ferguson went directly to the new Chancellor of the Exchequer (Finance Minister), Sir Stafford Cripps, and obtained a sufficient allocation of material for production to start.

The plant had 1,000,000 sq. ft. of space. Black and Ferguson also asked for one half million dollars for machine tools, $3,000,000 for certain implement parts and $5,000,000 for 25,000 engines. All this was approved by the government, and a 10-year contract was set up to manufacture the Ferguson tractor.

The engines were supplied by Continental Engines of Muskegon, Michigan, which at that time was the largest manufacture of gas engines in the United States. Their model Z120 was used. This engine had wet sleeves, 119.7 cubic inches of displacement, and was rated at 24 horsepower. The electrical system used was the English Lucas system. The Continental gave Ferguson the overhead valve engine he had always wanted. The arrangement with Standard Motor Car was the same as with Ford, but this time it was written down. Harry Ferguson controlled design, development, sales, and service through Harry Ferguson (Coventry) Ltd. while Standard manufactured the tractor and sold it to Ferguson. Implements were mainly contracted out to other firms.

Much of the tooling was brought in from the United States, with prototype tractors and implements being brought from Belfast and the United States in the latter part of 1945. Equipping the Standard factory at Banner Lane in Coventry, England, took most of 1946, with tractor production starting the last few weeks of that year. A last minute change in design allowed the hood to tip forward to allow for filling the gas tank and checking coolant and battery fluid levels.

This tractor was called the TE-20 (the TE indicating "Tractor England"). The weight of the tractor was around 2400 lbs. Speeds at 1500 engine rpm were 2.5, 3.5, 4.75, and 9.75 mph, with a reverse of 3 mph. The hydraulic system used a four-cylinder pump in the transmission housing driven by the pto, producing 1500 psi of working pressure. Front wheels were 4.00x 19 and the rears were 10x28. Track was adjustable from 48" to 78". The weight of the tractor was approximately 2500 lbs. The first 200,000 TE-20s had Lucas 6-volt systems, tractors after that had Lucas 12 volt systems. In 1947 and 1948, around 25,000 of these TE-20 tractors were shipped to Harry Ferguson Inc. in the United States to help fill demand until a new Ferguson tractor plant was operating running there.

In September of 1947, a new overhead valve engine built by Standard was ready. It was a 112.9 ci engine with a compression ratio of 5.77:1 producing a maximum belt hp of 23.9. Tractors with this engine were called TE-A20. The implement range continued to expand.

In 1949 a vaporizing engine was introduced to help farmers avoid the heavy tax on gasoline. Tractors with this engine were designated TE-D20. The displacement was increased to 127.4 ci to compensate for the lower efficiency of vaporizing oil. The compression ratio was lowered to 4.8:1 and it produced 25.4 hp. In 1950 a zero octane engine that burned lamp oil became available. It produced 22.9 hp

In July 1994, the Gray Ferguson Challenge was held in Lincolnshire, England. Over 100 "Little Gray Fergies" plowed a single field at the rate of 74 acres per hour.

The TE-20 on the left was build by Standard Motor in England. The nearly identical TO-20 tractor on the right was built in Ferguson's factory in Detroit.

with a compression ratio of 4.5:1. Tractors with this engine were designated TE-H20. A diesel engine was added to the line in 1951, producing 26 hp from the same 127.4 ci block. In 1952 a vineyard TE-20 tractor was introduced with 5.00x15 front tires and 9x 24 rear tires. This tractor was 20" narrower and 6" lower than the normal TE model. The vineyard models used the same engines and were designated TE-K20 gas, TE-L20 vaporizing oil and TE-M20 lamp oil. There was also a narrow width tractor with smaller tires which was 2" lower and 6" narrower than the normal tractor. It used the same engines as above and was designed to run on TE-C20 gas, TE-E20 vaporizing oil, and TE-J20 lamp oil. By 1952, a total of 12 industrial tractor models had been introduced. They could be fitted with gas, vaporizing oil, lamp oil or diesel. The models varied by the different types of fenders,

bumpers, tires, lighting system, etc. that they were fitted with. All industrial tractors were fitted with two independent brake systems, one mechanical and one hydraulic.

The TE-20 tractor was so well accepted that it became affectionately know all over the world as the "Little Gray Fergie." Production ended in October 1956 with 517,649 TEs produced. In the United Kingdom the TE-20 had captured over 60% of the tractor market.

On October 11, 1948, tractor production began in Detroit, Michigan, in the first factory ever owned by Ferguson. Ferguson had never liked the manufacturing part of the operation, and until then was able to have someone else do it for him. The tractors first produced at the Detroit plant were called TO-20s (TO for "Tractor Overseas"). The TO-20 tractors were similar to the TE-20s. They used the same Z-120 Continental engine but now had Delco electrics. The transmission, rear end, and hydraulic pump assemblies were produced by the Detroit gear division of Borg-Warner.

By the end of 1948, the plant was producing 100 tractors per day. During the Korean War, raw material availability, not demand, was the factor that limited production. Due to many presentations to the U.S. government, Ferguson was at least able to avoid a cutback in production. Sixty thousand TO-20s were produced in a three-year period.

In the fall of 1951 a slightly larger model, the TO-30, was introduced. Production started at serial number 60,001. The principal change was a larger 129 ci Continental Z 129 engine which produced around 29 hp. The rear end was built heavier for greater durability, and there were small changes such as locating the air cleaner in the dashboard and putting the oil filter outside the engine instead of in the oil pan.

There were over 63 Ferguson implements on the market along with the TO-30. Production ended at the end of 1954 with 80,000 being produced.

Ferguson marketed an extensive line of implements to go with its tractors. Most implements were manufactured for Ferguson by other companies.

The TO-30 was a slightly larger, more powerful tractor than the TO-20 and introduced a few refinements to the older design.

Harry Ferguson Builds a Tractor

Part 4 of a History of Ferguson Tractors

H. FERGUSON 1884-1960

by David Lory

The three previous installments of this series detailed the progress of Harry Ferguson's tractor enterprises through the production of the TO-30. The next step in Ferguson tractor development was the TO-35. Production began in early 1955 at serial number 140001. Production continued until 1963 with over 100,000 tractors produced in nine years. Many of the changes embodied in the TO-35 were made by Herman Klemm, who had been with Ferguson since the 1940s.

In the early 1950s, tractor and implement sales experienced a downturn. Harry Ferguson was almost 70 years old and felt it might be a good time to sell off his American interests. He had asked Massey-Harris in 1947 if they would be interested in manufacturing a tractor for him. They had declined, thinking that Ferguson was too big a risk!

By 1952 things had changed. Ferguson had established himself as a major force in world tractor production. Then Massey-Harris learned that Ferguson had not only developed a four plow tractor, but that plans were being made to manufacture the small TE-20 tractor in France. This, they felt, would threaten sales of the most popular Massey-Harris models in the United States and also the successful Pony model they were producing in France.

A basic agreement between Ferguson and Massey-Harris to manufacture a small combine for the Ferguson tractor was reached in 1953. The president of M-H, James Duncan, joined Ferguson in a meeting which he thought would finalize that deal.

Instead, Ferguson had a new plan for selling his American business.

Duncan told Ferguson he would have to discuss it with the board, then toured the Ferguson operation in Detroit with two of his top management people. They were very impressed with what they saw, especially the new implements and the quality of engineering.

Duncan reported to the M-H board that at that time close to a million Ferguson system tractors had been sold. Ferguson and Ford together had a 24% share of the tractor market in the United States and sold half of all the tractors in the two-plow class. He also told his board that he felt the Ferguson TO-30 could replace the M-H 22,

Mustang, and Colt, and that the new larger Ferguson tractor could replace the 33, 44, and 55. With this in mind, the M-H directors announced that they would only be interested in a worldwide association with Ferguson.

The fate of the new tractor Ferguson's engineers had designed was a critical issue for Harry Ferguson. This tractor, called the LXT, or TE-60, was the four-plow tractor that had worried Massey-Harris so much. It was basically an enlarged version of the TE-20, with a 190 ci gas or a 240 ci diesel engine. It was believed that six prototypes had been built.

On August 4, 1953, Ferguson agreed to merge with Massey-Harris on a worldwide scale. M-H agreed to

By the time of the merger of Ferguson and Massey-Harris, Ferguson's tractors were famous around the world for their efficiency and versatility, and Massey-Harris was a leading manufacturer of harvesting equipment. The merger should have built on the companies' strengths, but sadly, it was five years before internal rivalries and friction were put to rest. By then, many Ferguson people had left in despair. Harry Ferguson, demoralized, tired, and ill, left after one year.

In 1956, in the United Kingdom, production of the world renowned TE-20 ended after a total of 517,649 tractors were made. A tractor similar to the American TO-35 took the place of the venerable TE-20. The new tractor was called the FE-35. The sheet metal was gray like its American counterpart, but the castings were painted gold. It was sold with all the options of the TO-35, plus several different engine options that allowed farmers to use vaporizing oil, lamp oil, or diesel. The FE-35 was produced in the United Kingdom until 1958, when it was changed to the MF-35. Total production of the FE-35 was 387,800. The last one rolled off the line in 1964.

give Ferguson 1,805,055 shares of their stock, which was valued at $9 a share or a total of $16,000,000 U.S. dollars. Ferguson felt the price should be $17,000,000 Canadian. He suggested that the difference be settled by a toss of a coin. They agreed, and Ferguson lost. Undaunted by the loss, he then said, "Now I'll toss you for the coin. That is the sort of bet I win." And he did.

The announcement of the formation of Massey-Harris-Ferguson Ltd. was made on August 16, 1953. At that time, Ferguson had built over 800,000 tractors worldwide. About 50% of his tractors made in England had been exported. Ferguson tractors had captured about 60% of the market in England and 75% of the tractor market in Denmark. Ferguson had also set up local subcon-

tractors and distributors in countries worldwide.

During the years of the merged Massey-Harris-Ferguson companies they adopted a policy of producing and selling two competing lines which raised suspicion and fear among the dealers of both lines. Massey-Harris introduced the MH-50, which was based on the TO-35, and suddenly Massey dealers who

The Ferguson TO-35

The TO-35, introduced in 1955, was first powered by a Continental K-134 engine with a displacement of 133.6 ci producing around 34 hp. The TO-35 had a dual range transmission which allowed six forward speeds and two reverse speeds. There were two models of the TO-35, standard and deluxe.

One of the features offered on the TO-35 deluxe was the constant running layshaft Ferguson patented in 1937. This allowed the tractor to have "live power" with a two-stage clutch. Depressing the clutch part way disengaged the transmission. Pressing the clutch all the way down disengaged the transmission, PTO, and the hydraulic pump.

The deluxe model also had a tachometer. Included in both the standard and deluxe was the double acting draft sensing top link. This enabled implements that transmit either compression or tension on the top link to operate with the Ferguson System. The hydraulic controls consisted of two levers: one controlled the draft sensing system while the second lever

controlled the position of the lift arms, making it possible to select and maintain and desired height of the implement. This was very helpful when using non-soil engaging implements such as crains or loaders. The brake arrangement was improved by putting both left and right pedals on the right side of the transmission housing. The hydraulic pump capacity was improved to 2⅞ gallons per minute and 2000 pounds pressure.

There was also a ground speed PTO. This allowed PTO powered implements to be operated at a speed proportional to forward travel and not engine speed. Power steering was offered as an option. The TO-35 was the first Ferguson tractor to be painted two colors. The sheet metal was still the same Ferguson gray with the castings painted green.

The 40 was the first Ferguson to be available with a tricycle front end. The 40 is a repaint of a Massey-Harris 50 which is itself a modification of a Ferguson 35. The main differences were in sheet metal, steering design, and front axle design. The MH-50 was also several inches longer, to allow the use of mid-mounted implements, and was available in tricycle, high clearance, utility, or row crop models. The sheet metal on the MH-50 was painted red, with the castings painted copper.

had successfully sold against Ferguson were selling a tractor that basically *was* a Ferguson. Then the Ferguson division introduced a version of the MH-50 called the Ferguson 40. The only difference was that the sheet metal was painted beige and the castings were painted gray, so Ferguson dealers had nothing but color to sell over competing Massey-Harris dealers.

In an effort to increase the strength of the Ferguson dealers, the company decided to transfer the Massey-Harris Pony and implements to Ferguson. The Pony would be painted gray to match the rest of the Ferguson line. Within a month they realized the folly of this action. Some Massey-Harris dealers lost one of their better selling tractors, and Ferguson dealers were forced to try to sell a style of tractor that they

had successfully sold against for years. Soon more profitable Massey-Harris products were transferred to

By 1953, over 800,000 Ferguson tractors had been manufactured worldwide.

Ferguson dealers, and the morale of the dealers began to drop.

Morale within the company was sagging, too. Ferguson assumed that after the merger, his new four-plow tractor would be rushed into production. When it was not, he started a campaign to push the project forward.

By 1958, Ferguson's name was appearing on tractors such as this Oliver built Massey-Ferguson 98 that neither he nor his engineering staff had anything to do with.

When he was unsuccessful, he resigned as chairman of the new company and sold back his Massey-Harris stock.

Several reasons were given for the cancellation of the LTX tractor. Massey-Harris engineers felt that it could not be modified into a row crop tractor, and it could not be used with a mounted corn picker. Therefore, they felt it was unsuitable for use in the corn belt. Had they produced the LTX, M-H-F would have had an edge in the larger tractor markets. As it turned out, they had to play catch up with the market when they introduced the M-F 65 model in 1958, a tractor which was very similar to the LTX.

The policy of maintaining two separate and competing tractor lines obviously could not continue. In 1958, the lines were combined into one. Henceforth, the tractors were called Massey-Ferguson, and a red over gray color combination became the standard throughout the line.

After Ferguson resigned from Massey-Harris-Ferguson, he devoted much of his time to promoting and designing his four-wheel-drive system for cars. He made designs for Formula 1 race cars which were quite successful.

Harry Ferguson lived to see his dream of his Ferguson system tractors being used around the world come true. In 1958, three TE-20 tractors became

Ferguson's legacy to the tillers of the soil, his Ferguson System, opened up entirely new ways of farming to the world, and his TE-20 tractor became a firm favorite with farmers all over the globe, at one time taking over 70% of some markets. Between 1939 and 1956 nearly one million were put to work.

In 1958, Sir Edmund Hillary drove three Ferguson 20s to the South Pole. They were the first motorized vehicles to reach the pole.

the first vehicles ever to reach the South Pole overland in a trans-Antarctic expedition lead by Sir Edmund Hillary. Harry Ferguson died on October 25, 1960, a few days before his 76th birthday.

Randy Leffingwell's book, *The American Tractor*, best sums up the the influence of the Ferguson system on the development of farm tractors. He states the following, "The Ferguson System was copied at least in some form by every other tractor maker who wanted to stay in business." He also adds that, "Every competitor tried to better the Ferguson; they failed, and the best they could manage was to steal it, copy it, or license it." As you study the history of tractors in the 1950s and 1960s, you see that every manufacturer sooner or later incorporated the Ferguson System in their tractor. In fact, the Ferguson System was about the last major feature to be universally adopted on all farm tractors.

Photos used in this series were provided by: David Lory, George Field, Brian Cull, Reading University, T. Oedmotlad, The Ulster Folk and Transport Museum, and Sam Rea.

For more information on Ferguson tractors contact David Lory, 5604 SW Rd., Platteville, WI 53818-9610, in the United States 608-348-6344, or The John Cousins, Hulbertree, Farm Laxfield, Woodbridge, Suffolk, 1P13 8HR U.K.

Bibliography

"The Ferguson System," by George Field in Vol.6, No.2, *The Ferguson Club Newsletter.*

A Global Corporation, by E.P. Neufeld.

Harry Ferguson, Inventor and Pioneer, by Colin Fraser.

The author, David Lory.

David Lory has one of the most extensive collections of Ferguson tractors in North America.

CHAPTER 6

The first Ferguson tractor

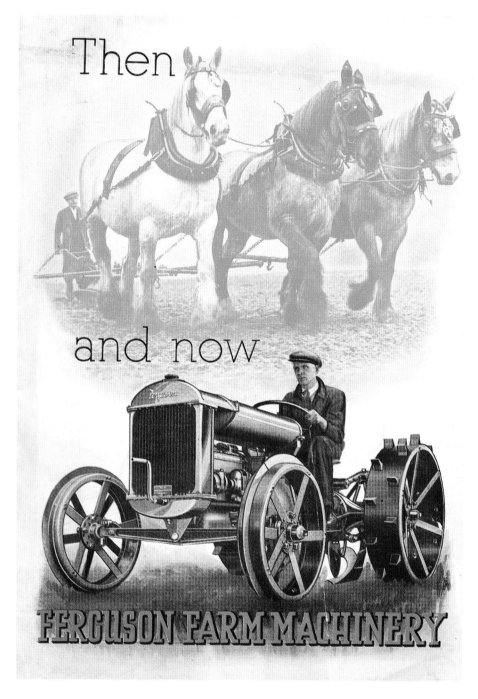

Harry Ferguson spent the early part of his agricultural engineering career fathoming how to change the traditional linking of a trailer plough to a tractor by a single point hitch, to a type of hitch which would allow weight transfer from plough to tractor, and integrate the tractor and plough as a single operational unit.

Harry Ferguson spent the early part of his agricultural engineering career fathoming how to change the traditional linking of a trailer plough to a tractor by a single point hitch, to a type of hitch which at one stroke would allow:

- a plough or other tillage implement to be integrally attached to a tractor and carried on the tractor when out of work

- economies of material use in plough (and other implement) construction

- avoidance of tractor rearing and overturning problems when trailer ploughs pulled by heavy tractors hit an obstruction

- complete cultivation of small fields and corners of fields

- use of lightweight tractors to effect the same work as heavier tractors

- reduction in fuel use per acre tilled or ploughed

- automatic control of implement working depth

- weight transfer from an implement's soil penetrative force to the driving wheels of the tractor

- a multiplicity of tillage implements to be attached to and operated by a light tractor.

Ferguson's early experiments at developing such a plough to tractor linkage were conducted on a Ford Eros tractor which was simply a Ford model T car modified to be a tractor. With this combination Ferguson achieved his objective of a "light weight" tractor of some 16 cwt and integrally attached plough weighing only 2 cwt. The two furrow plough had only about 80 parts as compared with conventional trailer ploughs which had about 300 parts. It could plough 4-6 acres per day.

Ferguson's first true tractor. A bird's
eye view of the Ferguson Black tractor
with ridger

The Motor Tractor in Use

The following is reproduced directly from the Coleraine Chronicle of December 1st 1917 and reports on the first public demonstration of the Ferguson plough and tractor combination.

"At Coleraine on Saturday a very successful demonstration of the utility of a new motor plough designed and put on the market by Messrs Harry Ferguson Ltd, Belfast was given in a field on the farm of Mr R W Jewell, Dundooan. The demonstration was arranged by Messrs Stuart and Co, Bridge Street, Coleraine, who are sole agents for the implements in this district and we understand that a number of orders were placed with Messrs Stuart for the complete outfit after the exhibition, so favourably impressed were those who saw it working. The morning turned out to be one of the worst as regards weather experienced in a particularly wet autumn, heavy rain drenching the ground and those who had gathered to witness the demonstration. There was a large attendance of interested farmers at both morning and afternoon displays and great appreciation of the work done was freely expressed. The conditions were excellent

for showing the advantage of a light tractor and plough over the heavy productions generally used, as in spite of the very soft ground and the fact that the wheels of the tractor were often in a foot of water, so that the "cleats" had very little catch, Mr Ferguson had no difficulty in turning an excellent furrow. Very considerable attraction was attached to the exhibition seeing that it was the first public exhibition of the Ferguson plough and widespread interest had been aroused in motor ploughing in Ireland lately, owing to the greatly increased acreage under the plough and the scarcity and cost of upkeep of horses. Heavy tractors have not been a success in Ulster, generally owing to the soft nature of the ground; beside the light tractor has all the advantage in economy of working as all the power of the engine is available for pulling the plough. The tractor used by Mr Ferguson is an attachment for an ordinary

Ford car chassis, the whole weighing only 15-17 cwt and the plough 2 cwt. The latter implement is constructed so as to plough up hills and through wet and marshy ground, and makes two furrows which the tractor draws at the rate of 2.5 miles per hour and can turn over 4-6 acres of soil/day according to the length of the day and nature of the ground.

A great advantage of the Ferguson plough is its simplicity and ease of control, this being done by a lever on the tractor, one man only being necessary and the mechanism is so simple and strong that even a lady could work it. Mr Ferguson was able on Saturday to vary the depth of his furrow from his seat on the tractor without interrupting the work. The machine does "flat" as well as "crested" ploughing and if it happens to strike a stone or stump it is impossible for anything to break as there is a safety pin to prevent such an occurrence. The plough makes a

Exhibition at Coleraine, N. Ireland

quick entry and clean finish and can be "wound" within its own space. The tractor when started upon petrol runs on paraffin and should do the work of four horses. It can be used for reaper or binder. Its upkeep is negligible and it is much easier handled than the heavier variety. The car being fitted with electric lighting, the tractor can be used at night and it is so easily detachable that the car body can be put on in a few minutes. Some idea of the simplicity of the Ferguson plough may be drawn from the fact that it has only 80 pieces as against some 300 in other ploughs and these are strong solid steel."

And so it was that the first combination of a Ferguson plough and tractor was launched – apparently with great success and in appalling ground conditions.

Ferguson went on to further develop his plough for attachment to the Fordson model F tractor – the first mass produced lightweight tractor, but designed only to pull trailed implements. Ferguson repeatedly redesigned his plough, improving at each step. Many Ferguson ploughs were sold for fitting to Fordson tractors. His constant experimenting with redesign of the plough to tractor linkage evolved from the single point linkage used with the

Ford Eros, through two point linkages and then to three point linkages. All were mechanically controlled, but finally a three point linkage with hydraulic control provided by an external hydraulic pump fitted on the Fordson tractor was evolved.

Despite successful sales of the plough for use on Fordson tractors, Ferguson was snagged when Ford ceased production of his tractor. This prompted Ferguson to design his own tractor. He gathered together a design team and from these efforts emerged his prototype tractor the "Ferguson Black" which was built in 1933. This incorporated his own design of three point linkage and automatic depth control with hydraulic lift and depth control powered by an internal hydraulic pump. The Ferguson Black was therefore a tractor specifically designed to accommodate the Ferguson principles of automatic depth control of implements, and an integral matching and linking of implement and tractor. Up to this point in time Ferguson had always had to modify a tractor to accept his linkage mounted implement principles. The Ferguson Black tractor was therefore the first Ferguson tractor which fully incorporated the Ferguson System of linking tractor to implement. This tractor is

now on permanent display at the Science Museum in London.

The prototype went on to be produced as the popularly known Ferguson Brown tractor, or more correctly the Type A. Over 1200 were made for Ferguson by David Brown between 1936 and 1938, but the arrangement between David Brown and Ferguson was ultimately discontinued due to disagreements between them. True mass production of a purpose built Ferguson System tractor had to wait until 1939 by which time Ferguson had linked up with Ford to produce the Ford tractor with Ferguson System.

In the following pages are reproduced an original advertising brochure for the Ferguson Brown tractor. This is a later rather than early edition of the brochure as an earlier one was produced by Ferguson-Brown Ltd. reflecting changes that went on in the short period of Ferguson and Brown working together. This is followed by illustrated price lists for the tractor, a confidential Hints for Salesmen brochure and finally an almost toy town sketch from a brochure titled "Hydraulics Harnessed" by Ferguson Brown Ltd. highlighting the lightweight of the Ferguson tractor.

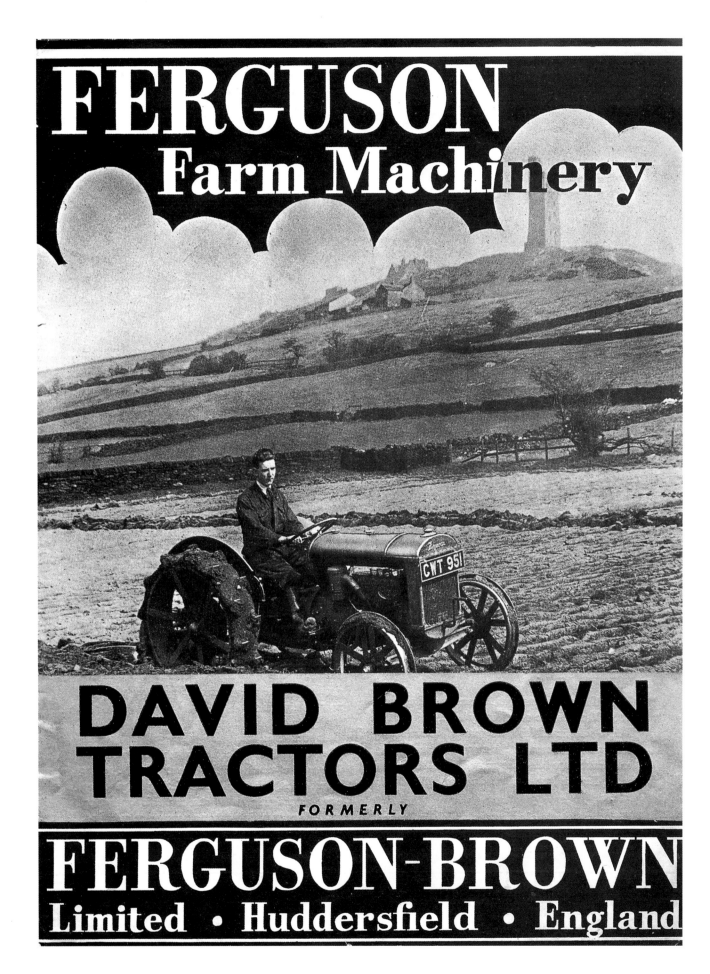

Early Ferguson Brown brochure

FERGUSON FARM MACHINERY

FERGUSON
The All British Farm Machinery

Scope

Much has been written regarding the minimum acreage of a farm where a tractor can be used with profit, and the main object of this booklet is to show that all farm work, whatever the size of the farm, can be carried out more economically by one or more "Fergusons," as their versatility enables them to entirely supersede horses.

Many farms as small as 20 acres and as large as 1,000 acres are completely mechanised with Ferguson Farm Machinery and all have shown substantial increases in revenue when land, previously used for the growing of fodder, has been diverted to the production of food for sale.

These are the main factors which influenced the 20 years of research and experiment which

are the background of "Ferguson Farm Machinery." We are all, to some extent, familiar with the shortcomings of tractors with hauled implements; for instance, how often do we see a tractor with hauled implement ridging and horses being used when splitting ridges? Even on extensive farms, horse drawn implements are still regarded as the safe and sure method of inter-row cultivation.

Compare this with the "Ferguson" where the patent linkage compels the implement to follow the track of the front wheels. Just think what this means! Splitting ridges is as easy as ridging and both for this operation and when working among row crops you just sit and steer.

Made by DAVID BROWN TRACTORS LIMITED

Unit Principle

The unit principle is the ideal design for which many manufacturers have striven in the past, but the rigid or semi-rigid methods of mounting the implements which they employed doomed them to failure and it was not until the Ferguson automatic hydraulic depth control and linkage became an accomplished fact that the enormous advantages of this principle could be realised.

Consider for a moment the action of a rigidly mounted implement. When the tractor is steered to the left, the implement veers to the right ; when the front wheels drop into a hollow, the implement, pivoting about the rear axle, lifts ; this makes it impossible to work on uneven ground and explains why the horse is still popular for inter-row cultivation. Now compare this with the " Ferguson " where the implement follows the track of the front wheels and floats behind the tractor, thus maintaining an even depth of cut whatever the contour of the land.

Another important point of comparison is that, when using rigidly mounted implements,

Ploughing with the " Ferguson "—easy and profitable.

it is necessary to employ a skilled operator to mount and adjust them and the time taken is considerable. With the " Ferguson," a child can connect the implements within two minutes and they are absolutely foolproof.

Turning Waste Land to Profit

A tribute to the efficiency of the " Ferguson " is the amount of land that has been brought under cultivation which had previously been unprofitable to work. This is only possible with machinery that is not deterred by hilly, stony or marshy conditions.

The behaviour of the " Ferguson " under these three conditions is of particular interest and is explained in the following paragraphs.

Hilly Ground

The superiority of the " Ferguson " on hilly ground is due in the first place to the implement following the front wheels thus eliminating the tendency to follow the slope when working transversely. Secondly, when operating uphill, the light weight and the scientific distribution of this weight together with the unit principle obviate the disadvantage experienced with a tractor and hauled implement whereby the line of draught tends to lift the front wheels, or conversely, makes

Ploughing with horses—laborious and costly.

Page Three

FERGUSON FARM MACHINERY

" Ferguson " implements—changed without tools in two minutes.

the rear wheels sink in the ground which is equivalent to increasing the slope of the hill. This explains why the " Ferguson " with its 20 H.P. and 16½ cwt. is successful where heavier machines with higher rated engines cannot work.

Stony Ground

This condition has previously been regarded as sufficient reason for the retention of the horse on the farm as, when ploughing or cultivating and the implement strikes an obstruction, the horse immediately stops, thus preventing damage to either the implement or itself. With a tractor and hauled implement, the energy stored in the flywheel is such that under similar conditions the adhesion of the rear wheels through torque reaction is increased to its maximum when the full tractive effort is applied to the implement, causing serious damage to implement or tractor.

Compare this with the " Ferguson." When an obstruction is encountered, the patent linkage increases the downward pressure on the front wheels and relieves the weight on the rear wheels, causing them to spin and stop all tractive effort, effectively preventing any damage to tractor or implement.

The operator reverses the tractor, lifts the implement with the hydraulic mechanism, and again travelling forward, drops the implement in front of the obstruction. As the hydraulic lift is controlled by a finger-tip lever, this operation is accomplished without effort and with no loss of time.

Marshy Ground

By the use of heat-treated high tensile steels and aluminium alloys, the weight of the " Ferguson " has been kept down to 16½ cwt.

Idle horses must be fed.

One third of the land cultivated by horses is used for growing their fodder.

BROWN TRACTORS LIMITED

which fact, together with the scientific distribution of this weight, gives a ground pressure per square inch of less than half that of horses. The combination was designed to minimise land packing and to give it the enormous advantage which it possesses when working on wet land.

Pneumatic Equipment

Recent orders have shown a notable increase in the demand for " Fergusons " with pneumatic equipment, as farmers are appreciating that 70% of all farm work can then be done without wheel changing.

Harvesting and mowing are particularly well carried out in this manner as the grass is not damaged; while being able to cross the highway and carry out general haulage is a definite advantage.

Implement Control

The implement control lever can be set to give a pre-determined depth and is only used for lowering and lifting the implement in or out of work. The hydraulic mechanism then maintains a uniform depth of cut without further movement of the lever.

Hydraulic control lever, simple and foolproof.

Facilities

Before giving the more technical data there are three important economic factors. Firstly—of special interest to the farmer who is working small fields—the implements can be changed in two minutes without the use of any tools. Secondly; the unit principle enables the tractor and implement to be reversed like a car making it possible to cultivate the whole of a small plot without leaving a wheel mark and for ordinary work reducing headlands to less than is required with horses. Thirdly—but of vital importance—the " Ferguson " does not require the services of a skilled operator.

Can be hitched to a farm cart in a few seconds.

70% of all farm work can be done with pneumatic equipment.

Page Five

FERGUSON FARM MACHINERY

1. Two furrow plough in action.
2. Ploughing with 16" digger plough.
3. General cultivator at work.
4. Hauling double disc harrow.
5. The Ferguson with Cambridge roller.
6. Pneumatic tyred equipment drawing farm cart.
7. The "Ferguson" ridging.
8. Hauling fertilizer spreader.
9. Drawing grass harrow.
10. Inter-row cultivation.
11. Moulding up potatoes.
12. Hop and Orchard model in action.
13. Mowing.
14. Sugar Beet lifting.
15. Reaping and binding with the "Ferguson."

Made by DAVID BROWN TRACTORS LIMITED

16. " *Ferguson* " *pulley drive to thresher.*
17. *Potato lifting.*
18. *Ferguson-Brown assembly line.*
19. *Implement assembly department.*
20. *Ferguson-Brown Works at Huddersfield.*

FERGUSON FARM · MACHINERY

Fig. 1. Line of draught with a hauled implement.

Hauled Implements

While it is not proposed to deal fully with the geometrical principles which govern the action of the various types of implement, these diagrams and notes are of the utmost importance in that they show that the adhesion of a tractor is not a matter of weight and that the power and draw-bar pull are not a basis for comparison.

The history of tractors with hauled implements is a sequence of increases in implement weight, tractor weight and power. A glance at Fig. 1 shows that the line of draught from " A " to " B " tends to pull the share out of the ground and to counteract this a long and heavy implement is necessary. In the event of the plough striking an obstruction the tendency is to lift the front wheels of the tractor off the ground and the additional weight thus thrown on the rear wheels gives maximum traction and damages the implement.

This difficulty has been met by increasing the tractor weight and providing a more powerful engine to haul its own extra weight. These factors naturally increase the calibrated draw-bar pull, but this is used in overcoming its own fundamental disadvantages and not in useful work.

The " Ferguson " Patented Linkage

Compare the foregoing with the " Ferguson " linkage. The line of draught is in the line of " C " to " D " and a rearward pull on the implement tends to pull the share point into the ground thus eliminating the necessity for the long and heavy implement. This means that a heavy tractor is not necessary—just

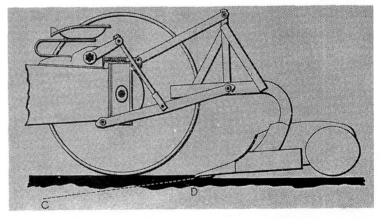

Fig. 2. Line of draught with Ferguson Patent Linkage.

Page Eight

Made by DAVID BROWN TRACTORS Limited

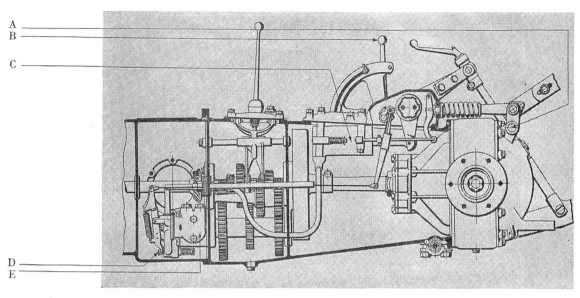

Fig. 3. Cross section showing hydraulic mechanism.

think what this means in running costs. The implement is not rigid with the tractor and the link connections allow free movement.

The line of draught keeps the implement in the hardest ground and when an obstruction is met the conditions described for a hauled implement are reversed and the front wheels of the tractor are pushed downwards when the weight on the rear wheels is relieved enabling one of them to spin and thus prevent damage.

Although the wheels spin under these conditions, they will not spin when ploughing the hardest ground.

Hydraulic Mechanism

While space does not permit a technical explanation of the hydraulic principle, Fig. 3 gives a good general idea of the simple mechanism and at the same time shows that, although compact, all the components are of sturdy design and are

totally enclosed, thus requiring no attention beyond the periodic verification of the oil level by means of the conveniently placed dip-stick.

The extraordinary success of the " Ferguson " is in no small measure due to the unique hydraulic mechanism which consists of a 4-cylinder, cam operated reciprocating pump which is direct coupled to an extension of the layshaft as shown at " E." The pump delivers to a double-acting piston operating in the cylinder at " C " and the inlet of pressure oil to this cylinder is controlled by the valve " D " operated by the conveniently placed handle " B." The top bar of the linkage couples the implement to the control point " A " so that when the driving wheels fall into a hollow or mount a ridge, the compensating lever automatically adjusts the valve " D " giving the necessary depth correction.

The drawing also clearly shows the implement levelling lever.

Page Nine

FERGUSON FARM MACHINERY

IMPLEMENTS and AUXILIARIES

The versatility of " Ferguson Farm Machinery " enables it to supersede horses for all farm work but this is by no means the complete story, as is shown by certain of the auxiliaries which are outlined below.

Fig. 4. Shows a spring mounted road band which can be fitted in a few minutes enabling the tractor with steel wheels to carry its implement on the highway.

Fig. 5. Illustrates the alternative Cultivator Shovels which are available.

Fig. 6. Where a tractor is required for universal purposes, pneumatic tyres of the type illustrated are particularly popular as they have excellent adhesive qualities and obviate frequent wheel changing.

Fig. 7. Shows an auxiliary box, which can be fitted to the standard machines, and is arranged to drive a belt pulley and is also the transmission to a power take-off shaft which extends to the rear of the tractor.

Fig. 8. Represents a Single furrow 16″ Digger Plough which can be supplied when required.

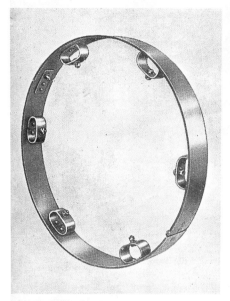

Fig. 4. Road Band.

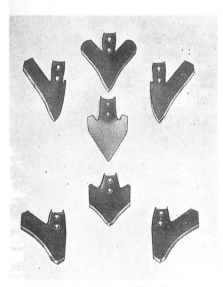

Fig. 5. Cultivator Shovels.

Fig. 6. Pneumatic Equipment.

Fig. 7. Power take-off and pulley drive.

Fig. 8. 16″ Single furrow plough.

Made by DAVID BROWN TRACTORS LIMITED

IMPLEMENTS and AUXILIARIES

Plough

The plough is of the two-furrow type, fitted with general purpose bottoms. It is manufactured from the highest quality heat-treated alloy steel giving tremendous strength combined with light weight. Brine-hardened three-ply steel mouldboards are fitted and the shares are chill cast. The standard equipment includes disc coulters and skimmers. Adjustments can be carried out easily and quickly. Weight, approximately $2\frac{1}{2}$ cwts.

General Cultivator

This implement embodies an exclusive and patented design of spring tine which extends rearwards when overriding obstructions and comes back into work instantaneously. The standard equipment includes seven spring-release tine units which are adjustable for spacing. This implement also is manufactured throughout from heat-treated alloy steels.

Ridger

The ridger has three adjustable ridging bottoms with high carbon steel mouldboards and chill cast shares. Spacing from 18″ to 30″ can be obtained easily as the frame is drilled at intervals of one inch. A patented steerage fin is also fitted which maintains the implement centrally behind the front of the tractor when working on hill sides and when splitting ridges.

Row Crop Cultivator

This cultivator is fitted with nine rigid tines which can be easily adjusted for row widths from 18″ to 30″ as the frame is drilled at intervals of one inch. In common with the other implements all parts are made from high-tensile steels, heat-treated to give lasting service. A steerage fin is fitted as described for the ridger.

Fig. 9. Two furrow plough.

Fig. 10. General Cultivator.

Fig. 11. Ridger.

Fig. 12. Row Crop Cultivator.

Page Eleven

FERGUSON FARM MACHINERY

Directors: F. E. Brown; David Brown, A.I.Mech.E.; Henry G. Ferguson, M.I.A.E., A.F.Ae.S., Joint Managing. Ernest de Silly Hamilton Browne, D.L., J.P.; Thomas MacGregor Greer, D.L., J.P.; Arthur Sykes, B.Sc., M.I.Mech.E.

SPECIFICATION

ENGINE
Cylinders cast monobloc, of special chromium alloy iron. Detachable cylinder head. 4 cylinders. Bore $3\frac{1}{8}$ ins. Stroke 4 ins. (79×100 m.m.). Capacity of engine 2010 c.c. Pistons of finest quality grey iron. Crank shaft to B.E.S.A. specification S.76 plus 1% nickel. Side by side valves of silchrome steel. B.H.P. 20 at 1400 r.p.m.

GOVERNOR
Governor is fitted as standard equipment and adjusted to 1400 r.p.m.

LUBRICATION
By gear pump supplying fully forced feed to all bearings. Capacity of sump 10 pints.

IGNITION
By magneto, with impulse starter specially designed to resist dust and damp.

COOLING
By four blade fan fitted with easy adjustment. Thermo-syphon ; radiator capacity four gallons.

FUEL SUPPLY
Nine gallon tank and two gallon reserve. Supply to carburettor by gravity, detachable fuel filter provided.

OIL CLEANER
Fitted as standard.

CARBURETTOR
Dustproof.

AIR CLEANER
Of the most efficient oil-bath type. Easily examined and cleaned.

SILENCER
Silencer is fitted as standard equipment. Pipes carry exhaust to rear of tractor.

CLUTCH
Exceptionally smooth in operation. Single plate. Dry type.

HYDRAULIC UNIT
Consists of four cylinder pump, valves, and ram cylinder. A small lever situated at the driver's right hand controls the lifting mechanism.

GEAR BOX
Centrally mounted gear lever. Three forward speeds and reverse. All shafts run on ball bearings.

GEAR RATIOS AND SPEEDS
At 1400 r.p.m.

	Final reduction.	Axle speed in r.p.m.	m.p.h.
Low	96.7	14.48	1.63
Intermediate	61.2	22.85	2.59
High	32.1	43.4	4.9
Reverse	75.5	18.57	2.1

Oil capacity of transmission housing three gallons.

REAR AXLE
Semi-floating. Spiral bevel.

STEERING
Of screw and nut type. All joints are Thompson Eccentric self adjusting and do not require attention apart from lubrication.

BELT PULLEY
Diameter 8 ins. Width $6\frac{1}{2}$ ins. Speed 1130 r.p.m. Belt speed 2366 feet per minute.

WHEELS
Steel.—Front ; diameter 2 ft. 2 ins. Width 5 ins. Rear ; diameter 3 ft. 2 ins. Width 10 ins. Supplied with twenty-four 4 in. spuds. Wheel track centres adjustable from 48—51 ins.
Narrow Wheels.—Diameter 3 ft. 2 ins. Width 6 ins. Wheel track centres $46\frac{1}{2}$ and $52\frac{1}{2}$ ins.
Pneumatics.—Front, 4.5×19 ins. Rear, 9×22 ins. Agricultural Pressure front 20 lb. rear 7 lb. Industrial pressure 20 lb., all round. Wheel track centres adjustable from 45—54 ins.

BRAKES
Internal expanding type, fitted as standard equipment, independently operated by pedals, with ratchet which enables brake to be left on. Provision is made for easy adjustment, 14 in. drums give efficient braking.

DIMENSIONS OF TRACTOR
Wheel base 5 ft. 9 ins.
Overall length from front wheel fin to end of lower link 9 ft. 5 ins.
Length over wheel fins and spuds 8 ft. $11\frac{1}{4}$ ins.
Overall width of tractor 4 ft. $10\frac{1}{2}$ ins.
Overall height 3 ft. 11 ins.
Height of drawbar 15 ins.
Turning circle 21 ft.
Ground clearance $10\frac{3}{4}$ ins., including depth of front wheel fin $12\frac{1}{2}$ ins.

ALTERATIONS TO SPECIFICATION
The Company reserves the right to make any alterations to or departures from the specification, design or equipment, without notice.

D/3806 FB104

Printed in England by Horrocks & Co. Ltd.

Distributed by :— KAY & BACKHOUSE, LTD
FOSSBRIDGE,
YORK.

L80-60

FERGUSON FARM MACHINERY

PRICE LIST

Tractor complete with Hydraulic unit and 10″ spudded wheels.	£230 0 0
Tractor complete with Hydraulic unit and pneumatic tyres.	£270 0 0
Tractor (Industrial) with pneumatic tyres but without Hydraulic unit.	£244 0 0

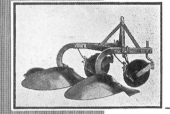

Two Furrow Plough ... £26 0 0

General Cultivator £26 0 0

Three Row Ridger £26 0 0

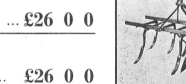

Row Crop Cultivator ... £26 0 0

Belt Pulley £6 10 0

Pneumatic Wheels ... £47 0 0

Road Bands £6 10 0

Steel Wheels (per pair)
10″ With Spuds £14. Without Spuds £8
6″ ,, ,, £12 10. ,, ,, £8
Front Wheels £8

FERGUSON-BROWN Limited HUDDERSFIELD

The Company reserve the right to alter list prices at any time and all goods are invoiced at the prices current on the day of delivery.

An early Ferguson Brown price list

℠80-76

FERGUSON FARM MACHINERY

PRICE LIST

	PRICE	REF.
Tractor on 10″ Steel Spudded Wheels without Hydraulic unit and Linkage (Petrol)	£175 0 0	A
Tractor on 10″ Steel Spudded Wheels with Hydraulic unit and Linkage (Petrol)	£198 0 0	B
Tractor on Adjustable Pneumatics front, 4.5″ × 19″, rear 9″ × 22″, variation of wheel centres from 45″ to 54″, with Hydraulic unit and Linkage (Petrol)	£238 0 0	C
Tractor on Industrial Pneumatics, front 6.00″ × 19″, rear 11.25″ × 24″, including adaptor plates and complete with Hydraulic unit (Petrol)	£246 0 0	D
As above but without Hydraulic unit (Petrol)	£223 0 0	E
Special Paraffin (vaporising oil) Carburetter, if supplied with tractor. Extra	£10 0 0	F
Pneumatic Equipment 9″ × 22″ and 4·5″ × 19″ wheel track centres adjustable from 45″ to 54″	£47 0 0	G
Belt Pulley	£6 10 0	H
Road Bands	£6 10 0	J
Pneumatic Equipment Heavy Industrial Type 11·25″ × 24″ and 6·00″ × 19″ with adaptor plates	£55 0 0	K

DAVID BROWN TRACTORS LTD. HUDDERSFIELD

DBT 106/1

D390

A later, June 1939 Ferguson Brown price list

FERGUSON FARM MACHINERY

PRICE LIST—continued

	PRICE	REF.
12″ Two Furrow Semi-digger Plough ...	£26 0 0	L
10″ Two Furrow Plough	£26 0 0	M
16″ Single Furrow Plough	£26 0 0	N
Three Row Ridger	£26 0 0	P
Extension Drawbar	£2 2 0	Q
General Cultivator	£26 0 0	R
Power Take-off and Pulley	£15 10 0	S
Row Crop Cultivator	£26 0 0	T
Paraffin (Vapourising Oil) Carburetter ...	£15 0 0	U

ALL PRICES EX WORKS, HUDDERSFIELD

DAVID BROWN TRACTORS LTD. HUDDERSFIELD

Directors : F. E. Brown, Chairman ; David Brown, A.I.Mech.E., Managing. Arthur Sykes, B.Sc., M.I.Mech.E.

CONFIDENTIAL

FERGUSON
FARM MACHINERY
HINTS FOR SALESMEN

KAY & BACKHOUSE L™
FOSSBRIDGE. YORK.

Issued by the makers—

FERGUSON-BROWN LTD.,
HUDDERSFIELD.

Publication No. 102.   **1st Edition D/3709.**

Copyrights reserved.

FERGUSON   FARM   MACHINERY

Ferguson Sales Organisation.
Hints for Salesmen.

Confidential.

Ninety per cent of the troubles experienced with tractors can definitely be traced to the misuse of paraffin, and the strenuous efforts now being made by prominent tractor manufacturers to educate farmers to use petrol show that troubles due to the misuse of this fuel have reached a critical stage.

During the War, when tractors were first introduced, the price of petrol was prohibitive and in addition, the weight of the average tractor was in excess of 3 tons.

The price of petrol has now been reduced, even including tax, to a reasonable level, but no manufacturer other than ourselves has been able to reduce the tractor weight sufficiently to justify taking full advantage of this. In the Ferguson this has been made possible by the unique unit principle adopted and it is actually more economical to run our tractor on petrol than any other tractor on paraffin.

Thus it is obvious that, by insisting on the use of petrol, we are giving the farmer advantages which he cannot obtain with any other machinery.

A farmer depends more on the unfailing performance of his tractor than on any other piece of machinery he owns, and it is absolutely necessary that it should be kept in a workable condition at all times, as the loss of a day's work may make all the difference between the success and failure of a crop.

BY USING PETROL, THE ONLY POTENTIAL SOURCE OF TROUBLE IS ELIMINATED.

It is significant that although the farmer has alternative means of personal transport, he nevertheless runs his car on petrol—the only reliable fuel—and it is therefore a strange anomaly that he should even consider a different fuel for his tractor where he has no such alternative means.

———— PAGE ONE.————

Ferguson Farm Machinery, hints for salesmen

FERGUSON FARM MACHINERY

Skilled, experienced and therefore costly operators are needed to carry out the complicated instructions issued by tractor manufacturers when paraffin is used. The Ferguson controls are simple and easily understood, and with a safe fuel unskilled operators can successfully carry out intricate cultivating work.

It pays you, as a trader, to advocate the use of a safe fuel which ensures that every owner, however inexperienced, will be as satisfied with the long life of his Ferguson as he is with its remarkable adaptability.

Ferguson machinery is full of selling points and our exclusive ownership of master patents, which cover the only successful application of the unit principle, is your safeguard against future competition.

These comments supplement the circular letter of September 6th, which was sent to all distributors and read as follows :—

FERGUSON TRACTOR FUEL.

A canvass recently completed of several hundred Ferguson owners, and discussions with Ferguson Distributors, have convinced us that in the best interests of the owner, Trader, and ourselves, petrol must be used exclusively.

No reasonable resistance can be offered to this recommendation, because the Ferguson has always been acknowledged the cheapest tractor to run, and the carburettor we now fit has still further reduced fuel consumption.

A large saving is effected in engine oil consumption, as with petrol the crankcase oil need only be changed once every full working week, whereas the normal instruction for paraffin is to drain one quart of oil daily and renew every third working day. Petrol ensures maximum engine life and minimum expenditure in upkeep.

Given proper explanation, with all the advantages presented as they should be, the farmer will readily agree that the safest fuel is the best, permitting him to benefit by the unique capabilities of our machinery, with the comforting knowledge that no harm can result from unskilled operation.

When he is brought to realise that in addition to maximum trouble-free life it is actually cheaper to run the Ferguson machinery on petrol, all further resistance is readily overcome.

The Distributor, in overcoming the farmer's prejudice against the use of petrol, has removed the greatest potential source of friction between himself and his customer, for the farmer still expects free service even if his engine is damaged by the misuse of paraffin.

We are just as capable of producing a paraffin-burning engine as any other Manufacturer, and in fact many Ferguson owners have been operating their tractors for 18 months on T.V.O. with perfect satisfaction, but we know from our records that more and more of our tractors are being bought by farmers who have not previously owned mechanical equipment ; their conditions being such that only the Ferguson could replace their horses.

Over 80 % of the farms of Great Britain have still to be mechanised, the vast majority being of such a nature that no machinery other than the Ferguson could profitably be applied to enable these farms to be commercialised successfully.

——— PAGE TWO ———

FERGUSON FARM MACHINERY

Our decision to insist on the exclusive use of petrol is one which should be warmly supported by Ferguson Distributors and the Trade generally as being an important contribution both to Farmers and Distributors towards limiting the need for service, and in helping to pave the way for the universal application of tractor power to the farm.

From this date, therefore, Ferguson tractors are warranted only if petrol fuel is used exclusively.

Salesmen's Hints.

CONFIDENTIAL.

MECHANICAL.

1. Modern tractors are being designed for petrol fuel for the following reasons :—

(a) Freedom from engine damage caused by the misuse of lower grade fuels.

(b) Influence of motor-car design—the farmer would not attempt to run his car on paraffin, and is beginning to realise that a similar argument applies to his tractor.

(c) Reliability is the farmer's first consideration— the use of petrol increases his security against breakdown and consequent loss of valuable time.

(d) Greater power and flexibility is obtained, and much cleaner running.

(e) Work can commence immediately the engine is started, even in cold weather, and the operator is not encouraged to leave his engine running.

(f) Considerable weight reduction can be effected— less land compression.

2. Other mechanical advantages are :—

(a) Engine can be designed to give maximum efficiency and lowest fuel consumption.

(b) Oil consumption is reduced by 2/3rds.

(c) Engine wear is halved.

(d) Decarbonisation and valve grinding less frequently required.

(e) Fewer running adjustments necessary.

—— PAGE THREE ——

FERGUSON FARM MACHINERY

3. PRACTICAL ADVANTAGES.

(a) Simplicity and ease of operation and use of unskilled labour.

The operation of Ferguson machinery is so simple that unskilled labour can be successfully employed, whereas even with skilled labour the danger of damage due to the misuse of paraffin is always present. The increasing difficulty of securing tractor drivers makes it more and more essential that all complications and risks be removed from tractor operation.

(b) Ease of Control.

Due to the unique hydraulic control of our implements, the Ferguson is the easiest and lightest machinery in the world to handle. Operators are not tired after a full day's work, and there are many cases recorded where this feature alone has enabled farmers to retain their drivers' services.

4. Other practical advantages are as follows :—

For light work petrol fuel should be used in any tractor, and as, in many cases, this instruction is neglected, much engine damage results.

By standardizing on petrol, forgetfulness or carelessness on the operator's part cannot damage the machinery.

By installing a fuel tank, a farmer can buy the whole of his requirements of petrol at trade price, and so save himself 2d. per gallon on the fuel he uses in his car and truck.

5. CONSUMPTION FIGURES.

The Ferguson costs between 8d. and 1/- per hour to run, including lubricating oil.

These costs are substantiated by hundreds of Ferguson owners throughout the British Isles.

————— PAGE FOUR —————

DIRECTORS
F. E. BROWN, CHAIRMAN
DAVID BROWN, A.I.MECH.E.   } JOINT
HENRY G. FERGUSON, M.I.A.E., A.F.Ac.S. } MANAGING
ERNEST DE SILLY HAMILTON BROWNE, D.L., J.P.
THOMAS MacGREGOR GREER, D.L., J.P.
ARTHUR SYKES, B.Sc., M.I.MECH.E.

Producing and using the Ferguson Brown

Reproduced in the next pages are 21 photos relating to the production of the Ferguson Brown tractors and implements and photos of the tractor in use. These are from the *originals* used in the preparation of the Ferguson Brown Machinery brochure shown earlier in this chapter.

ABOVE **Ferguson Brown Tractors and implements leaving the David Brown factory site on the once very common Scammel three wheel articulated trucks. Note the "Ferguson Hydraulic Farm Machinery" stamped on the tractor covers**

THIS SPREAD **The Ferguson Brown tractor assembly line**

Manufacturing the Ferguson Brown implements at the David Brown factory, 1937

57.

A big field for a small tractor making an impressive job of the task

BELOW **Over the crest of the hill on pneumatic wheels and without wheel spin**

RIGHT **Making a perfect job at 9 in. depth**

BELOW RIGHT **A good finishing of the lands as the mist comes down, 1938**

ABOVE LEFT **Only a three and a half yard wide headland was required when ploughing with the Ferguson Brown**

BELOW LEFT **Ploughing up a hill of 1:4 gradient. The wheels are thought not to be original Ferguson Brown equipment**

BELOW **Cultivating stony ground was no problem for the Ferguson "General Cultivator" equipped with spring release tines**

ABOVE **After harvest stubble cultivation**

BELOW **An early adaptation of a Ferguson Brown toolbar for inter row cultivation of sugar beet**

BELOW RIGHT **Inter row cultivation of sugar beet. The Ferguson Brown toolbar is equipped with Saxonia weeding equipment.**

ABOVE LEFT **Rowcrop cultivator and rowcrop width wheels in a crop of spring cabbage**

BELOW **A final pass through well grown sugar beet**

ABOVE RIGHT **No hydraulics used when pulling this Bamford's self cleaning harrow**

Splitting potato ridges

ABOVE LEFT **No wheel marks after a Ferguson Brown tractor!**

BELOW LEFT **Light duties only for this Ferguson Brown pulling a Bamford's Supreme fertiliser spreader**

BELOW **Demonstrating a Bamford's hay rake well in advance of the season!**

CHAPTER 7

Introducing the Ford Ferguson

This chapter is a reproduction of the Souvenir Official Introduction brochure of the Ford Tractor with Ferguson System at St. Stephen's, Bedfont, Middlesex in May 1940. The production of Ford Ferguson tractors had started almost a year earlier in the USA. It is a 14 page brochure printed in England bearing the Ford Ferguson System logo on the rear cover. Interestingly the brochure features a more than significant note about the UK Ford plant at Dagenham. However the Ford Ferguson tractor never came to be manufactured there.

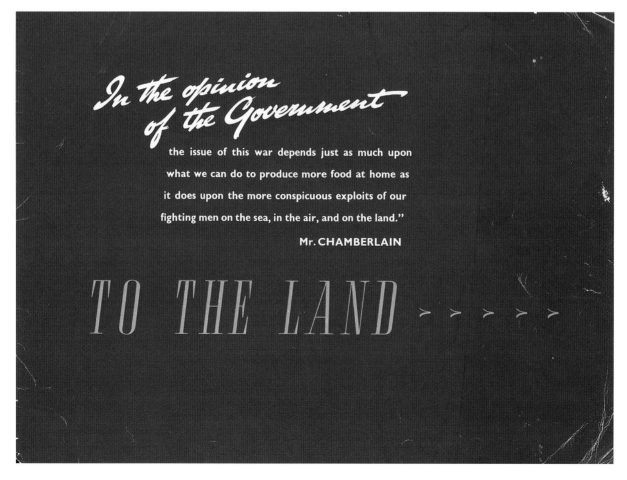

THE LAND! That is where our roots are. There is the basis of our physical life. The farther we get away from the land, the greater our insecurity. From the land comes everything that supports life, everything we use for the service of physical life. The land has not collapsed or shrunk in either expanse or productivity. It is there waiting to honour all the labour we are willing to invest in it, and able to tide us across any local dislocation of economic conditions. No unemployment insurance can be compared to an alliance between man and a plot of land.

Henry Ford

THIS SIGNIFICANT meeting and friendly agreement between Mr. Henry Ford and Mr. Harry Ferguson means the end of the unprofitable drudgery of animal farming. It means the beginning of a new era in agriculture, for the farmer can make more profit without increasing the cost of foodstuffs to the consumer.

With one foot on the Land and one in Industry— Great Britain is safe

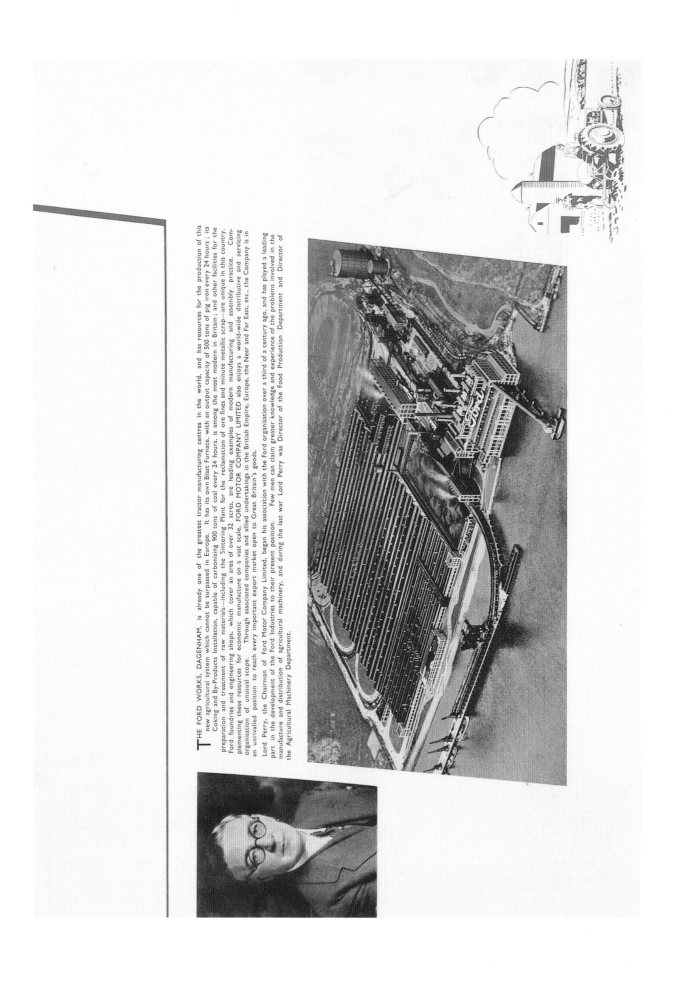

THE FORD WORKS, DAGENHAM, is already one of the greatest tractor manufacturing centres in the world, and has resources for the production of this new agricultural system which cannot be surpassed in Europe. It has its own Blast Furnace, with an output capacity of 500 tons of pig iron every 24 hours; its Coking and By-Products Installation, capable of carbonising 900 tons of coal every 24 hours, is among the most modern in Britain; and other facilities for the preparation and treatment of raw materials—including the Sintering Plant for the reclamation of ore fines and minute metallic scrap—are unique in this country. Ford foundries and engineering shops, which cover an area of over 32 acres, are leading examples of modern manufacturing and assembly practice. Complementing these resources for economic manufacture on a vast scale, FORD MOTOR COMPANY LIMITED also enjoys a world-wide distributive and servicing organisation of unusual scope. Through associated companies and allied undertakings in the British Empire, Europe, the Near and Far East, etc., the Company is in an unrivalled position to reach every important export market open to Great Britain's goods.

Lord Perry, the Chairman of Ford Motor Company Limited, began his association with the Ford organisation over a third of a century ago, and has played a leading part in the development of the Ford Industries to their present position. Few men can claim greater knowledge and experience of the problems involved in the manufacture and distribution of agricultural machinery, and during the last war Lord Perry was Director of the Food Production Department and Director of the Agricultural Machinery Department.

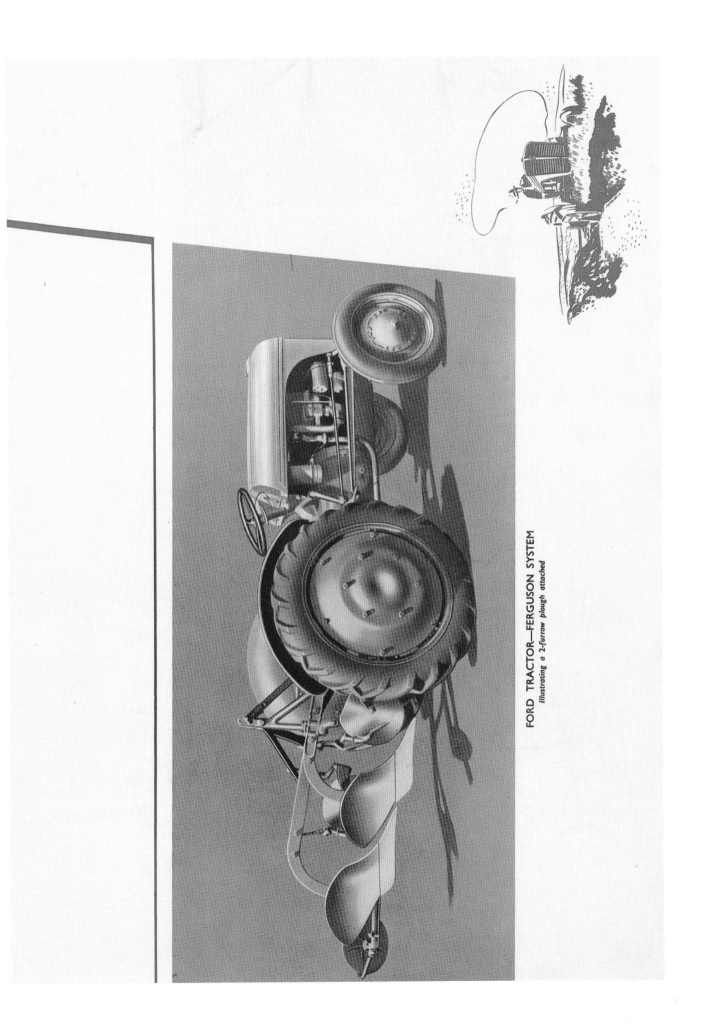

FORD TRACTOR—FERGUSON SYSTEM
Illustrating a 2-furrow plough attached

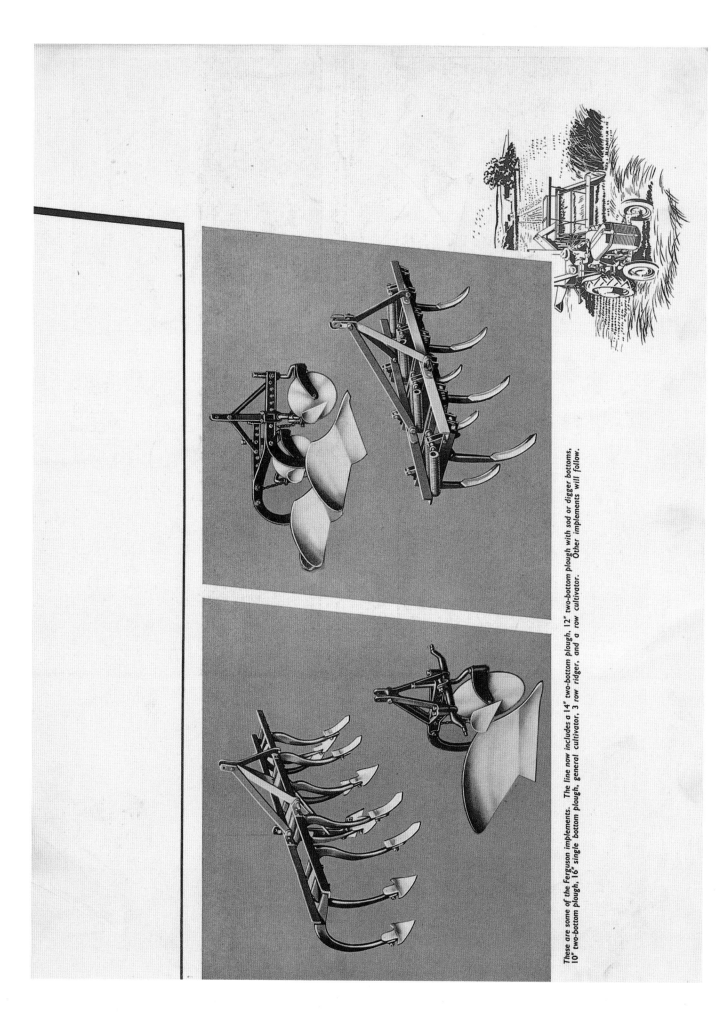

These are some of the Ferguson implements. The line now includes a 14" two-bottom plough, 12" two-bottom plough with sod or digger bottoms, 10" two-bottom plough, 16" single bottom plough, general cultivator, 3 row ridger, and a row cultivator. Other implements will follow.

Row crops—the now vital potato ! For the growing of this crop the new system is ideal. The above illustration shows how ridges are made. A young girl or young lad can operate the tractor with ease.

Splitting ridges to cover the potato seed. Wooden pegs were used to represent potato stems. The light tractor does not pack the land.

Cultivating hard ground between fruit trees. The system of linkage employed holds the implement in the hardest ground.

Orchard cultivation. It will be noted in the above illustration that each tine is fitted with two coil springs. When the tine encounters an obstruction, such as a tree root, it automatically releases without causing damage to either tine or root, and goes back to work again without stopping.

Ploughing an acre an hour ! The Ford Tractor with Ferguson System handles this two-bottom 14 in. plough with ease in medium land. One implement can be detached and another fitted instantaneously.

Every inch of land should be cultivated in this war ! In small fields and awkward corners the new System far eclipses the horse. Note that the whole of the small plot—too small for horse operation—has been cultivated without leaving a wheel mark.

Hauling a binder with power take-off in operation. The new tractor has ample power for hauling the average binder in the hilliest conditions.

Hauling manure spreader. The distributor can be driven by the power take-off.

Belt work. The engine has ample power for all work on the farm. The attachment of the belt pulley is a simple operation.

The tractor is fitted with a built-in power take-off and handles a 5 ft. Combine on pneumatics with ease.

Cultivating between the ridges. In this class of work a young land worker of either sex can do as much work in one day as can be done in six days by a man and a pair of horses.

Moulding-up after cultivation. Rapid work ensures maximum yield, because the farmer can catch the best weather.

One of the most difficult problems in perfecting the Ferguson System was how to haul a big load with a light tractor. This problem was solved by utilising the tractor linkage in such manner as to make the tractor carry most of the load being hauled. The load is so applied through the patented linkage that the weight is divided as required over the four tractor wheels.

Tipping is the easiest thing in the world ! ! At the touch of a finger the hydraulic mechanism in the tractor tips the trailer. The trailer can be unloaded from the tractor seat.

The Ford Tractor, Ferguson System, is revolutionary in its operation on steep hills. With the ordinary tractor there is a tendency on steep hills for the front wheels to be lifted off the ground. With the Ferguson System of linkage the front wheels are held down. When an obstruction is encountered no damage is done to the implement.

For many reasons the new System will prove a vital factor in the war. Vast quantities of food can be produced from land which it would not be possible to cultivate with other tractors or with horses. In addition, the new tractor can be operated by very young and older people of both sexes who could not operate the ordinary tractor or horses.

Corn Drilling. The new tractor is ideal for this purpose, because it does not pack the land.

The new tractor will do every job on the farm, thus eliminating the need for costly horse-operation. The above picture speaks for itself.

SPECIFICATION

ENGINE—Four-cylinder L-head. Bore 3.18 x 3.75 in. Displacement 120 cu. in. Brake Horse Power—23 at 1,400 R.P.M. (recommended for ploughing).

GOVERNOR—Variable speed governor. Controlled from steering column. Working range—1,200 to 2,200 R.P.M.

LUBRICATION—By gear pump supplying direct pressure oiling to crankshaft, camshaft and connecting rod bearings, also to timing gears. Crankcase oil capacity—6 quarts.

IGNITION—Direct driven battery distributor in unit with coil in waterproof housing. Fully automatic spark advance.

GENERATOR—6-volt shunt wound with vibrator type voltage regulation.

STARTER—6-volt conventional type automobile starter with finger operated switch on dash.

BATTERY—6-volt—85 ampere hour capacity—13 high plates.

COOLING—Pump circulation of water through tube and fin type of radiator. Fan—4 blade 16 in. driven by belt. Pumps are of the packless type with prelubricated bearings.

FUEL SUPPLY—Welded steel tank carried in engine hood, capacity 9 gallons with 1 gallon reserve. Fuel outlet to carburettor is through glass sediment chamber and strainer.

OIL FILTER—Removable cartridge type of large capacity.

VAPORISER—New Improved Type Holley.

AIR CLEANER—Oil bath type with dust receptacle removable for cleaning.

MUFFLER—Muffler is fitted as standard equipment to carry exhaust to the rear of the tractor.

CLUTCH—Single dry place 9 in. effective diameter. Spring pressure increased by centrifugal force.

TRANSMISSION—Sliding gear—3 speeds forward and one reverse. All shafts run on tapered roller bearings.

FINAL DRIVE—Spiral bevel gear drive with straddle mounted pinion 6.66 to 1 ratio. Four pinion differential mounted on tapered roller bearings. Drive axle of the semi-floating type with axle shaft and wheel hub integral, also carried on tapered roller bearings.

SPEEDS—At 1,400 R.P.M.

Low ... ...   2¼ M.P.H. approx. High ...   ...   6 M.P.H. approx.
Intermediate (ploughing) 3 M.P.H. approx. Reverse... ...   2¼ M.P.H. approx.

NOTE.—Higher speeds than these can be obtained by speeding up the engine.

STEERING—Bevel pinion and twin bevel sectors controlling both front wheels independently. Tread of front axle adjustable without disturbing any steering connections. Rubber covered steel steering wheel 18 in. diameter.

POWER TAKE-OFF—Shaft extends from rear of axle housing. Has standard spline end for fitting to drives of power driven equipment. 727 R.P.M. at 2,000 R.P.M. engine speed.

BRAKES—14 in. x 2 in. internal expanding, two shoe, full energising type. One simple accessible adjustment. Brakes operating independently on each rear wheel, controlled by separate pedals to facilitate short turning.

WHEELS—Front—Steel disc fitted with 19 x 4 single rib pneumatic tyres on drop centre rim, tyre pressure—28 lbs. Rear—Steel disc fitted with 28 x 10 traction tread pneumatic tyres on drop centre rim, tyre pressure—12 lbs.

HYDRAULIC IMPLEMENT CONTROL—Consists of 4 cylinder pump supplying oil under suitable pressure to ram cylinder and controlled by an ingenious valve. An operating handle convenient to the operator's right hand gives him instant control of the implement.

DIMENSIONS OF TRACTOR—

Wheelbase—70 in.
Normal tread—Front and rear—48 in.
Front tread—Adjustable by means of telescoping axle beam and reversible wheel disc to 76 in. in 4 in. steps.
Rear tread—Adjustable by means of reversible wheel disc and reversible tyre rim to 76 in. in 4 in. steps.
Overall length—Front tyre fin to end of lower link—115 in.
Overall width—64 in.
Overall height—52 in.
Ground clearance—13 in. under centre. 21 in. under axles.
Minimum turning circle—15 ft. with use of brakes.

EXTRA EQUIPMENT—1. Belt Pulley. Carried by self-contained drive unit quickly attachable to rear of tractor. Pulley diameter—8 in., width 6.5 in.   Speed—1,352 R.P.M., belt speed—2,831 ft. per minute at 2,000 R.P.M. engine speed.   2. Lighting System. 3. Steel Wheels with Lugs.

ALTERATIONS TO SPECIFICATIONS—Ford Motor Company Limited, whose policy is one of continuous improvement, reserves the right to change specifications, design, or prices, without incurring obligation.

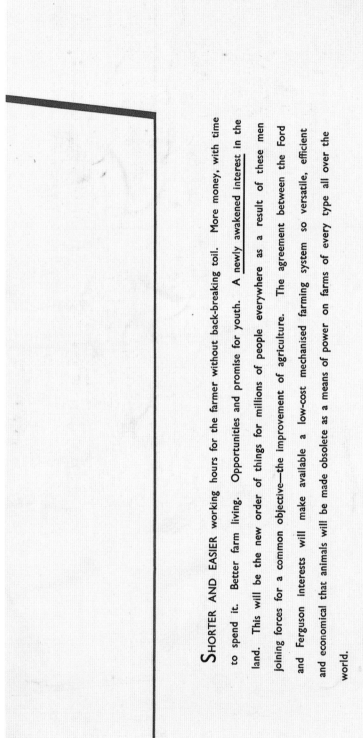

SHORTER AND EASIER working hours for the farmer without back-breaking toil. More money, with time to spend it. Better farm living. Opportunities and promise for youth. A newly awakened interest in the land. This will be the new order of things for millions of people everywhere as a result of these men joining forces for a common objective—the improvement of agriculture. The agreement between the Ford and Ferguson interests will make available a low-cost mechanised farming system so versatile, efficient and economical that animals will be made obsolete as a means of power on farms of every type all over the world.

From left to right: Mr. Harry G. Ferguson, Mr. Henry Ford, Mr. Edsel Ford, Mr. Charles E. Sorensen, Mr. George B. Sherman, Mr. J. L. Williams, Mr. Eber C. Sherman.

IN 1917, under the impetus of Mr. Lloyd George's food campaign, the "Ferguson System" of land cultivation was conceived. It has taken 23 years to perfect!

The Plan on which the System was founded was as follows :—

1. To halve the cost of food production and make farming prosperous without increasing the cost to the consumer.

2. To make farming attractive to youth and largely solve the unemployment problem by stopping the drift from the land.

3. To assist all other industries through a prosperous agriculture, and to establish a great new British industry for manufacturing agricultural machinery for the Home and Export Trade.

4. To lay the foundation of a greater National security in war.

When the inventions had been perfected to a point where this Plan could be fulfilled, the System was demonstrated to Mr. Henry Ford in the U.S.A. He at once agreed that it had all the possibilities claimed for it, and put his genius and vast resources behind manufacture. His success has been phenomenal. Although production only started in August last, the present output exceeds 350 tractors and 1,500 implements per DAY.

The new System applies to world conditions, and Ford Motor Company Limited desires to commence production of the machinery as soon as possible for the home market, and for export throughout the Eastern Hemisphere. I hope the British Government will take advantage of the vital help this new System can give in the war, and in the reconstruction period afterwards.

Harry Ferguson

BRITAIN today faces urgent problems. To the solution of these, no less than to the ultimate regeneration of her agriculture, this new machinery will provide a new and vital contribution. Its manufacture is simplified and made economical and rapid by its design and the unique elimination of excess weight and parts.

The new tractor and four implements can be built with *less than half* the material required for the ordinary tractor and four implements of the same operating capacity. Therefore, their manufacture can effect invaluable savings in steel and other raw materials, and, at the same time, provide British farmers with new power, combined with universatility of application, to assist them in their great endeavour to increase and safeguard the Nation's food supplies.

E_{VERY} country needs the advantages which are provided by this new agricultural System. Vast new export markets are thus within reach of British industry. In the economic phase of the struggle in which the Country is now engaged, this machinery can provide a new and especially effective weapon, because the consumption of steel entailed by its manufacture is low in relation to the value of the finished product in export markets. Ford manufacturing resources will, at the earliest opportunity, produce this new machinery for the waiting markets of the world, and thereby help to pay for the food and raw materials which Britain must continue to import.

A.5286/054   *Printed in England.*

S O U V E N I R

OFFICIAL INTRODUCTION OF THE
FORD TRACTOR WITH FERGUSON SYSTEM
ST. STEPHEN'S, BEDFONT, MIDDLESEX

MAY, 1940

CHAPTER 8

The Museum: Collecting, restoring and building the Hunday collection

The building for the collection was completely renovated in 1990 and has an insulated area of 8,500 sq. ft. It contains a small workshop with facilities for basic mechanical repairs, cleaning and painting. Any mechanical work requiring use of machine tools is contracted out.

Collection of items of equipment for the Ferguson collection started in earnest in 1985. Prior to this some literature had been collected as part of the Hunday Countryside Museum Programme. The model collection has also been ongoing since 1980.

A general view of the museum building and part of the Hunday collection

THE MUSEUM

The building for the collection was completely renovated in 1990 and has an insulated area of 8,500 sq ft. It contains a small workshop with facilities for basic mechanical repairs, cleaning and painting. Any mechanical work requiring use of machine tools is contracted out.

Collection of items of equipment for the Ferguson collection started in earnest in 1985. Prior to this some literature had been collected as part of the Hunday Countryside Museum Programme. The model collection has also been ongoing since 1980.

The equipment has been collected from all over the UK as well as Canada and the USA. In the USA David Lory, a well known Ferguson enthusiast in Wisconsin, was a great help and assisted in locating North American equipment for this collection. The effort was reciprocated by British equipment being collected and sent over to him.

The finding of equipment for the collection was a painstaking effort with many false leads and interesting exploits into quite diverse parts of the UK and the USA.

All possible preservation and restoration has been undertaken in the museum's own workshop. In charge of this has been George Potts. Although now retired he was the foreman on the family farming business for over 40 years. In so called retirement, George has been kept well occupied on restoration of the equipment for the several years over which the collection has been assembled. The restored condition of the equipment is a tribute to George's quiet perseverance, everything first having been sand blasted and etch coated. Where parts had to be made, outside assistance has been sought.

Two fascinating pieces of equipment which proved impossible to obtain had to be made. The side mounted combine harvesters were only made as prototypes and as far as can be ascertained none survive. Equally, few of the side mounted balers were made and these are now very rare – so one of these had to be made too! For the "manufacture" of these machines professional engineers had to be involved and it was a stroke of luck that a nearby facility – Greenline Engineering - could be used for the difficult fabrication work.

BELOW With the acquisition of some original 1950 banners and buntings, one end of the museum is now set up as a Ferguson exhibition stand

ABOVE Occasionally every tractor is brought out of the museum for a photo opportunity
TOP RIGHT A TEA 20 under restoration in the museum workshop
BELOW RIGHT A general shot inside the museum

BELOW LEFT The Ferguson 35 corner
ABOVE LEFT The museum site is occasionally used to host Ferguson events. Seen here is a vintage rally line up in 1997 with both visiting and resident items of Ferguson equipment

MAIN PICTURE A long shot through the museum – all 210 ft. of it – and becoming evermore crowded!

INSET When all the tractors and implements are on display outside, accessories and wheel section in the end of the building are revealed. On the lower shelf, the middle four wheels are original Ferguson equipment, whilst those to right and left were made by other manufacturers. The two cabinets on the top shelf are Ferguson mobile tractor servicing equipment

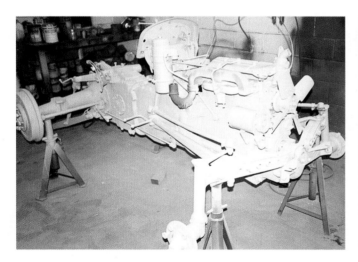

ABOVE A TEA tractor purchased from Mr Joll in June 1996 having received a full cleaning, starts going through the paint sequence
ABOVE RIGHT Mass application of primer paint to a selection of implements

TOP The "on arrival" condition of this Ferguson 40 standard tractor was typical of many items that were purchased by the museum

BELOW The side mounted forage harvester in "as found" condition having just crossed the Atlantic from the USA

ABOVE LEFT Most machines are sandblasted before painting. This manure spreader had the treatment in August 1996

TOP Standard Vanguard vans were widely used as Ferguson service vans in the UK. (Fergusons were made in a Standard Motor Co. factory at Coventry) Here restoration will involve a complete colour change!

ABOVE RIGHT John Moffitt inspecting detail on a tractor under restoration
BELOW The forage harvester was dismantled for restoration. This is the main chopping cylinder assembly before cleaning

Making the side mounted combine

In 1995, during John's quest for all things Ferguson, a photo of one of the prototypes was found, but attempts to trace any surviving machines drew a blank. Only perhaps a dozen or so of them had ever been made. They were designed in the 1950s and tested in many parts of the world including Newcastle University farm at Nafferton.

The only few drawings that could be traced of the side mounted combines were in magazines at the Museum of English Rural Life in Reading. Apart from these the only specifications that

had come to light were three pages of general data about the machine, dated 1956, which are reproduced here. Further enquiries produced little to add to these other than the similarity of the working mechanism to the MF 735 combine in terms of the drum width, the three straw walkers, and the grain separation area. It was therefore decided to build a good replica of the side mounted combine using pieces from two 735 combines as the starting point of the operation. From the outset it was recognised that such a replica could not be identical, but at least it would bring back into existence   a live version of the original concept.

ABOVE The Museum's aim was to create a working full scale replica of this "extinct" side mounted combine harvester. This is a rare surviving colour photograph of one of the originals at work, probably in the north east of England

RIGHT One of the prototype side mounted combine harvesters which failed to survive, but which at least provided some visual detail

1956 FERGUSON MOUNTED COMBINE.

PROVISIONAL SPECIFICATION.
(NOT FOR GENERAL RELEASE)

Tractor.	TE.20 with epicyclic reduction unit giving 3 : 1 reduction. FE-35 (TO-35)
Basic Type Combine.	Two-spout bagger.
Overall Dimensions.	Length : approx. 21'6" Width : approx. 8'6" Height : approx. 7'9"
Weight of Combine and Attachments.	approx. 2,300 lbs
Overall Weight.	approx. 5,000 lbs.

Ground Speeds Available for Combining.

TE-20.

Standard: 2000 engine r.p.m. 1.1, 1.5, 2.1, 4.4. m.p.h.

Optional: 1400 engine r.p.m. .77, 1.1, 1.5, 3.1 m.p.h.

FE-35 & TO-35

Standard: 1750 engine r.p.m., 1.05, 1.55, 2.83, 4.2 m.p.h.

Optional: 1200 engine r.p.m. .71, 1.05, 1.95, 2.83, 4.2 m.p.h.

Reel.

Standard Bat type.

Optional Universal type, with tines maintained in vertical plane by eccentric cranks. Chain driven

6 speeds available - 6, 10, 14, 20, 33, 46 r.p.m.

Standard: Manual height control

Optional: Hydraulic height control.

Knife. 7'9"

Top-serrated blades.

Driven by oscillating con-rod and bell-crank with a bronze slider in the knife-head.

Chain driven with slip-clutch provided.

500 r.p.m. approx.

N.B. The slip-clutch also protects the table auger and reel.

Table Auger.

Open structure with feathering fingers and plastic bearings, running at 145 r.p.m.

Chain driven

Flight diameter 20".

Table.

Integral, spot-welded structure.

7'6" cutterbar

7'9" gather

Standard: Hydraulic lift control.

1956 FERGUSON MOUNTED COMBINE (cont'd).

Crop Elevator.	Three spot-welded, five-bladed, closed beaters.

Bottom beater : 18" diameter.   185 r.p.m.
Centre beater : 15" diameter   270 r.p.m.
Feeding beater :12" diameter   400 r.p.m.

Width of elevator casing 23½"

Dust cowling provided.

Main Body.	Integral, spot-welded structure 24" wide.

Cylinder.	Rasp-bar type - 6 bars 18" diameter.

Chain driven.

4 sprockets available giving the following speeds :-

360, 455, 510, 800, 910, 1020, 1140, 1290, 1440 r.p.m.

Concave.	Bar and wire type (Grill)

Manual adjustment gives a 3 : 1 ratio between front and rear settings.

Limits of front adjustment : 3/16" to 15/16"

Two-position adjustment provided at rear of concave to allow easy clearing of cylinder blockages.

Straw Beater.	Spot-welded, five-bladed beater, 15" diameter.

Belt driven at 720 r.p.m.

Gearbox.	Normally provided with one output location only but a second may be added, allowing the tractor engine to be operated at a lower speed, giving the following :-

TE.20.   Normal Speed : 2000 engine r.p.m.
              Extra speed : 1400 engine r.p.m.

FE-35 & TO-35.   Normal speed : 1750 engine r.p.m.
                 Extra speed : 1200 engine r.p.m.

In its complete form the gearbox consists of one spur pinion and two gears, belt driven from the P.T.O. pulley adaptor.

Straw Walkers.	Three spot-welded, two-cascade straw walkers.

7½" wide and 8'9" long.

Chain driven at 190 r.p.m.

Supported on two three-throw crankshafts.

Plastic bearings.

Shaker Pan.	Stepped, spot-welded structure, 23½" wide.

230 cycles per minute.

3" stroke.

Shaker Shoe.	Spot-welded structure

230 cycles per minute.

1½ stroke

Driven in the reverse direction to that of the shaker pan from an eccentric on the end of the grain auger, through a con-rod and appropriate linkage.

Sieves.	(a) Top Sieve. Universal fixed type with arched openings.
	(b) Bottom Sieve. Round hole type - 9 sieves available.

1956 FERGUSON MOUNTED COMBINE (cont'd).

Standard hole sizes : 5/16", 7/16", 5/8"
(for cereals)

Optional extra sieves available :
1/16", 3/32", 1/8", 5/32", 3/16", 1/4"
(for special crops)

Both sieves 23-3/16" wide by 36" long.

Gleanings Re-thrasher.

Comprises on the same shaft a conveying auger, a set of thrashing blades and a fan impellor for conveying the re-thrashed gleanings to the top sieve through an appropriate duct.

Chain driven from the P.T.O.Pulley adaptor at 1150 r.p.m.

Grain Auger
and Elevator.

Auger diameter 5"

Cup and link chain elevator

Belt driven at 230 r.p.m.

Bagging Arrangement. Two-spout bagger with quick action sack holders.

Bagging Platform. Tubular steel frame integral with the body.

Fanning Mill. Paddle type. Four radial paddles.

Belt driven at 1680 r.p.m.

Air controlled from the driver's seat.

Tractor Attachments. (a) Extension to the nearside rear axle and load relieving bracket.

(b) Front bracket providing front attachments for the main body and for the table lifting jack.

(c) Hydraulic valve for table lift control and operating mechanism.

(d) Special P.T.O.Pulley incorporating an over-run clutch.

(e) Tractometer - standard on TO-35
extra on TE-20

General. All drives guarded.

Empty sacks holder.

Sealed bearings throughout.

Fire extinguisher.

Optional Equipment. (1) Three rotary screen, giving two grades of corn.

(2) Grain tank with unloading auger.

(3) Hydraulic control of reel height adjustment.

(4) 2nd gear for low engine speeds.

(5) Universal reel.

Graham Johnstone of Greenline Engineering in Hexham was approached for help and gladly accepted the challenge. George Byerley, a neighbour, stepped in to assist with fabrication of the front part and the wheel extension. Friend and colleague Andy J. Sewell from Bardon Mill who had worked as a draughtsman at the Silsoe National Institute of Agricultural Engineering undertook to do the drawings of the tricky parts that needed

to be scaled down e.g. the various drive arrangements for the drum and beaters. George Potts was also involved with John in the general co-ordination of the project and locating numerous second-hand parts.

By the autumn of 1995 there was no turning back for the project. A target date of completing it for the Royal Agricultural

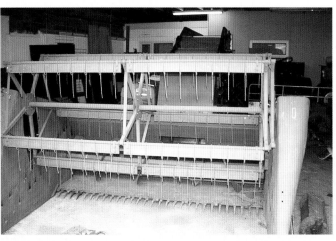

ABOVE Left hand rear axle extension and combine support under manufacture
BELOW George Byerley, who was responsible for the manufacture of the axle extension, checking the finished component

ABOVE Headers from two M-H 735 combine harvesters were used in the manufacture of this one unit
BELOW An early side view of the header and threshing units coming together to give the first impressions of what the final machine would look like

Show in 1996 was set where it would partake in the 50th anniversary of the start of production of the TE 20 Ferguson tractors in the UK. This was achieved – just!

Perhaps it was a crazy idea but everyone involved had great fun. The total cost, including labour, was about £11,500 which

included the purchase of two 735 combines and new bearings etc. This was more or less the budget figure as an original target of £10,000 was set without really knowing what was involved. More illustrations of the final product are shown in Chapter 9, and in Chapter 12 Nigel Liney recounts some of his experiences in demonstrating the prototypes.

ABOVE The main threshing and separation area being assembled on to the tractor and its sub frame

BELOW The near complete machine is driven from the workshop for the first time

ABOVE RIGHT View through the internal workings of the separation and threshing areas

ABOVE Time for thought and consideration of the final product

BELOW LEFT Museum owner John Moffitt compares his replica of the 1950s combine with a monster from the late 1990s.

BELOW RIGHT The first public outing of the combine was at the Royal Show in 1996 where it took part in celebrations to mark the 50th anniversary of the start of TE tractor production in the UK

Making the side mounted baler

John, on one of his many visits to the US had seen an un-restored side mounted baler in Ohio in 1997. Desperate attempts to buy it failed, but the workmanship that had gone into the machine left an indelible impression. Research revealed that it would be like looking for a needle in a haystack to find another survivor. Apparently they were all recalled to the factory to be scrapped at the time of the Ferguson and Massey-Harris merger. There were reportedly some 40 owners who were given M-H No.1 balers in exchange. However not all the machines were traced and two are known to have escaped the scrap bin.

The tricky bit was getting the chassis and sub frame constructed. Good friend Richard Kemball in Ohio, where John had seen the first example of an original specimen, provided dimensions of his machine which were imposed on drawings. The most difficult task was how to get the PTO drive from the tractor round the gearbox. A gearbox reversal was necessary and hope was in the air that the drive to the knotters and feed rakes

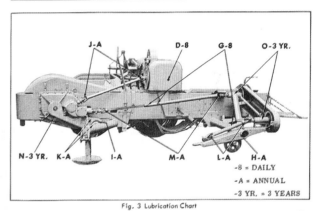

Fig. 3 Lubrication Chart

Fig. 4 Lubrication Chart

RIGHT Two of the best shots we had of an original machine were the lubrication charts from an operators manual
ABOVE 1955 shot of a dealer/customer demonstration of the side mounted baler in central Michigan. (Photo courtesy of Delbert Gentner)

could be established! In the event the machine was finished for a Ferguson Rally Day held at Hunday on August 24 1997.

The gearbox arrangement proved not to be wholly satisfactory and surprisingly an original gearbox turned up in a scrapyard in Nebraska, which has produced a smoother running machine altogether.

A 701 baler already "in stock" at Hunday bore many similarities in basic design to the side mounted model. This formed the basis for this second "manufacturing" project. Greenline Engineering was again enlisted to build the baler, whilst John Moffitt and George Potts co-ordinated the undertaking. A parts and instruction book were obtained from David Lory in Wisconsin. Then came the stripping down and sand blasting of pieces from the 701 baler.

The total cost for the project was about £5,000, and more illustrations of the final product are shown in Chapter 9.

BELOW LEFT The main frame which carries the baler under assembly. This proved to be a complicated piece of engineering and is here shown upside down as welding proceeds

ABOVE The main assembly of a 701 PTO drive baler was used as the basis for the side mounted baler. Here in the early stages of construction the main drive gearbox is seen reversed to accept the PTO drive from the rear of the tractor, and provide a drive to the packers etc.

BELOW RIGHT Developing the hitch of the main frame to the rear of the tractor

ABOVE The main frame is now hitched to the tractor and the main baler body mounted on it for the first time

ABOVE RIGHT Working detail of the attachment of the pick up to the main baler body

RIGHT Taking the drive from the main gearbox to the packers presented a problem and had to be invented. An original gearbox has been found in North America and will be fitted retrospectively

ABOVE LEFT Almost complete!

BELOW Employees of Greenline Engineering who made the baler heave a sigh of relief after the first successful demonstration. George Potts, the Moffitts' retired farm foreman who has been the backbone of restoration activities at the museum, looks on from the left rear of the tested product

ABOVE RIGHT The first successful outing of the baler was at a local vintage working day

A Listing of the Hunday Fergusons

The following are listings of equipment held in the museum as of the end of 1999. To many it may seem very comprehensive, but the more expert enthusiasts will realise that it is still not a complete collection, especially if all the USA style implements are included. French equipment also has limited representation so far. Experts will also notice that a few items of equipment are included in the collection which were not sold or approved by Ferguson. In practice many such items of equipment were made, and it seemed appropriate to include a few examples.

Tractors

NO.	TRACTOR TYPE	MODEL	SERIAL NO.	YEAR
1	Ferguson Brown	A	130	1936
2	Ford Ferguson	9N aluminium bonnet	738	1939
3	Ford Ferguson	2N	missing	1941
4	Ford Ferguson	2N fitted P3 engine	missing	1941
5	Ford Ferguson	9N Moto Tug	157	1942
6	Ford	8N-AN	266832	1952
7	Ferguson TE	TE fitted P3 engine	2223	1947
8	Ferguson TE	TE	15596	1948
9	Ferguson TE	TEA	36385	1948
10	Ferguson TE	TEA	40183	1948
11	Ferguson TO (USA)	TO 30	82673	1953
12	Ferguson TE	TEA	47880	1948
13	Ferguson TE	TET industrial	70340	1948
14	Ferguson TE	TEA half track	85362	1949
15	Ferguson TE	TEA	141207	1950
16	Ferguson TE	TED	141665	1950
17	Ferguson TE	TEA	166326	1950
18	Ferguson TE	TED	194540	1951
19	Ferguson TE	TED Reekie adaption	213546	1952
20	Ferguson TE	TED	286268	1952
21	Ferguson TE	TED	305603	1952
22	Ferguson TE	TEF	309642	1952
23	Ferguson TE	TED narrow (maybe replacement serial number)	319933	1952
24	Ferguson TE	TEL orchard	328794	1953
25	Ferguson TE	TEF with digger	359602	1953
26	Ferguson TE	TEF	224112	1951
27	Ferguson TE	TEF with reduction box	344610	1953
28	Ferguson TE	TED full track	224471	1952
29	Ferguson TO (USA)	TO 35 green	148997	1954
30	Ferguson 35	SDM grey/gold	56537	1957
31	Ferguson 35	SKT grey/gold	118361	1958
32	Ferguson 35	SDF red	149805	1959
33	MF 65	SNY	519712	1960
34	Ferguson F 40	C GM	404980	1954
35	Ferguson F 40	S GM	408261	1956
36	MF 50	S GM	528590	1958
37	MF 25 (French)	Standard	200108	1958
38	Standard Vanguard	Service van diesel		1955
39	Ford Ferguson	Funk 6 cylinder conversion		1943
40	Ford Ferguson	Funk Ford V8 100 hp conversion		
41	Ivel	16 hp	131	1903

In the following tables are some specimen prices that have been traced.

Ploughs and subsoilers

TYPE	MODEL	SERIAL NUMBER	PRICE £
Ferguson 2 furrow by R Lean	Made Aug. 1923	6560	
Plough 3 furrow 10" general purpose	10HC-AEOA99	006441	76.0.0
Plough 2 furrow 10" general purpose	10H-AE-A28	003407	44.0.0
Plough 2 furrow 14 in. (USA)	14-AO-28	92652	
Plough 2 furrow 16" semi digger	12-OAE-28	3001189	
Plough 1 furrow 16"	16-CF-AE-28	12365	41.0.0
Plough slatted mouldboards	14-AO-40	7952	
Plough, Ford, 2 Furrow			
Single furrow reversible plough 16ins	T-AE-28	001995	102.10.0
Disc plough 2 furrow	2-P-AE-20	2163	66.0.0
Disc plough 3 furrow	3-P-AO-21	20304	117.0.0
Disc terracer (USA)	A-FO-20	7160	
Subsoiler	D-BE-28	8481	
Subsoiler (Canada)	D-BO-22	04646	

Cultivators, harrows and discs

TYPE	MODEL	SERIAL NUMBER	PRICE £
Spring tooth harrow 2 gang	K-BE-A21	16454	28.10.0
Spring tooth harrow 3 gang	K-BE-A31	12101	35.0.0
Spring tine cultivator	9S-KE-20	18579	46.0.0
Tiller	9-BE-20	61265	49.0.0
Tiller, orchard width	6-BE-20	322	44.0.0
Weeder	M-KE-A21	4612	34.0.0
Steerage hoe + Reekie weeder	1PKE-20	3484	86.0.0
Steerage hoe independent gang	4PKE-20	81	117.0.0
Spike tooth harrow, folding	S-BE-31	25154	41.0.0
Spike tooth harrow, heavy duty	S-BE-41	W6404	
Rigid tine cultivator, Sherman (USA)	KP	1414	
Rigid tine cultivator with crop guards	KO	1929	
Lister cultivator with crop guards	LKO-B-20	3246	
Rigid tine cultivator	9-KE-A20	48712	46.0.0
Trailed discs 6ft.	6 ABE 21	16345	90.0.0
Mounted tandem type discs 6ft.	7 ABE 22	193	
Offset discs	9-BE-20	842	
Heavy duty discs	SH-BE-20	3874	
7 disc tiller	P-BO-20	1071	
Single row discs	50A-BO-21	73694	
Rotary hoe 7ft	R-KO-20	10877	
Mid mounted inter row cultivator	Ford Ferguson 40		
Middle buster	D-O-21	32965	

Potato, sugar beet and seeding equipment

TYPE	MODEL	SERIAL NUMBER	PRICE £
Ridger	R-DE-20	21642	43.0.0
Potato planter hopper attachment	P-PE-B20	9704	25.10.0
Potato spinner	D-HE-20	7461	84.0.0
Chitted seed Potato planter	P-PE-B20	32459	22.10.0
Potato planter fertiliser attachment	P-RE-20 type 726	2447	54.15.0
Potato front ridger,	Reekie		
Weight tray front mounted MF	A-TEE-129 type 737	R167	
Sugar beet lifter, 1row	1L-HE-20	N229	
Sugar beet lifter, 2 row M-H-F	2L-HE-20	380	
Row crop thinner 4 row (gapper)	4P-KE-20	808	
Sugar beet seeder 4 row (MF)	32	S225	
Sugar beet topper 1 row	L-HE-21	5	
Corn planter and ridgers (USA)	DO-21	34028	
Corn planter/fertiliser drill (USA)	D-20-A21	8061	
Corn and cotton planter	D-PO-10	1606	
MF Seed drill universal 13 disc	G-POE-A2	A69651	157.10.0
Ferguson Seed drill universal 13 coulter	G-PE-A2001	S52286	145.0.0

Manure loaders, spreaders, forklifts and excavators

TYPE	MODEL	SERIAL NUMBER	PRICE £
Manure loader, front axle mounted	L-UE-20	197	
Manure loader, high lift	M-UE-20	2164	112.0.0
Tipping earth bucket	M-UE-1000		
Manure fork, push off	M-UE-822		
Manure spreader, steel body	A-JE-A20	1777	83.10.0
Concrete balance weight			
Manure loader for FE 35 tractor	FE35 loader HK	1014721	57.10.0
Mill loader for Ferguson	Model H		
Rear loader, Cameron Gardner	HL-1 (Handy Loader)	726	
Fork lift (Fewsters) (MHF)	FE-34 Model 737	P 127	
Excavator digger, Pippin, (USA)	DX-102	5299	
Fertiliser broadcaster (MHF)	477-101-701	1371	

Trailers, transport boxes and wagons

TYPE	MODEL	SERIAL NUMBER	PRICE £
Ferguson 2 ton trailer USA	JO	1818	
Trailer 30 cwt. Tipping	L-JE-40	29	112.10.0
Trailer 3 ton tipping	F-JE-A40	16141	162.10.0
Dump skip	R-JE-20	532	41.5.0
Transport box	T-JE-21/22	11652	10.10.0
Transporter tipping	F-JE-A20	17641	37.15.0
Wheelbarrow conversion kit	TE-JE-90	H5765	8.0.0
Wagon, 4 wheel (USA)	W-JO-22	1032	

Mowers and hay equipment

TYPE	MODEL	SERIAL NUMBER	PRICE £
Mower 5 ft. rear mounted	5A-EE-B20	10553	82.10.0
Mower 5 ft. mid mounted M-H-F	FE 779	P 6893	98.15.0
Mower 7 ft. rear mounted (USA)	F-EO-A20	00404	
Side delivery rake PTO drive	D-EO-20	4892	130.0.0
Game flusher	PA-EE-20	12	27.10.0
Mower stands	A-BE-B780		1.15.0
Buckrake 12 tine	S-EE-20	1894	38.0.0
Kale cutrake	G-HE-20 type 596	M 420	116.0.0

Harvesters, balers and power unit

TYPE	MODEL	SERIAL NUMBER
Baler, trailed, PTO drive (USA)	F-12	3897
Baler, side mounted	Made from 703 baler parts	
Forager, side mounted (USA)	F-HO-20	1518
Combine, side mounted	Made using 735 combine parts	
Corn picker, Belle City (USA)	Model E	17508
Power unit detached (USA)	A-HO-60	1577
Power unit on forager (USA)	A-HO-60	1394

Other equipment

TYPE	MODEL	SERIAL NUMBER	PRICE £
Cordwood saw	A-LE-A20	1613	34.10.0
Post hole borer 9"	9D-FE-20	1398	53.10.0
Winch	WU-L-20	1035	88.0.0
Winch, Boughton and Sons Ltd.	SN35 direct coupled	10217	
Multi-purpose grader blade, rear	B-EE-20	30531	
Earth leveller and blade terracer	B-FE-20	10533	
Earth scoop	B-JE-A20	24386	
Earth scoop, reversible (USA)	S-JO-20	7007	
Earth mover, front, Bomford	Bomford Sapper		
Crane, rear mounted	O-BE-20	1490	15.0.0
Low volume sprayer	S-LE-20	2938	84.0.0
Medium pressure sprayer	S-LE-21		
Hydrovane 25 compressor	A-UE-20	463	
Hydrovane 60 compressor	MZ-Z4-2075	105	
Hammermill, rear mounted	H-LE-A20	1673	107.10.0
Electromatic hammermill	H-LE-21	made by Newman Scotmec	
Roller, Tractamount	Made by Twose	160232	
Sack lifter			
Cult harrow, Horstmann			
Rotovator	Howard	F 22826	
Manless Bale and Sack lifter			

Other accessories

TYPE	MODEL	SERIAL NUMBER	PRICE £
Lighting kit 9in box	A-T-O-76-A1		
Front wheel weights, 19"	A-TE-91		6.10.0
Dual rear wheel kit conversion	A-TE-78		5.5.0
Epicyclic reduction gearbox	A-TE-118		81.0.0
Howard reduction gearbox			
Everett reduction gearbox 10:1			
Front axle brackets	A-TE-130		
Automatic hitch assembly	A-TE-90		9.5.0
Rear wheel girdles 10"	A-TE-109		19.10.0
Skeleton rowcrop steel wheels	ATE-1101		
Rubber rear rowcrop wheels, Allman			
Steel wheels 10"	ATE-1100		31.0.0
Opperman strakes			
Tractor jack	A-TE-70		4.15.0
Belt pulleys (4)	A-TO and A-TE66		14.0.0
PTO extension (USA)	A-TO-73		
PTO, raised (USA)			
Swinging drawbar kit (USA)	A-TO-88		
Tractor canvas storm cover	A-TE-68		3.15.0
Vertical exhaust pipe	A-TE-82		
Half tracks	A-TE-113		
Stabiliser kit (USA)	A-TO-59		
Stabiliser bracket assembly	A-TE-59		
Hour meter kit (tractormeter) (USA)	A-TO-69		11.5.0
Hour recorder for dynamo	A-YE-69		
Grease gun, lever type 16 oz.(USA)	A-TO-17125		
Grease gun, pump type, 8 oz			
Hinged seat and stepboards	A-TE-61		3.10.0
Tractor cab by Cengar			45.00
Tractor cab by Reekie		670520	
Tractor cab			
High cutter 3 ft.	AU-E-60		
MF Draft transfer device	537	032253	
Wheelbarrow conversion kit for	TE-JE-90	31	
Transport box			
Bomford hedge cutter			
Hedge cutter, chainsaw and			
Trimmer by Tarpen			

CHAPTER 9

Dissecting the Hunday Fergusons

In this chapter a detailed look at most of the Hunday Ferguson collection is presented by means of photographs of individual implements accompanied where possible by some original spare parts diagram(s). The selection of diagrams had to be limited because of the large number of them – we have endeavoured to select one or more informative diagrams for each implement. The larger implements, or machines with very numerous parts are generally shown in section or overview form only. The diagrams are accompanied by the date of the publication from which they were taken when known. Where possible dates of introduction of equipment to the UK market are also given and these have been researched from the Farm Implement and Machinery Review. Photographs of some of the museum's tractors are also shown.

Readers should not assume that the diagrams shown here are absolutely definitive for their machines because some minor design modifications will inevitably have been made over time. Also conversion kits were sometimes required for fitting implements to different models of tractors.

A few non-Ferguson implements and machines are included at the end of the chapter. These are only a few of the very many which were made by outside manufacturers for use on Ferguson tractors, but never badged or approved by Ferguson.

"Beauty in engineering is that which performs perfectly the function for which it was designed and has no superfluous parts."

- so said Harry Ferguson! Judge for yourself through this archive mix of photographs and diagrams.

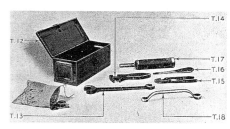

Tractors

ABOVE **FERGUSON BROWN MODEL A**
At serial no. 130 this is an early Ferguson Brown model A, but typical of the limited run of Ferguson Brown tractors made. It is driven here by enthusiast Arthur Hughes. Shown also is a page from the spare parts book, a copy of which recently sold for £1,350! Note the boldness of the "Ferguson" on the tractor cover

BELOW **FORD FERGUSON - 1939**
One of the earliest surviving Ford Ferguson tractors is serial no. 738. The very early tractors of this range were typified by their aluminium bonnet which had a reputation for cracking, hence few survive with their original bonnet

BELOW RIGHT **PERKINS P3 ENGINE**
This Ford Ferguson has been fitted with a Perkins P3 engine. This was a popular conversion engine for both Ford Ferguson and Ferguson tractors in the UK. It was offered by Perkins but was never an approved Ferguson item

BOTTOM RIGHT **FORD FERGUSON 2N**
The Ford Ferguson 2N was the economy model produced in wartime to conserve materials. They usually had no self starter and were often fitted with steel wheels. A popular machine for land reclamation and with vegetable growers. This example is fitted with an optional furrow width adjuster (1955). Model 16A

RIGHT "MOTO TUGS"

Ford Ferguson industrial tractors –"Moto Tugs" –
were used by the military in the war, particularly
on airfields. Here George Potts demonstrates
how serial no. 157 might have pulled a 500
lb bomb. 275 of these tractors are reported
to have been made. Depending on the all up
weight of specific models they had drawbar pulls
of 4,000 or 2,500 lb. They were originally
designed in response to a US Navy request for a
compact mechanical mule!

RIGHT TE FERGUSON TRACTOR

TEA 40138 is typical of the UK produced TE
Ferguson tractor range. TEA is an all petrol
model. It is difficult to appreciate that nearly
half a million similar tractors were to be produced
after this one!

LEFT Another type of Funk conversion is the V8 flat head type engine which produced 100 hp at 2,400
rpm. Although many thought that these were too powerful for the basic tractor they were successful
and apparently many were sold with few problems. To improve the inadequate gear ratio Sharman Bros.
provided a simply fitted transfer box with a step-up and step-down ratio of 1.513:1 giving a crawling
speed of 1.32 mph and a top speed at full throttle of almost 30 mph. This could be further modified by
fitting the Ferguson reduction gearbox. These tractors are in big demand in the USA and conversion kits
are still available from R.L. Shauffer in Portland Indiana

BELOW FUNK ENGINES AND GEARBOX CONVERSIONS

Funk fitted larger hp engines and gearbox conversions for the Ford Ferguson
tractors. Shown here is one such conversion whereby a six cylinder Ford
side valve engine has been fitted. The tractor is shown here on its arrival in
unrestored state at the Hunday collection

Funk
More Power
FOR YOUR
Ford Tractor

**8 Cylinder Engine
Tractor Conversion**

FITS ALL MODELS

BELOW Serial no. TED 319933 is a petrol / paraffin narrow version tractor seen here fitted with a Ferguson crane. Sadly the front wheel hubs are missing but shown in the parts diagram

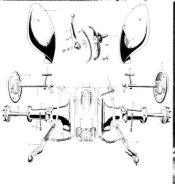

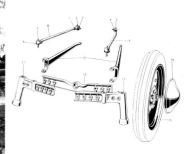

LEFT FULL INDUSTRIAL

TET 70340 is a "full" industrial version of the UK Ferguson tractor and here is seen to have made an impressive job of the hedges by use of a Hydrovane 60 compressor and Ferguson hedge cutter!

MAIN PICTURE NARROW TRACTOR

Serial no. 213546 is a narrow tractor conversion made by the Reekie company in Scotland. Some correspondence on this subject is presented in Chapter 4

FAR LEFT VINEYARD FERGUSONS

TEL 328794 is a rare vineyard version of the UK built Fergusons. Note the smaller size front and rear wheels

LEFT JOHN REEKIE

Mr John Reekie who designed the narrow conversion of the Ferguson tractor. The tractors bore both a Ferguson and Reekie badge

ABOVE LEFT **TO 20 AND TO 30**

TO 82673 (a TO 30 model) is typical of the USA built TO 20 and TO 30 tractors which were fitted with Continental engines. The USA built grey Fergusons are easily distinguished from the UK grey Fergusons by the side badges on the bonnet

BELOW **CONTINENTAL ENGINE**

TE 2223 would have originally been fitted with a Continental engine. Later it received a Perkins P3 diesel engine transplant and a swap to wider front wheels. The P3 engine was a very popular conversion engine to be adopted as original engines wore out or as farmers came to appreciate diesel engine economy

ABOVE RIGHT **FERGUSON 35**

The Ferguson 35 brought dual lever hydraulic control to the Ferguson System. USA Ferguson TO 35s kept the same styling as the TO 30s which they succeeded, but the UK built Ferguson 35 received both new styling and livery. They were popularly known as the "grey-gold" Ferguson. Serial no. SDM 56357 is a petrol/tvo version

ABOVE AND RIGHT FERGUSON 40

The Ferguson 40 made in the USA was in essence a Ferguson 35 but with radical new styling which paved the way for the later MF 65 tractors. It also broke with Ferguson tradition by the offering of tricycle and high clearance models. Serial no. 404980 is a high clearance model and seen here fitted with a mid mounted cultivator. Mechanically identical tractors to this were the Massey-Harris 50 and Massey Ferguson 50 tractors which had red livery and individual stylings. Also shown is a standard tractor

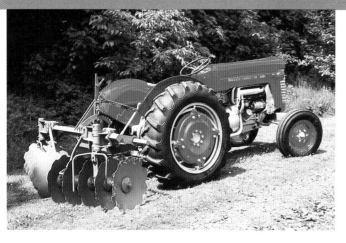

ABOVE MASSEY FERGUSON 50

The Massey Ferguson 50 tractor was mechanically identical to the Ferguson 40

ABOVE MASSEY FERGUSON 65

It is plain to see how this British built Massey Ferguson 65 tractor serial no. SNY 519712 grew out of the Ferguson 40 design

TWO PHOTOS LEFT
MASSEY FERGUSON 25

Massey Ferguson in France had a market for small hp tractors in the early days of Massey Ferguson. MF 25 serial no. 200108 has a 25 hp four cylinder Perkins diesel engine. It is shown here immediately after restoration in January 2000

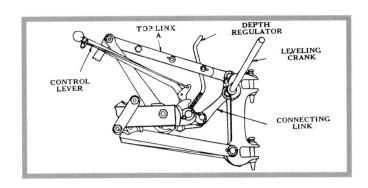

Ploughs and Subsoilers

THIS PAGE **RODERICK LEAN PLOUGH**

In 1922 Ferguson established plough production in the USA with Roderick Lean, but this arrangement was only to last for about two years. Then in 1924 Ferguson-Sherman Inc. was established; the link between Ferguson and the Sherman brothers was to last a considerable time. Seen here are photos of an original Roderick Lean Plough accompanied by parts diagrams from a Ferguson-Sherman Plough instruction book. Note that the linkage is only two point at this stage – the Duplex hitch. The plough was specifically for the Fordson tractors of the day. (Date on badge March 1923)

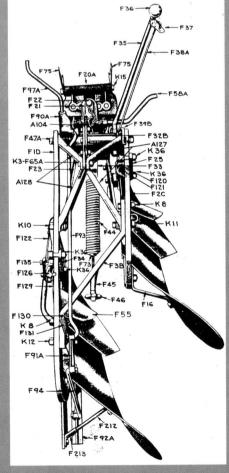

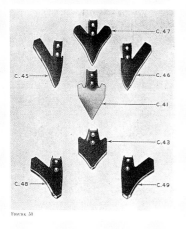

FIGURE 51

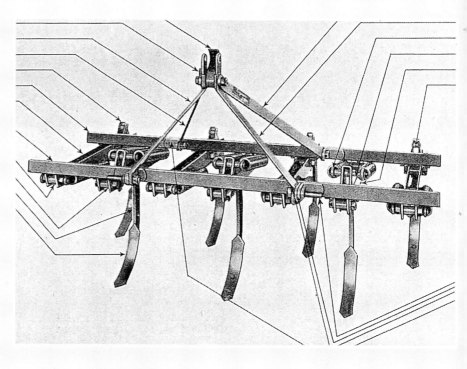

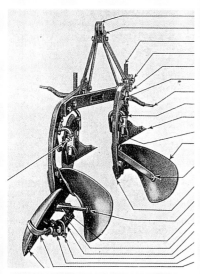

THIS PAGE FERGUSON BROWN IMPLEMENTS
Three original Ferguson Brown implements.
The back plate to the top point is
characteristic of Ferguson Brown implements

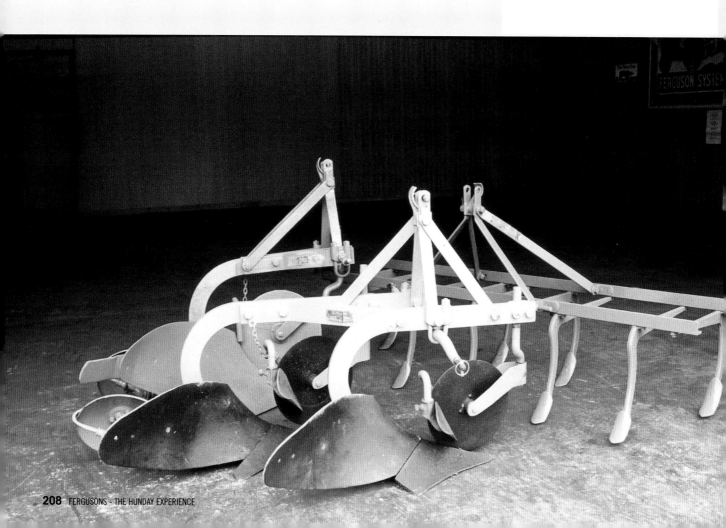

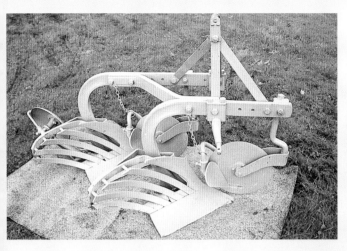

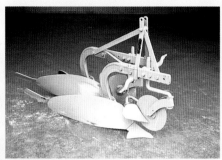

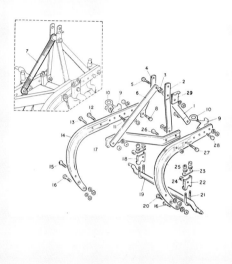

BELOW **SINGLE FURROW DEEP DIGGER PLOUGH**
The Single Furrow Deep Digger Plough cut a 16 in. furrow. A popular machine for land reclamation and with vegetable growers. This example is fitted with an optional furrow width adjuster (1955). Model 16A

ABOVE **TWO FURROW PLOUGH**
Three examples of the familiar Two Furrow Plough. Middle left is a Ford Ferguson version, top left is slatted mouldboard version marketed in North America and top right is a standard British type. (1955). Model: Several according to type

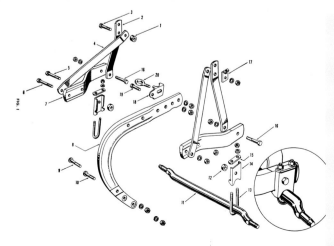

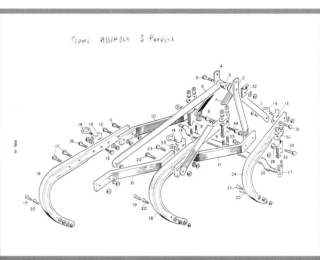

ABOVE THREE FURROW PLOUGH

The Three Furrow Plough was available with 8 and 10 in. furrows and ley, general purpose or semi digger bodies. (1955). Model: Several according to type

BELOW AND RIGHT DISC TERRACER

The side mounted Disc Terracer was never marketed in the UK but achieved successful adoption in areas of the world where terraces or bunds had to be created along the contour to prevent soil erosion and water run off. It was available for many years on the North American market but it was 1950 before it was introduced to the British market. (1944). Model: AFO-20

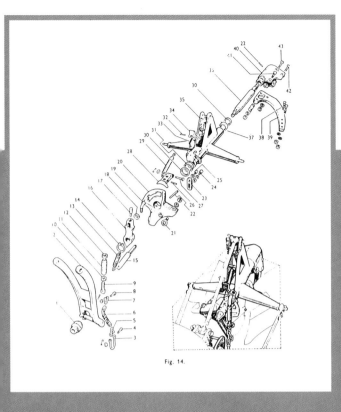

Fig. 14.

ABOVE SINGLE FURROW REVERSIBLE PLOUGH

Commonly known as the "butterfly" plough – for obvious reasons! - the Single Furrow Reversible Plough had a positive automatic change over as the plough was lifted. It was announced on the British market in1952. (1955). Model: T-AE-28

BELOW DISC PLOUGH

The Disc Plough was available in two or three disc versions. The third disc was added as a conversion to the two disc model. These ploughs gave excellent penetration in hard ground. It was announced on the British market in 1950. (1957). Model: 2-P-AE-20

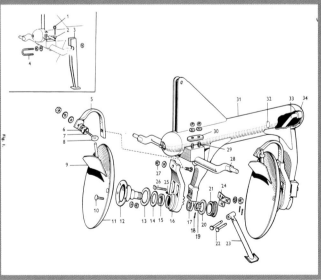

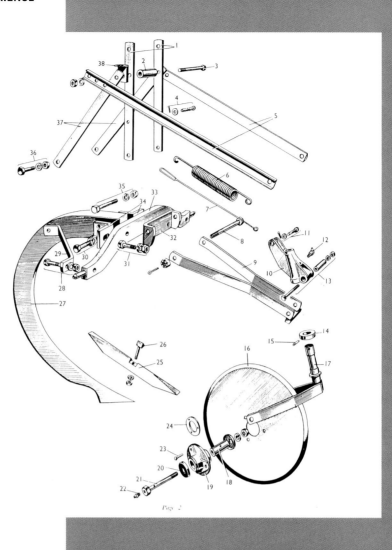

THIS PAGE **C TINE TYPE SUBSOILER**

The C Tine Type Subsoiler appears to have been uniquely British. It is shown here being compared with the straight leg type which was used in North America and Australia. The C tine has a break back feature which avoids damage if an obstruction is encountered. This implement was ideal for breaking up the subsoil without disturbing the topsoil. (1951). Model: D-BE-28

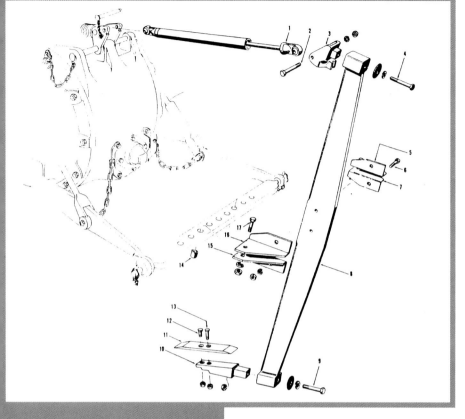

THIS PAGE STRAIGHT LEG SUBSOILER

The Straight Leg Subsoiler was reversible. The top link had a compression feature which acted as a safety device when the implement hit an obstruction. An underground pipe and cable laying attachment (not shown) could be fitted which could lay pipe of 0.5-1.5 in. diameter. (1954). Model: D-BO-22. (Note the prop at the rear of the implement is not part of it)

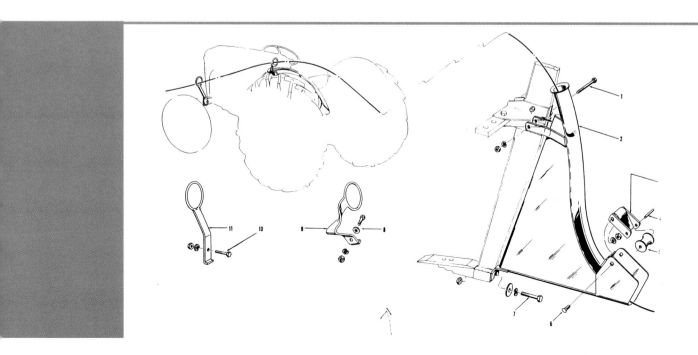

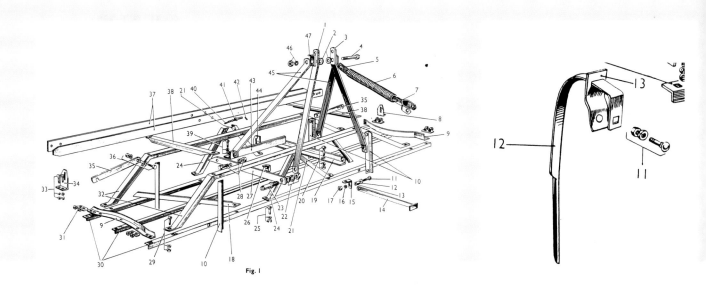

Fig. I

THIS PAGE **WEEDER**

The Weeder has 71 delicately sprung tines spread across a 13 ft. span. No young broad leaved weed could ever hope to be missed!

The claim was that "never before has such speedy weeding been offered for your corn, potatoes and peas". (1951). Model: M-KE-A21

Cultivators, Harrows and Discs

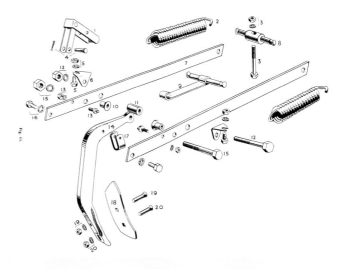

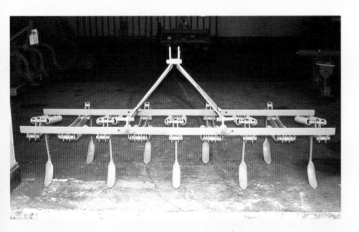

LEFT AND ABOVE TILLER
The Tiller was made as a 7 and 9 tine machine. Each tine has a strong spring release to avoid implement breakage when hitting unseen obstructions. The reversible shovels were claimed to be hard wearing. (1953). Model 9-BE-20

RIGHT AND BELOW TANDEM SEMI TRAILED DISC HARROW
The Tandem Semi Trailed Disc Harrow came in 5 and 6 ft. widths. A product mainly of the Ford Ferguson era it was eventually replaced by mounted types. No weight transfer was achieved with this implement, but the three point linkage was used to alter the angle of the disc gangs. (1951)

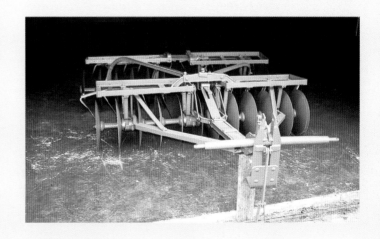

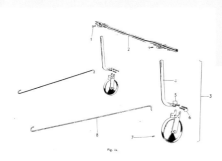

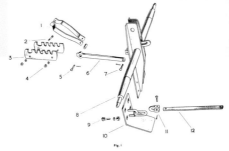

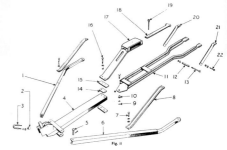

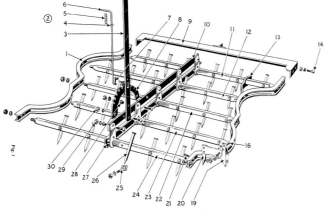

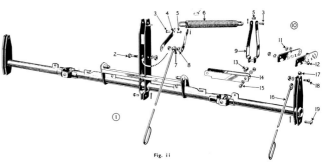

ABOVE THREE SECTION SPIKE TOOTH HARROW

In the UK a Three Section Spike Tooth Harrow was marketed whilst in the USA three and four section models were made. It was ideal for seed bed preparation, sqitch (rhizomatous grasses) clearing and bringing potatoes to the top after harvesting. The implement folds to tractor width. (1951). Model S-BE-31

BELOW LISTER CULTIVATOR

A development of the spring tine cultivator is this North American Lister Cultivator seen here fitted with crop shields

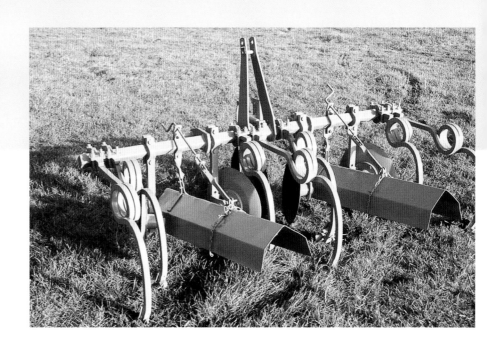

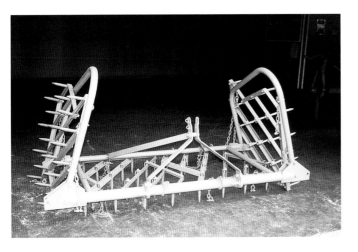

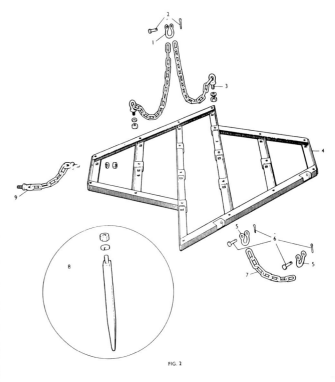

FIG. 2

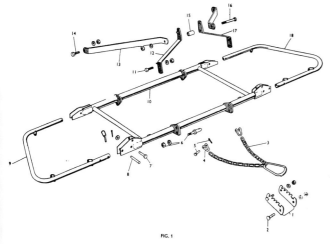

FIG. 1

ABOVE AND RIGHT HEAVY DUTY SPIKE TOOTH HARROW
The Heavy Duty Spike Tooth Harrow was recommended for reclamation work where rough work can be tackled without straining the frame from which the harrow gangs freely hang when in work. (1956). Model: S-BE-41

BELOW AND RIGHT SPRING TINE CULTIVATOR
A most popular implement with rowcrop farmers was the Spring Tine Cultivator. It dates back to Ferguson Brown times as one of the original few implements offered with the Ferguson Brown tractor. It was exceptional for pulverising soil between root crops where dry weather has baked the soil surface. It had minute adjustment for all types of crops. The late Billy Smith, the tractor modeller, is at the wheel. (1949). Model: 9S-KE-20

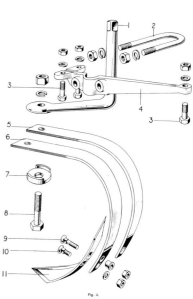

Fig. II.

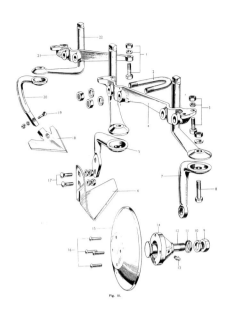

BELOW LEFT INDEPENDENT GANG STEERAGE HOE

The Independent Gang Steerage Hoe was an advanced design of the rigid steerage hoe in that there is in built depth control of each hoe unit. Fine side steerage of the implement was achieved by a second operator as for the rigid steerage hoe. It was introduced to the British market in 1952. (1953). Model D-KE-20

ABOVE RIGID STEERAGE HOE

The Rigid Steerage Hoe brought about a revolution in the weeding of root crops, and in particular sugar beet. The provision of a steerage mechanism operated by a second operator enabled extremely close weeding of small seedlings. (1951). Model: B-KE-20

BELOW RIGHT ROTARY HOE

A rarely seen machine in the UK, but relatively common in North America, this Rotary Hoe is mounted here on a TO 30 tractor. It was used for general seedbed preparation or inter row work. The implement could also be used in reverse for compacting or clod busting. (1955)

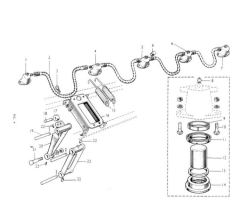

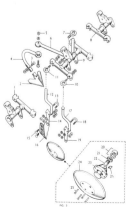

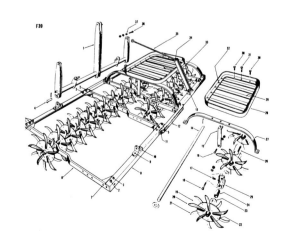

THIS PAGE **RIGID TINE CULTIVATORS**

Seen here are examples of the British and American styles of Rigid Tine
Cultivators. The American one, mounted on a Ford Ferguson tractor, is fitted
with crop guards which as far as can be established were not offered in the
UK. A rolling steerage fin was also offered in the USA. (1955). Models:
British 9KE-A-20, American N-KO

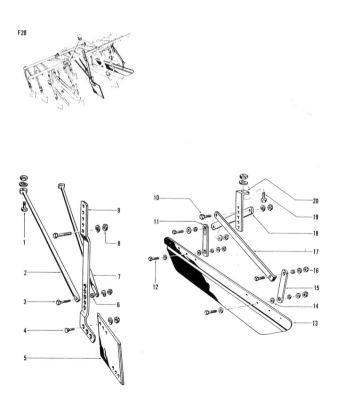

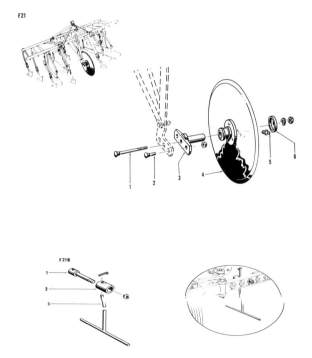

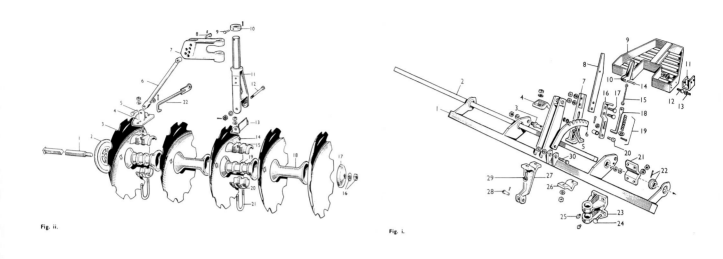

Fig. ii.

Fig. i.

THIS PAGE **REVERSIBLE HEAVY DUTY DISC HARROWS**

Reversible Heavy Duty Disc Harrows were made as 8 or 10 disc machines. They are primarily used to shift soil away from or to the centre of the implement. This was required for such tasks as making planting beds, bunds, or water channels. (1952). Model: BE-20 (with a number prefix according to number of discs and disc size)

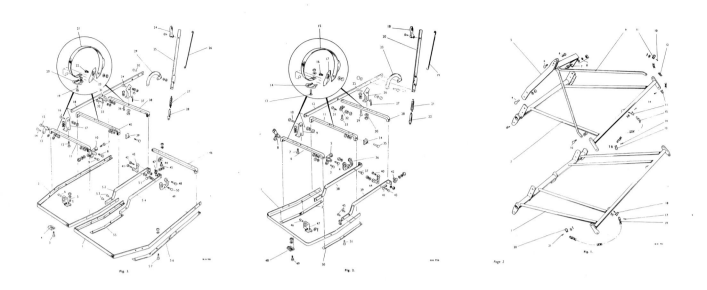

THIS PAGE **F 714 SPRING TOOTH HARROW**
The F 714 Spring Tooth Harrow was introduced to the British
market in 1955

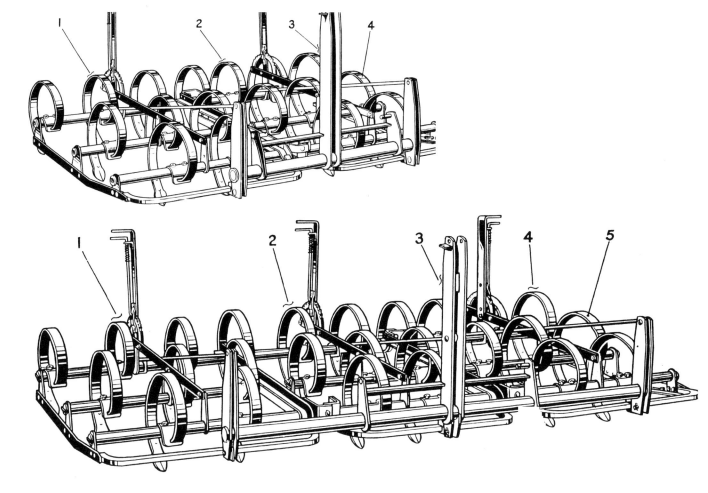

THIS PAGE A second type of spring tooth harrow. The Spring Tooth harrow was available as a two or three gang implement. (1951). Model: K-BE-A21 or K-BE-A31

THIS PAGE **OFFSET DISC HARROW**
The Offset Disc Harrow could achieve all that a normal mounted one could but would work even closer to fences, hedges and trees. It could be offset by up to 4 ft. Model: G-BE-20

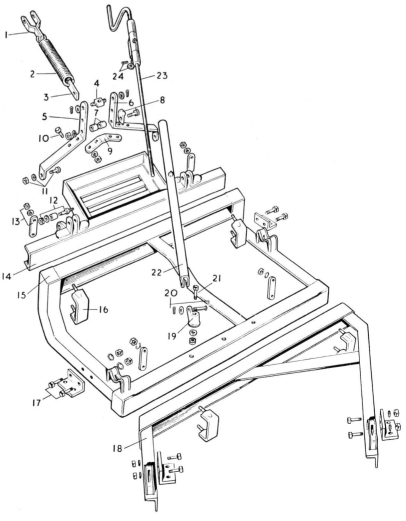

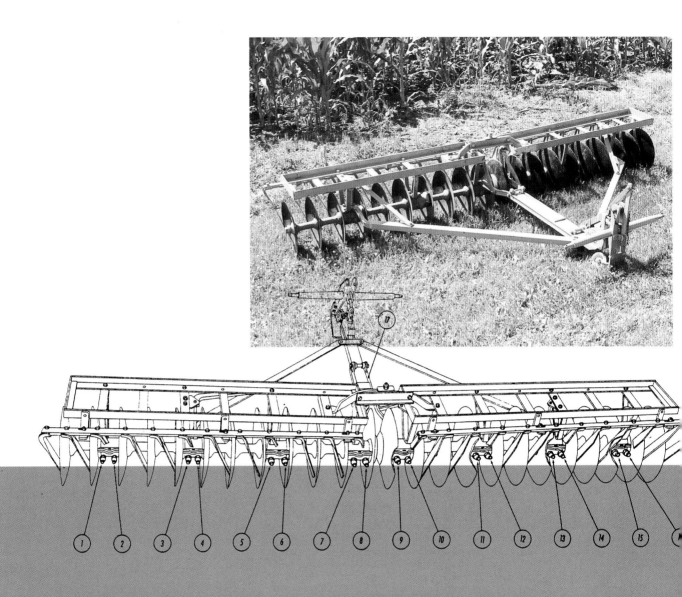

ABOVE SEMI TRAILED SINGLE DISC HARROWS

These Semi Trailed Single Disc Harrows date back to Ford Ferguson days.
This is photographed in the USA before joining the Hunday collection. Model:
50-AB0-21

BELOW DISC TILLER

The Disc Tiller was available as a 7 or 9 disc model with plain or notched
discs. It could be fitted with a seeder box for a one pass cultivate and
seed operation. Some similar implements were called Polydisc cultivators or
Polydisc Seeder and Cultivator. The Polydisc seeder was introduced to the
British market in 1953

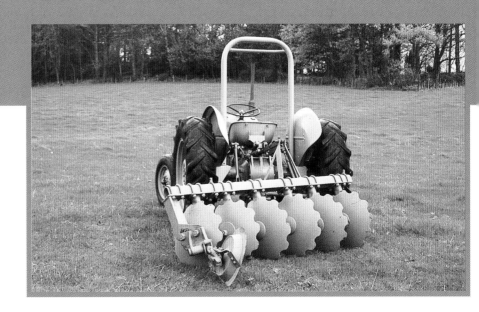

BELOW HORSTMAN CULTARROW

The Horstman Cultarrow was made by Midland Industries of Wolverhampton. Some machines were badged Ferguson. It cost £70 and was said to give three directional harrowing in one operation, break down any type of ploughed land to any tilth and clean land like no other implement. It was also advocated for levelling off cart tracks and the spreading of hard core or ballast. It is powered by the PTO – who thought that power harrows were a relatively recent invention?! It was introduced to the British market in 1948

ABOVE THE MOUNTED TANDEM DISC HARROW

The Mounted Tandem Disc Harrow was a very popular implement in the UK and offered with five or six disc gangs. It was introduced to the British market in 1953. Its main attractions were ease of transportation down roads and ability to work right into the corner of fields. Model: 4A-BE-22

Equipment for potatoes, sugar beet and seeding

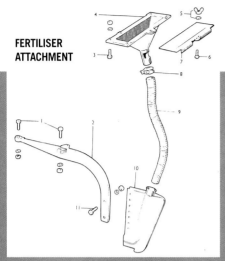

FERTILISER ATTACHMENT

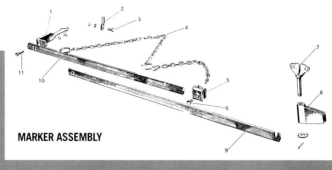

MARKER ASSEMBLY

ABOVE THREE ROW RIDGER

The Three Row Ridger was one of the original implements launched with the Ferguson Brown tractor. This one is shown with its original marker and marker hinge unit on the rear of the frame – these are often missing with surviving examples of this machine. (1953). Model: R-DE-20

BELOW UNIVERSAL SEED DRILL

The Universal Seed Drill, also later called the Multi-Purpose Seed Drill had a splendid reputation for accurate sowing. The coulters were lifted out of work by the three point linkage. It could be converted from a 13 row grain drill to a 6, 5 or 4 row root drill. Both disc and Suffolk coulters were offered (1952). Model: G-PE-A20

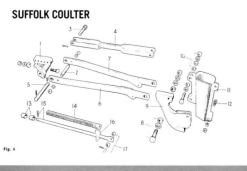

SUFFOLK COULTER

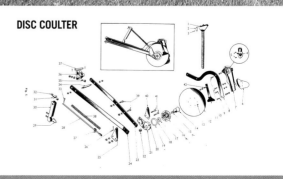

DISC COULTER

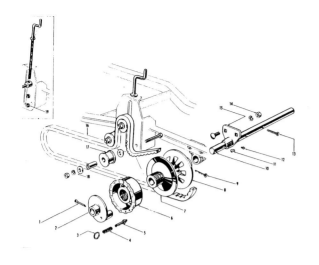

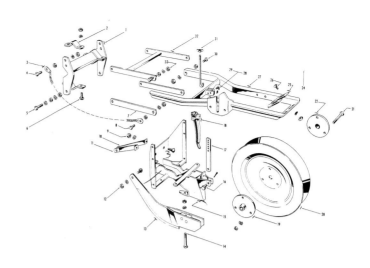

ABOVE AND LEFT CORN PLANTER, FLAT LAND DRILL ROLL

A classic Ferguson implement from North America is the Corn Planter, Flat Land Drill Roll. (1947). Model: D-PO-10

BELOW DRILL PLANTER WITH FERTILISER ATTACHMENT

This Drill Planter with Fertiliser Attachment was typical of many such machines offered by various manufacturers in North America. This was offered to the British market in 1951. (1955). Model: D-PO-A (A-RO-A60 and A-RO-B-60 were similar)

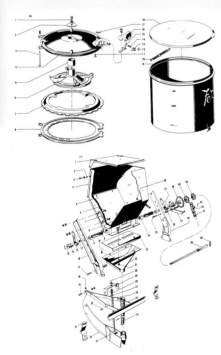

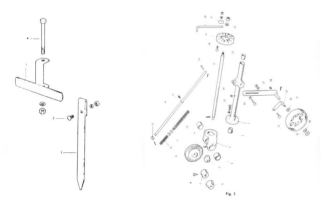

Fig. 2

ABOVE MIDDLE BUSTER

A Middle Buster shown in basic form or with seeder attachments. Middle busters, because of the share design, are used for making ridges in hard land. This combination had the designation DO-21

LEFT AND BELOW ROW CROP THINNER

George Potts, responsible for so much of the Moffitt Ferguson museum's restoration shows off a Row Crop Thinner. In its day this enabled thinning of such crops as sugar beet, swedes, mangolds and carrots at a fraction of the cost of hand labour. It was made as a four and six row model and introduced to the British market in 1955. (1956). Model: 4P-KE-20

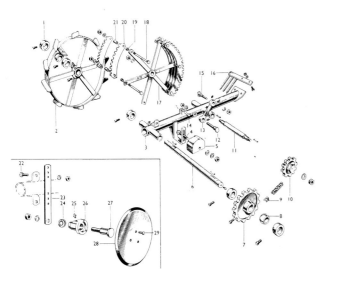

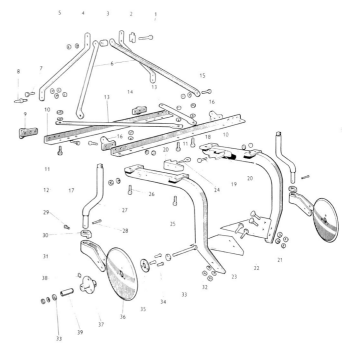

ABOVE BEET TOPPER

A Beet Topper mounted on a Ferguson 35 "grey-gold" tractor. It was introduced to the British market in 1955. It could remove a fixed proportion of beet top irrespective of size, and losses incurred through over or under topping were reduced to a minimum. (1957). Model: L-HE-21

ABOVE AND BELOW SINGLE AND TWO ROW BEET LIFTER

Examples of a Single and Two Row Beet Lifter. These had high clearance for trash or heavy top conditions. The beet was squeezed out of the ground rather than lifted to avoid breaking the tap root. (1956). Model: 1L-HE-20 and 2-HE-20

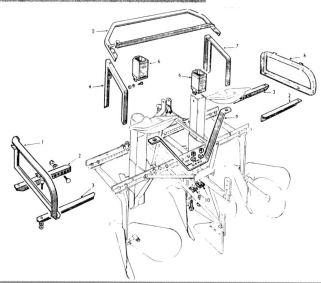

ABOVE MF 32-7 SEEDER

The MF 32-7 Seeder was available in 2-6 row configurations with PTO or land drive. This four row model has land drive units. A ridge type model (with large ridge rollers ahead of the seeder units) was also made. It was first announced in the UK in 1951

BELOW HOPPER TYPE POTATO PLANTER

The Hopper Type Potato Planter was for planting of seed which was generally not chitted, and placed in bulk in the hopper. This too was an attachment for the ridger. (1951). P-BE-B20

ABOVE POTATO PLANTER ATTACHMENT

The Potato Planter Attachment was a simple pack of fittings which were fitted on to a three row ridger to make a two row potato planter. This included the fittings for carrying the chitted seed boxes. (1955). Model PPE-B20

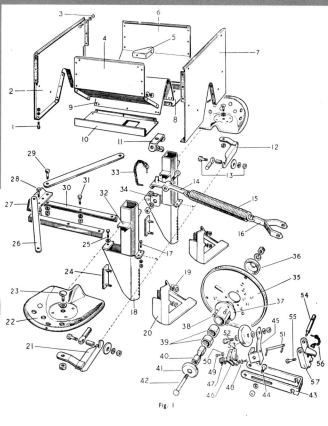

Fig. I

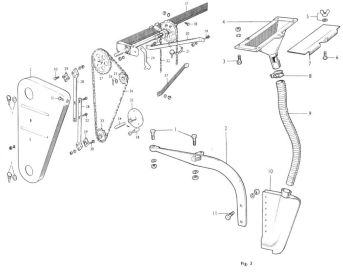

Fig. 3

FERTILISER ATTACHMENT FOR POTATO PLANTERS

Either of the two potato planters could be fitted with a Fertiliser Attachment for Potato Planters. It was mounted behind the driver's seat and the distributors driven from the rear wheel of the tractor. It was supplied in kit form. (1955).
Model: P-RE-20

POTATO SPINNER

The Potato Spinner is driven by the PTO. The rotating tines were claimed to "lift the potatoes with such gentle action that the crop suffers no damage". Potatoes are left above the surface and separated from the tops. (1951).
Model: D-HE-20

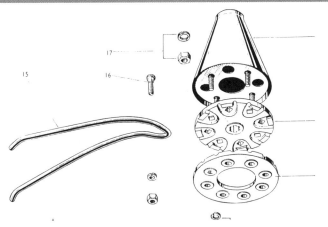

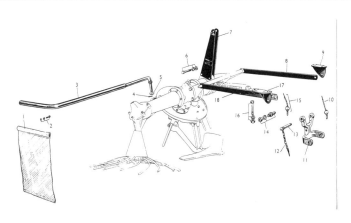

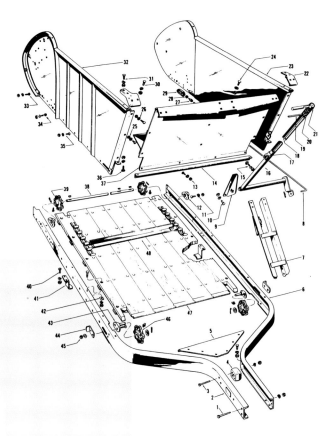

ABOVE AND RIGHT **MANURE SPREADER**

The Manure Spreader has a sheet metal body. This was very prone to severe rusting caused by the acid in manures. Consequently finding a machine in good condition is quite rare and they command a premium price. Later the Ferguson style spreader was replaced by the wooden body style Massey-Harris spreader which was designated the F 712. (1955). Model: A-JE-A20 (the parts diagram is for a USA built A-J0-21/22 spreader)

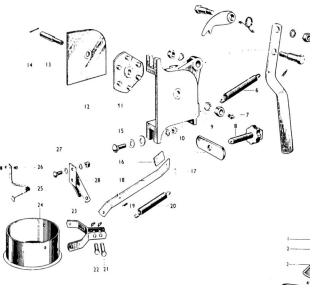

Manure loaders and spreaders

ABOVE AND RIGHT **721 FERTILISER SPINNER**

Shown here is a 721 Fertiliser Spinner. The original Ferguson spinner designation was FF-30 or FE-30. Like the manure spreader they were prone to rusting and end of season cleaning with de-watering anti-rust fluid was recommended.

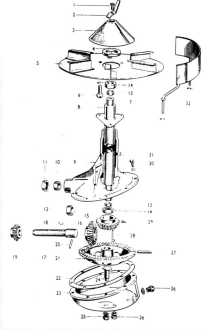

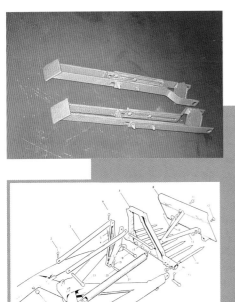

ABOVE AND LEFT HIGH LIFT LOADER

Commonly known as the "Banana Loader" because of the shape of its frame, the High Lift Loader has come to be regarded as one of the classic Ferguson implements. Very much ahead of its time in having a hydraulic tip facility for the bucket and hydraulic push off for the fork, it was however an uncomfortable driving experience with the arms and rams very close to the driver and two hydraulic control levers to be operated. The parking stands are also shown. (1956). Model: M-UE-20 (and some variant models)

BELOW MANURE LOADER

The first Ferguson Manure Loader was a light duty machine with a capacity of only 600 lb. Because of this limited capacity some farmers called it a "Teaspoon Loader"! However the loader was quite popular and certainly saved many hours of otherwise backbreaking manual work. (1951). Model: L-UE-20

TRAILERS

RIGHT THE FOUR WHEEL WAGON

The Four Wheel Wagon was only offered in North America. The wagon has a 6,000 lb capacity

It is shown here being pulled behind a Ferguson baler. (1955). Model: W-J0-22

TRANSPORT BOXES

RIGHT TWO WHEEL TRAILER

This is the original Ferguson Two Wheel Trailer produced to go with the Ford Ferguson in North America. It hitches to the standard drawbar and top link – the latter by the telescopic arm shown here. It weighs 1200 lb and has a capacity of 51 cu. ft. or 4,000 lb. Original Ferguson Badge Number J.0.1818. Here the trailer has arrived at the Hunday collection but awaits the fitting of a new body.

AND WAGONS

RIGHT THREE TON TIPPING TRAILER

Two wheel trailers extended the principle of weight transfer from a cultivation implement to tractor. This is shown here with the Three Ton Tipping Trailer which was a very popular and widely used Ferguson implement. This one has not been restored as it still shows much of its original paint. It allowed the small Ferguson tractors to pull loads that previously would have been pulled by larger hp or heavier tractors using four wheel trailers. A non tipping version was also sold. (1957). Model: F-JE-A40 (the diagram shown here is for a later designation FE-17 trailer)

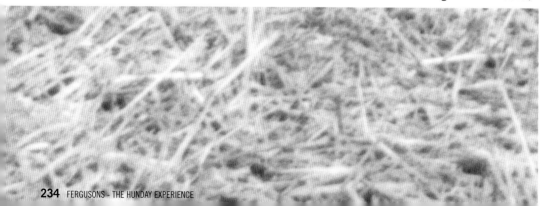

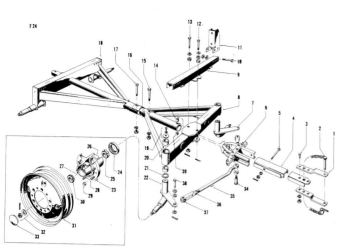

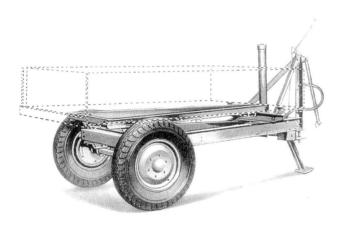

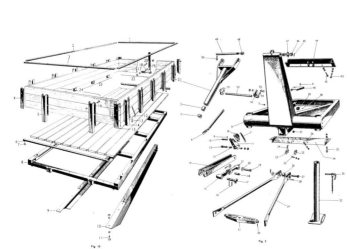

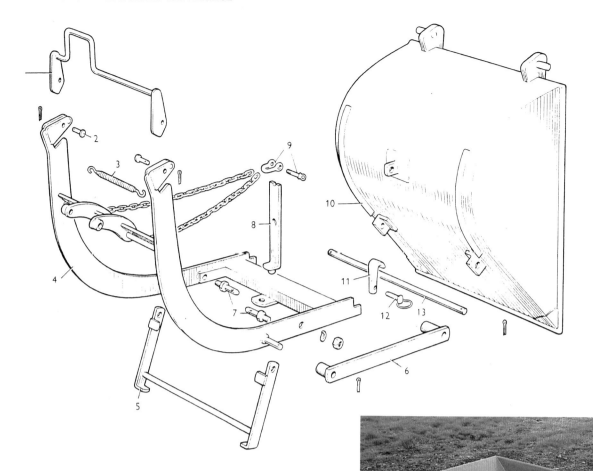

ABOVE DUMP SKIP

Having a capacity of 10 cwt, the Dump Skip found use mainly in the construction industry rather than on farms. Today it is quite a rare item. It was recommended for use in conjunction with the High Lift Loader, because when full it gave excellent balance to the loader and ballast to the tractor rear wheels. The dump skip was made by Fewsters of Stocksfield – very near to the home of the Hunday collection. It was introduced to the British market in 1954. (1956). Model:R-JE-20

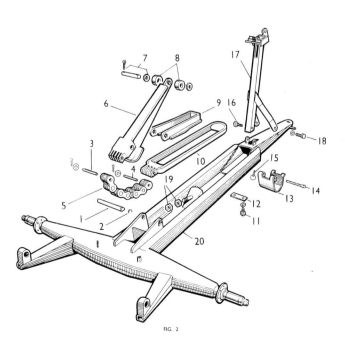

FIG. 2

LEFT AND BELOW 30 CWT TRAILER

The 30 cwt Trailer was available in tipping or non tipping form. It was not widely used on farms but found considerable use with local authorities and on building sites. This example is shown fitted with non original extension sides. It was introduced to the British market in 1952. (1955). Model: L-JE-40

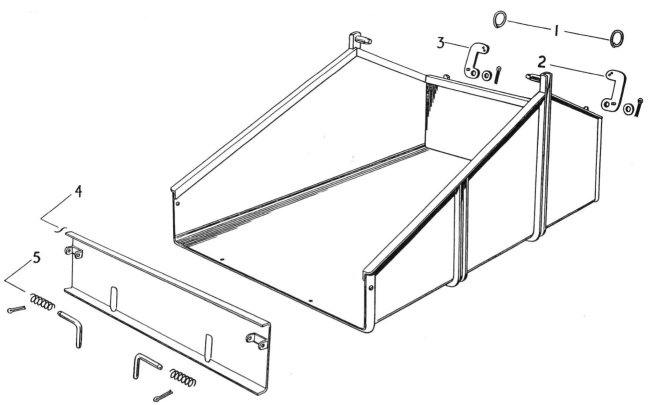

ABOVE **TRANSPORT BOX**

Two shots of the Transport Box. One shows it fitted with the Wheelbarrow Conversion Kit. This was a most useful implement and widely used.

Good second hand ones are in strong demand and replicas are being made commercially. Model: F-JE-A20

RIGHT **TRANSPORTER**

The Transporter was made in both tipping and non-tipping forms. They have a capacity of 1 cu.yd. They enabled ground level loading of heavy items. It was introduced to the British market in 1955. Model: T-JE-2

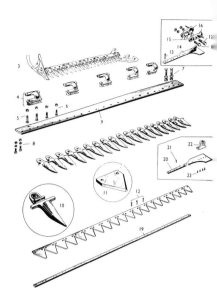

Mowers and Hay Equipment

ABOVE 5 FT REAR MOWER

A British 5 ft Rear Mower shown mounted on a tractor. In North America where crops tended to be thinner and drier, a 7 ft Rear Mounted Mower was offered and is shown in the parked position to emphasise its length. The diagram is for parts for a British rear mounted mower which were only offered as 5 or 6 ft. models. (1955). Models: 5A-EE-B20 (British) and 7A-EO-A20 (USA 7 ft)

BELOW 10 AND 12 TINE BUCKRAKES

10 and 12 Tine Buckrakes were made in the UK and a popular piece of equipment for silage makers. Due to the nature of their work these machines often had a hard life and ended up with bent or missing tines and often twisted frames. When abandoned outside, the main tubular frame member often rusted away with the result that good specimens of this implement are few and far between. Buckrakes were also used for carrying anything from hedge trimmings to pallet trays of fruit. (1956). Model: S-EE-20

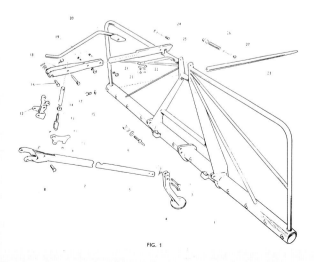

FIG. 1

THIS PAGE **SIDE DELIVERY RAKE**
More commonly found in drier areas of the world such as North America and Australia, the Side Delivery Rake is driven by the PTO. The PTO drive could be geared down for conditions where a slow forward speed is required. It was introduced to the British market in 1954. (1954). Model:D-EE-20

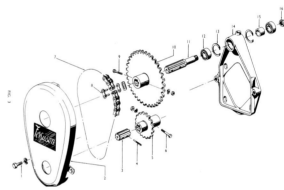

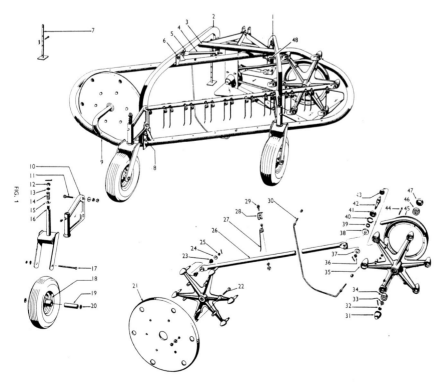

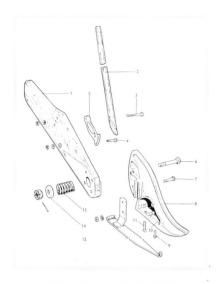

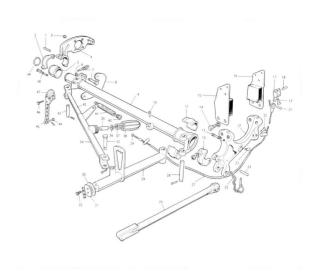

ABOVE MID MOUNTED MOWER

The Mid Mounted Mower was made as a 5 or 6 ft. model, and as a left or right hand side mounted machine. They were popular with highway authorities. It was introduced to the British market in 1955. On farms they were less common than the cheaper rear mounted mowers. A development of this mower was the 736 which had hydraulic control of the blade between vertical and 45 degrees below horizontal. Model: FE79

BELOW KALE CUTRAKE

The Kale Cutrake saved many a back breaking hour for men who previously had to cut and load often wet tall kale in winter conditions. It was however not a widely sold implement and good surviving examples are uncommon. Often the main tubular frame is rusted away. It was introduced in the UK in 1955. (1957). Model G-HE-20

BELOW GAME FLUSHERS

Only a limited number of Game Flushers were sold. They were designed to scare birds out of the grass or whatever crop was being cut and thereby save them from certain death or mutilation by a mower. Their initial development stemmed from concern for the welfare of game birds on large shooting estates. It was introduced to the British market in 1952. It can be seen how the Flusher moved sitting birds out of the path of the following mower. (1953). Model: PA-EE-B20

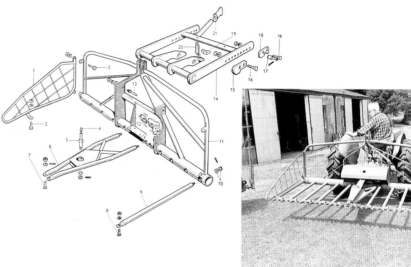

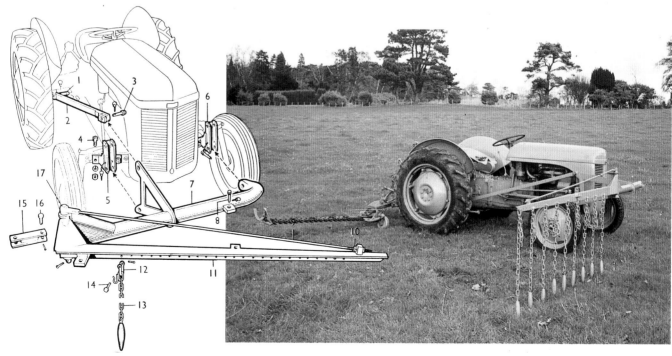

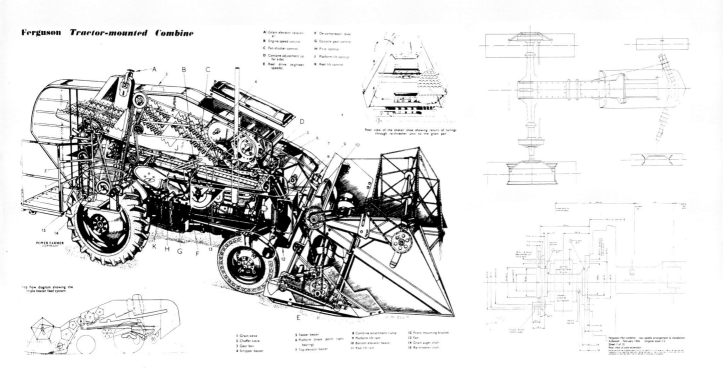

Ferguson Tractor-mounted Combine

A Grain elevator (tension-er)
B Engine speed control
C Fan shutter control
D Concave adjustment (at far side)
E Reel drive (eighteen speeds)
F De-compressor lever
G Epicycle gear control
H P.t.o. control
J Platform lift control
K Reel lift control

Rear view of the shaker shoe showing return of tailings through re-thresher unit to the grain pan

Top flow diagram showing the triple beater feed system

1 Grain sieve
2 Chaffer sieve
3 Gear box
4 Stripper beater
5 Feeder beater
6 Platform break point (split bearing)
7 Top elevator beater
8 Combine attachment clamp
9 Platform lift ram
10 Bottom elevator beater
11 Reel lift ram
12 Front mounting bracket
13 Fan
14 Grain auger shaft
15 Re-thresher shaft

Ferguson FE2 combine - rear saddle arrangement & installation
A.Gerald February 1996. Original scale 1:2
Sheet 1 of 10
Rear view of axle extension

Harvesters, Balers and power unit

THIS PAGE **SIDE MOUNTED COMBINE**

The Side Mounted Combine of Ferguson design - but made by John Moffitt! This was necessary as there are no survivors of these machines which were only ever made as prototypes. The diagrams show an original cut away view of the machine and two of the many engineering drawings that had to be made up prior to the construction of this replica machine

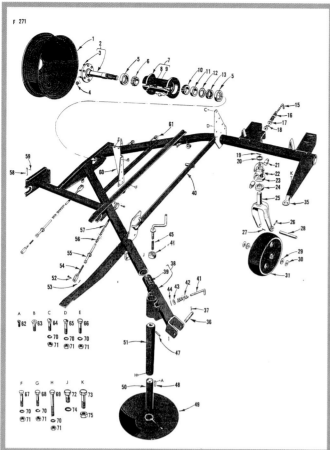

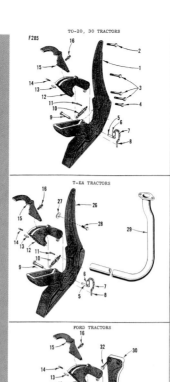

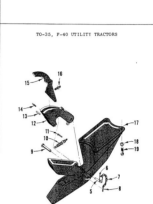

THIS PAGE SIDE MOUNTED BALER

Another John Moffitt special construction is the
Side Mounted Baler. These did reach limited commercial production, hence original parts drawings
were available to assist in construction. Model:
B-EO-20

THIS PAGE SIDE MOUNTED FORAGE HARVESTER

No need to construct a Side Mounted Forage Harvester. This machine was imported from the USA and restored to working condition. Both the baler and forage harvester were described as "Tractor Mate" implements. The diagrams shown here are original patent drawings. (1957 and 1955). The black and white photo is from 1955 and shows a side mounted forage harvester being demonstrated in central Michigan (photo courtesy of Delbert Gentner)

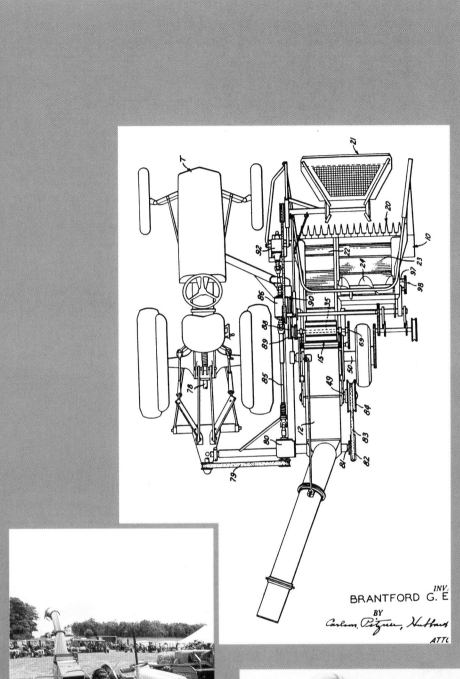

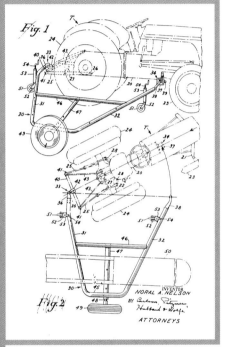

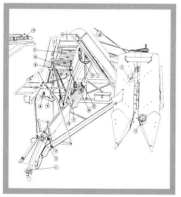
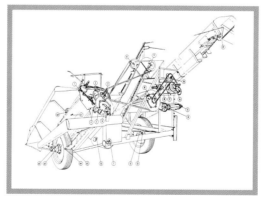

ABOVE CORN PICKER

The Corn Picker was a pto drive trailed implement badged Ferguson but made by Wood Brothers. In the Ford Ferguson era Wood Bros were approved suppliers of equipment to Ferguson. They were known as Belle City Corn-Picker Husker or Picker Snappers. The diagrams shown here are from Wood Bros days. (1946). Model:WB-1-P for diagrams

LEFT POWER UNIT

The Ferguson Power Unit was sometimes used as the power source on the side mounted forage harvester or the prototype side mounted balers

THIS PAGE **PICK UP BALER**

The Pick Up Baler was only produced in small numbers in North America. It is similar to the Massey-Harris No. 3 baler. Examples of the machine have also been noted to have reached Australia.

This one is seen on display after restoration at the Royal Agricultural Show in 1998 and at work with the three ton trailer at one of the Hunday collection open days. Model: F12

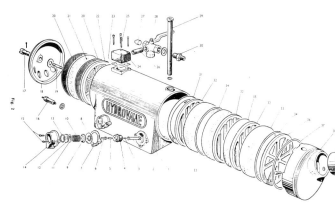

BELOW HYDROVANE 60 CFM COMPRESSOR

The Hydrovane 60 cfm Compressor was a heavy duty compressor. It required a speed control unit to be fitted to tractors. It was described as being suitable for demolition, reconstruction and paint spraying tasks. It is shown here on a Ferguson industrial tractor going hedge cutting. (1957)

ABOVE HYDROVANE 25 CFM COMPRESSOR

The Hydrovane 25 cfm Compressor was the lighter duty of two compressor units offered by Ferguson in the UK. It was used to power a wide range of power tools, one of the most common of which was the Ferguson Hedge Cut (1956). Model: A-UE-20

Other Ferguson Equipment

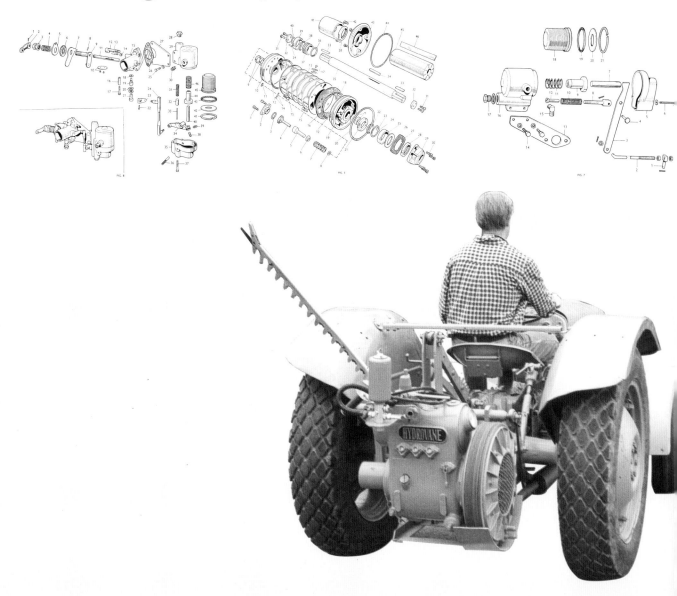

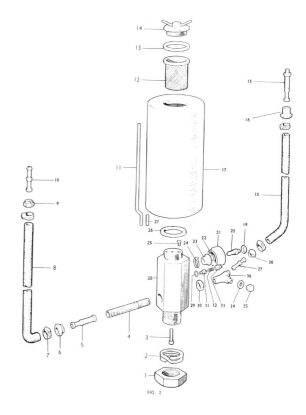

FIG. 2

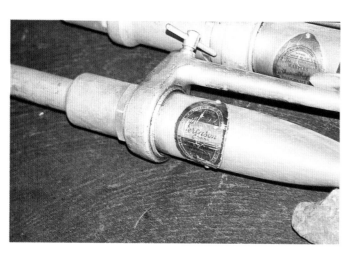

THIS PAGE **HEDGE CUTTER**

The Hedge Cutter was classed as an accessory. It was light to use due to its aluminium/alloy type construction and available in two models for either thin or thicker material. The hedge cutters were made by Marples and most had Ferguson and Marples dual badging. It was introduced to the British market in 1954. Shown here is a version of each and a tree pruner. (1956). Model:AU-E-60

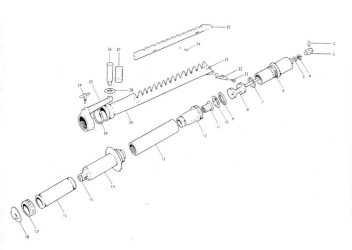

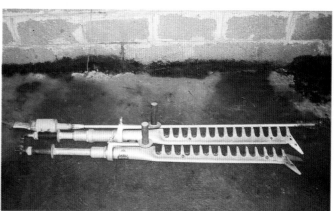

THIS PAGE LOW VOLUME SPRAYER

The Low Volume Sprayer has a 45 gallon tank and was recommended for use with hormone weed killers where application rates of 5-20 gallons/acre were required. The sprayer was made by Fisons Pest Control. Although badged Ferguson, some surviving examples are found in the yellow Fisons livery. It was introduced to the British market in 1953. Model: S-LE-20

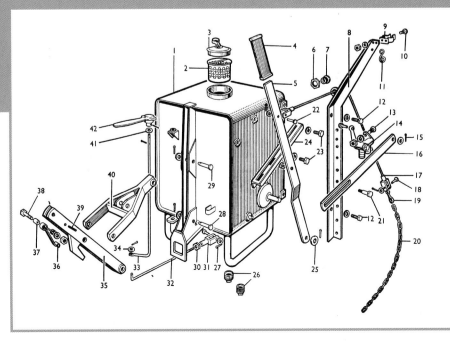

The Medium Pressure Sprayer has a 92 gallon tank. Special features include three stage filtration and anti drip device. (1955). Model S-LE-21

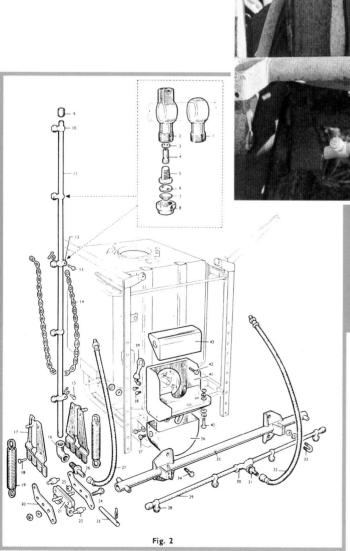

Fig. 2

THIS PAGE EARTH MOVER

The Earth Mover had an exclusive feature of "load control" which was reputed to increase working speed, make full use of engine power and keep the load within the tractor's capacity. It was appaently made by Bomfords for Ferguson and known as the "Sapper" before being officially adopted as a Ferguson implement. It was advertised as the Sapper in 1948 and announced by Ferguson in the UK in 1950. Seen here fitted to a Ferguson tractor fitted with the popular Perkins "P3" conversion diesel engine. (1955)

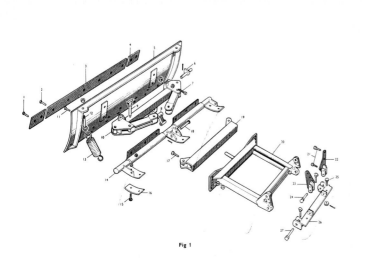

Fig 1

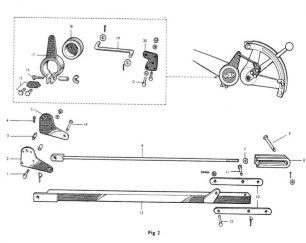

Fig 2

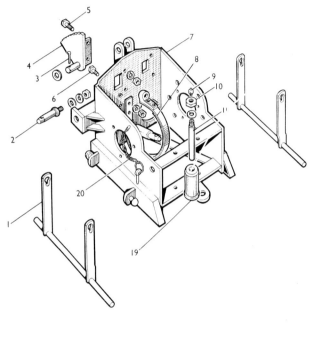

THIS PAGE **WINCH**

Still a highly sought after implement for work today is the Winch. Although only a light duty machine, it has a wide application and favour in hill farming areas and for light forestry work. The winch was made by Hesfords of Ormskirk and usually had joint Ferguson and Hesfords Badging. (1953).
Model: W-UE-20

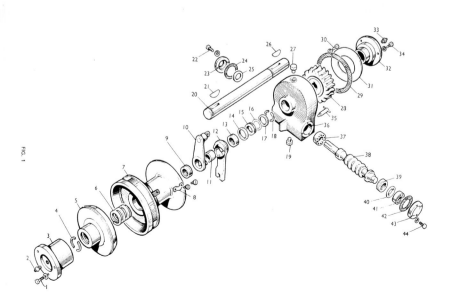

FIG. 1

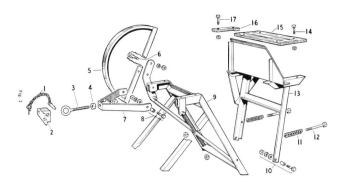

ABOVE CORDWOOD SAWS

There are still many of these popular Cordwood Saws in operation, and indeed many being reconditioned for work. Take care when using these machines and make sure they are guarded to comply with current regulations. Model: A-LE-A20

BELOW AND RIGHT Electromatic Hammer Mill

The Electromatic Hammer Mill is thought to have reached the Ferguson stable from the Massey-Harris stable after their merger. Few examples of the grey Ferguson or red Massey-Harris machines appear to have survived. It was introduced in the UK in 1954. (1955). Model:H-LE-21

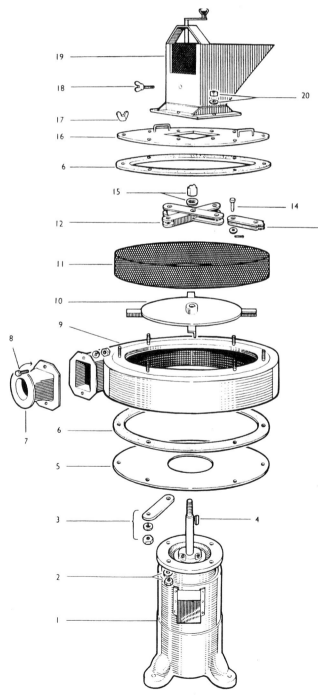

Figure 1

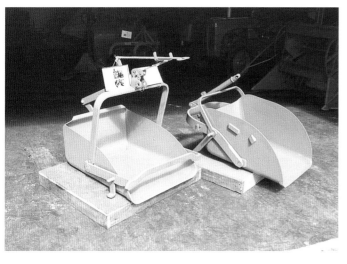

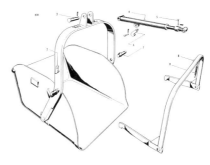

ABOVE AND LEFT EARTH SCOOP AND REVERSIBLE EARTH SCOOP

Shown here are examples of the UK made (left) non reversible Earth Scoop and USA made (right) Reversible Earth Scoop. The diagram is for the USA version. They were small and simple in appearance but high in output! (1955). Model:B-JE-A20 (UK) and S-JO-20 (USA)

LEFT AND BELOW EARTH LEVELLER AND BLADE TERRACER

More commonly known as the "Blade Terracer", the Earth Leveller and Blade Terracer preceded the later more heavy duty multi-purpose blade. The Blade Terracer was widely used in drier areas of the world for soil conservation work, levelling fields and creating surface drainage or irrigation channels. It was introduced in the UK in 1950. Model: B-FE-20

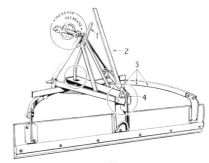

BELOW AND RIGHT MULTI PURPOSE BLADE

The Multi Purpose Blade replaced the Blade Terracer. It is a stronger and more sophisticated implement which came in with the Ferguson 35 era. A scarifier, depth wheel and blade extensions are notable extras above the Blade Terracer specification

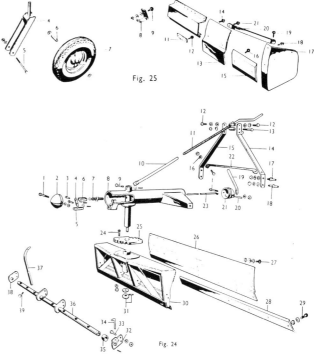

Fig. 25

Fig. 24

THIS PAGE AND OPPOSITE TOP TYRE TRACKS
Tyre Tracks gave the Ferguson tractors much enhanced flotation and traction. Both full and half tracks versions were fitted, but the full track versions are very rare and seem to have had most use on South Pole expeditions. The diagram is for a half track version. (1957).
Model: A-TE-113 (half tracks)

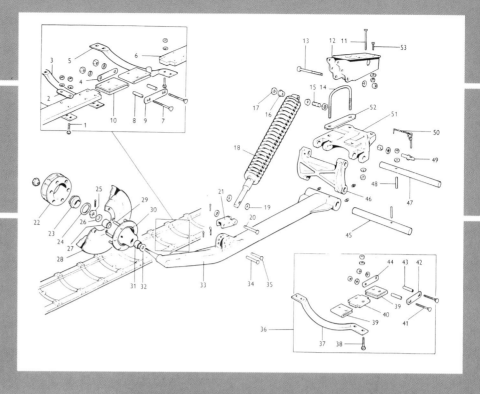

BELOW **FORK LIFT**
The Fork Lift was made by Fewsters but badged Ferguson. Although introduced in the Ferguson 35 era it could be fitted to the TE 20 type Fergusons

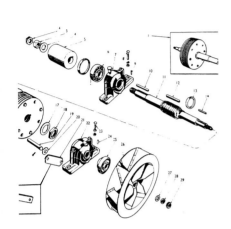

ABOVE AND BELOW LEFT PORTABLE HAMMER MILL

The Portable Hammer Mill made no use of the Ferguson weight transfer feature! These are much sought after by collectors as they can be used as static working exhibits

BELOW CRANE

The Ferguson Crane is a rare item, but a version of it is still made by the licensed MF producers in India. It can lift 350 lb. with the jib fully extended. It was introduced in the UK in 1953

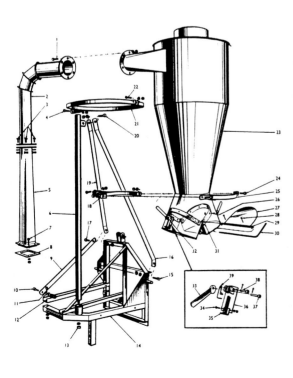

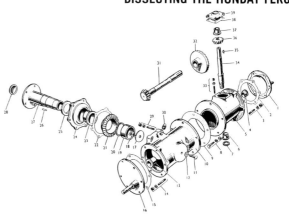

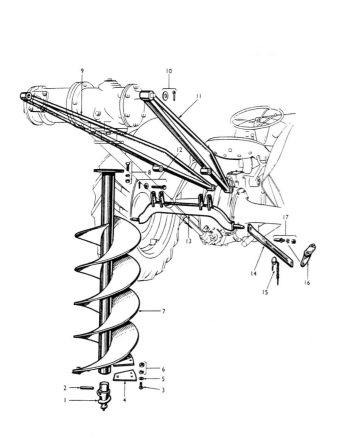

Other Ferguson Attachments

ABOVE POST HOLE

The Post Hole Digger was available with 6, 9, 12 or 18 in. augers. This one is unusual in that it has safety guards fitted for the PTO shaft – perhaps it is a feature of later versions. A major design deficiency of these machines is that they have no slip clutch in the PTO shaft. Model: 9D-FE-20

BELOW SHADE

An original 1940s Ferguson Shade showing its umbrella structure

BELOW FRONT MOUNTED WEIGHT TRAY

The Front Mounted Weight Tray was deemed to be particularly needed when using the Ferguson Rick Lifter. Model: A-TE-129

BELOW TRACTOR JACK

The Tractor Jack was made in several successive versions. This is an early version. Model: A-TE-A70

ABOVE, BELOW AND TOP OPPOSITE PAGE ON FARM SERVICE UNIT

North American On Farm Service Unit is comprised of two cases. One contains the compressor and the other the diagnostic tools and gauges. Also shown is the diagrammatic instruction panel

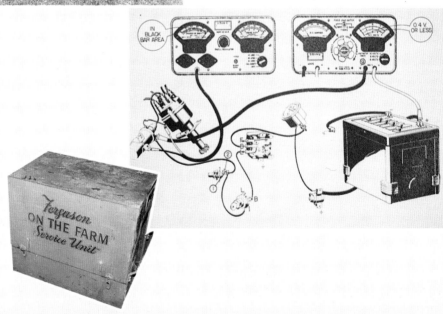

TRACTOR DIAGNOSIS

BELOW TRACTOR COVER
A Tractor Cover. This is an original 1948
example. Commercially reproduced ones are
now available as few originals have survived.
Model: A-TE-A68

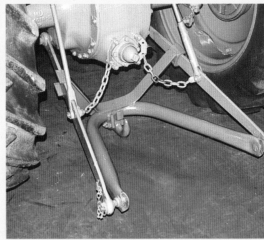

ABOVE **EPICYCLIC REDUCTION GEARBOX**

A Ferguson Epicyclic Reduction Gearbox gives a 3:1 reduction, a set of extra gears and 4.75 in. of extra length when fitted. A reduction gearbox made by Howard was more widely adopted for low speed work, and did not increase tractor length. It was introduced in the UK in 1955

ABOVE **NORTH AMERICAN STYLE PICK UP HITCH**

A North American style Pick Up Hitch which is reported as very successful

ABOVE **ROWCROP SKELETON STEEL WHEELS**

Ferguson Rowcrop Skeleton Steel Wheels. These could have all the lugs fitted on one side to give a working width of only 4 inches

BELOW **BRITISH STYLE MULTI PULL HITCH OF THE MASSEY-HARRIS FERGUSON ERA**

A British Style Multi Pull Hitch of the Massey-Harris-Ferguson era. This is one of several designs manufactured and used for effecting weight transfer from a trailed implement (usually a four wheel trailer) to the tractor

BELOW AND BELOW RIGHT **SWINGING DRAWBAR**

The Swinging Drawbar was widely adopted in North America, but few are to be found in the UK

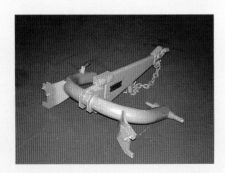

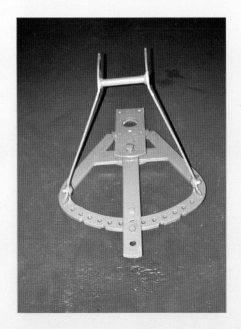

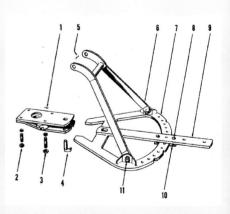

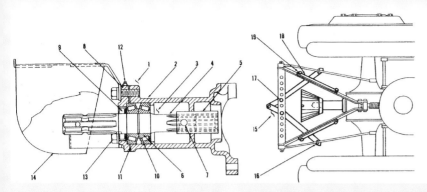

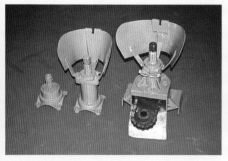

ABOVE **EXTENDED PTO DRIVES**
Three examples of Extended PTO Drives. Extension drawbars were sometimes required for use with these

ABOVE **FRONT AND REAR WHEEL WEIGHTS** Front and Rear Wheel Weights for the British built TE tractors

ABOVE **TRACTOR HOUR RECORDER**
Tractor Hour Recorder

BELOW **TRACTORMETER**
Tractormeter shown complete with drive gear and cable. The meter shows rpm, hours and speed in top gear.

BELOW **PTO DRIVEN PULLEYS**
Three types of PTO Driven Pulleys. Left North American type with non-metal face, centre as manufactured for British TE tractors, right as manufactured for British Ferguson 35 and MF 35 tractors

BELOW **FERGUSON DRAWBARS**
Different types of Ferguson Drawbars. The one to the rear is front mounted and was offered by Ferguson in North America. The other two are thought not to be original Ferguson equipment

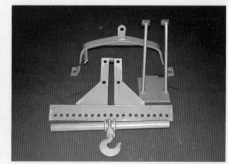

GENUINE *Ferguson* ACCESSORY

A-TO-76-A1
LIGHTING KIT-6 VOLT
FOR FERGUSON TRACTORS WITH
6 VOLT ELECTRICAL SYSTEMS ONLY

Printed in U.S.A.

Made in U.S.A.

HARRY FERGUSON, INC., DETROIT, MICHIGAN

TOP AND ABOVE
LIGHTING KIT
A new boxed Lighting Kit for the American Ferguson tractors

ABOVE CENTRE AND BELOW DUAL WHEEL KIT
A dual wheel kit gave both added flotation and traction and was particularly useful in seed-bed preparation to minimise wheel markings. The photos show the spacer and extension studs required to fit the twin wheel

ABOVE RIGHT
WHEEL GIRDLES
Ferguson Wheel Girdles were a considerable traction aid and of low cost. They are shown here in the fitting position

Some Non-Ferguson Attachments

LEFT EVERETT REDUCTION GEARBOX
An Everett Trencher could be fitted to Ferguson tractors, but it required fitting of this 98:1 Everett Reduction Gearbox. This enabled the machine to travel as slow as 30 yards/hr in work or as fast as 15 mph when moving between jobs

BELOW HOWARD ROTOVATOR
A Howard Rotovator made for fitting to Ferguson TE tractors

BELOW SACK LIFTER
This type of Sack Lifter is commonly thought to be of Ferguson origin, but it was made by outside manufacturer E.O. Culverwell of Lewes in Sussex

BELOW "HEDGE-MAKER" HEDGE CUTTER
John Moffitt in the driving seat, George Potts making final adjustments and then off to the hedges with a "Hedge-Maker" Hedge Cutter made by Bomford Bros. of Evesham. It could cut A or square shaped hedges, and work over ditches or cut ditch banks

BELOW "STEP UP" GEAR
This Sherman "step up" gear was made for fitting into Ford Ferguson and Ferguson tractors. It has a 4.2:1 ratio

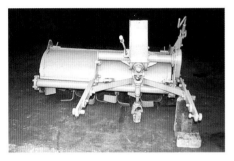

THIS PICTURE PIPPIN DIGGER
The Pippin Digger seen fully mounted on a Ferguson diesel tractor

ABOVE REAR MOUNTED CRANE
A Rear Mounted Crane by an unknown maker

BELOW REEKIE WEEDERS
A set of four Reekie Weeders fitted to a steerage hoe

ABOVE AND BELOW THE "MANLESS" BALE AND SACK LOADING DEVICES
The "Manless" Bale and Sack Loading Devices. Note that a different arm is needed for each application. This was made by E and G Norbury of Redditch. The bale loader cost £33.0s.0d and the sack lifting attachment an extra £15.7s.6d One hundred bales an hour was claimed as the potential for the bale loader and the sack lifter could handle 2.5 cwt

BELOW

CAMERON GARD-NER
A "Handy Loader" made in Reading, Berkshire

BOTTTOM LEFT FRONT MOUNTED RIDGE SPLITTER
Front Mounted Ridge Splitter made by Reekie which would have been used for covering hand planted potatoes. It would not have been used, as suggested in the photograph, in conjunction with the rear mounted planter

BELOW "TRACTAMOUNT ROLLER"
Made by E.V. Twose of Devon, the "Tractamount Roller" was recommended for car parks, football pitches, cricket fields, athletic cinder tracks, golf courses, public parks, tar-macadam roads and estate drives with ballast. The total weight is 4.5 tons. This roller was actually approved by Ferguson and included in Ferguson industrial equipment advertising. The prototype was announced in 1953

ABOVE OPPERMAN FOLDING WHEEL STRAKES
Opperman Folding Wheel Strakes added very considerable weight and traction when fitted to the rear wheels

ABOVE BOWER ADJUSTABLE WHEEL STRAKES
The Bower Adjustable Wheel Strakes differed in that the depth of penetration of the strakes was fully adjustable

ABOVE TARPEN HEDGE CUTTER, GRASS CUTTER AND CHAIN SAW
Tarpen Hedge Cutter, Grass Cutter and Chain Saw which are driven by flexible drive from the PTO through one or other of two gear connections

ABOVE ROWCROP WHEELS
A pair of Rowcrop Wheels

ABOVE LINDEMANN 16 IN. SINGLE FURROW REVERSIBLE PLOUGH
This Lindemann 16 in. single furrow reversible plough was marketed for use with Ferguson tractors in N. America and may have been offered officially by Ferguson

ABOVE SUNSHADE
A type of sunshade fitted to the Ford 8N tractor

LEFT STANHAY WHEEL STRAKES
A pair of Stanhay Wheel Strakes. These were attached to the rear wheels to give extra traction. The strakes retract for road travel; they are self-opening and closing. The depth of penetration of the strakes was adjustable within a small range

CHAPTER 10

Ferguson Models and Memorobilia

"The majority of the "one-off" models in my collection are the work of a very talented craftsman, Billy Smith, who unfortunately passed away two years ago at the age of 88 years." John Moffitt

MR BILLY SMITH – MODEL MAKER EXTRAORDINAIRE

A personal recollection by John Moffitt:

"The majority of the "one-off" models in my collection are the work of a very talented craftsman, Billy Smith, who unfortunately passed away two years ago at the age of 88 years.

I first met Billy in 1975 at a vintage show where he was displaying some of his models. We began chatting as I expressed a wish to have a model made of my "Ivel" tractor. To cut a long story short and some three years later, the model was complete right down to the finest detail. The Ivel went down to Billy's home where he was able to extract the finest detail in his drawings allowing him the opportunity to revisit the actual machine to check details. He produced his own patterns and made his own castings of the somewhat complex arrangement of the opposed cylinder piston engine.

Billy was completely self-taught and in fact, did very little modelling until he was 50 years old but he possessed an incredible eye for detail.

With some persuasion he entered the "Ivel" for the 1981 International Model Exhibition at Wembley, London and came back with the prestigious "Westbury" Memorial Trophy. This was the beginning of numerous Silver Awards at the great event.

Right up until Billy's death at 88 years he had kept very active not only modelling but painting, drawing and gardening which was his love. I am justly proud not only of the fifteen different Ferguson tractors and machines, but also of the further twenty models of various machines and a beautiful set of Fowler Ploughing machines complete with balance plough, subsoiler, cultivator, sleeping van etc.

ABOVE The late Billy Smith shown with a model Ferguson Brown
RIGHT John Moffitt and Billy Smith at Westside in 1983 in deep discussion about plans for a model
BELOW RIGHT In amongst the Ferguson models is an Alchin Ploughing Engine, also by Billy Smith

Billy Smith came from a family farm background. He had originally wanted to go to sea to be a ship's engineer. However, he settled for a land-based career, acquiring a Ferguson Brown tractor and implements, becoming a wartime farm contractor around his home in North Yorkshire. (The guarantee for the Ferguson Brown is shown in Chapter 4). Billy became a firm believer in the merits of the Ferguson System, which was to become apparent in later years.

Contracting led to developing an equipment repair business but as farm machinery got bigger, Billy then began to focus on smaller machinery, specialising his business in grass and horticultural machinery sales and repair. Whilst he officially "retired" in 1977 he probably spent more hours modelling than he worked in his earlier business. Billy will be remembered as a very humble and plain speaking North countryman, able to converse with all levels of society and

perhaps his finest hour was chatting to the Queen Mother when she opened the Hunday Museum in 1979."

Shown here are the Ferguson tractors and implements; also the Ivel tractor and an original Ferguson company model used for demonstrating the advantage of a mounted plough over a trailed plough. Billy Smith's models are all at 1:12 scale – beware! the reality of them when photographed on grass is quite exceptional.

ABOVE LEFT Another model from Billy Smith is this one of a pair of Fowler BB Ploughing Engines

BELOW Note the attention to detail with even a brass serial number plate on the ridger

ABOVE RIGHT An 1886 Crossley Gas Engine by Billy Smith

THIS PAGE The first ever Ferguson tractor – the Ferguson Black which is now at the Science Museum in London

ABOVE LEFT Ferguson hammer mill

ABOVE A TE Ferguson with Continental engine, sawbench and transport box. The axe tells us that Ferguson never thought of a log splitter - but he could easily have designed one for use with the tractor hydraulic system!

BELOW A Ferguson Brown line up – but the tractors pre-date the buckrake made for the TE 20 era tractors

ABOVE A grand display of Billy Smith's Fergusons

BELOW Ferguson Brown tractor and 30 cwt trailer – but the trailer was not manufactured until the era of the TE tractors

ABOVE AND BELOW A Ferguson company demonstration model shown in its original box and ready for demonstrating. One plough is trailed and demonstrates how the tractor rears when it hits an obstruction, the other is hitched the Ferguson three point hitch way and demonstrates the in built hydraulic safety mechanism of the Ferguson System hitch

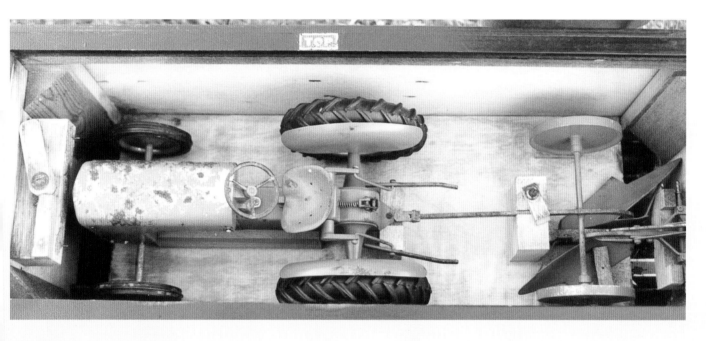

LEFT AND RIGHT Two views of the side mounted combine – totally complementary to the life size re-creation described in Chapter 8 (Not owned by J Moffitt)

There is an increasing range of modern models to be had which are not shown here. Some of these have been very good investments which have increased in value more rapidly than many vintage tractors!

ABOVE A selection of china and cast models by other makers

BELOW LEFT 1950s model of a TO 30 Ferguson with disc plough made by Topping Models. Made in Ohio USA and complete with a child's instruction book

BELOW RIGHT A cut away real TE 20 made for the Moffitt museum

Other Memorabilia

All things associated with Harry Ferguson seem to be becoming collectible, not least of which is literature and correspondence which is reviewed in other chapters. Another sector is the quite diverse range of small memorabilia which is becoming increasingly sought after. Then there are larger items such as dealers' signs.

Shown here is a selection of such items including some from the Massey Ferguson era.

BELOW LEFT A farm sign issued to some Ford Ferguson tractor owners

ABOVE Original Ferguson dealer's signs have become quite rare. Left is a Ford Ferguson sign (note the radiator access flap in the bonnet), centre is a TE or TO type Ferguson sign, and right is a double sided neon illuminated sign for Ford Ferguson tractors

BELOW RIGHT Not forgetting the present and the future of Ferguson, a relatively recent MF dealer's sign. This measures 3 ft x 2 ft and is fitted with a florescent light

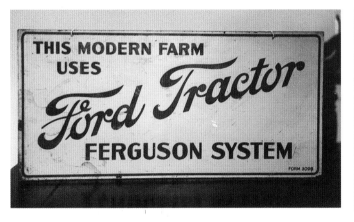

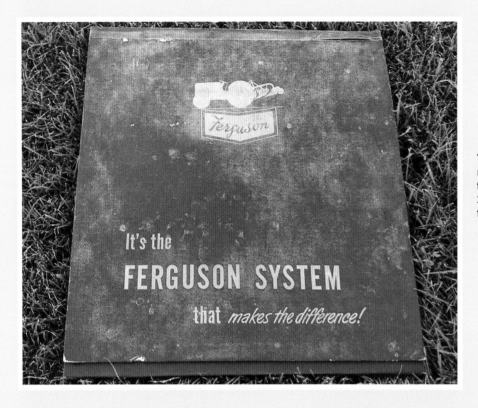

The cover and seven sheets contained in a salesman's flip chart used for explaining the workings of the Ferguson System tractors. The chart measures 23 in. x 25 in. As far as can be established, this flip chart was only used in North America

The FERGUSON SYSTEM gives you
PENETRATION without EXCESS WEIGHT

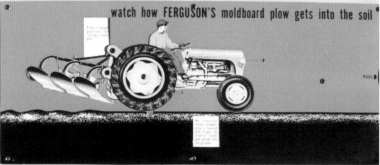

watch how FERGUSON'S moldboard plow gets into the soil

Ferguson's advanced engineering has made it possible to eliminate the costly, power-consuming deadweight often built into tractors and pull-type ground-engaging implements to provide penetration. Strength is provided with high alloy steel where strength is needed—but there is no weight "hung on." The result is implements that are light weight, compact and highly maneuverable—economical to buy and operate.

Ferguson System Implements are integrated with the Tractor through a linkage so designed that they are pulled into the soil by the forward movement of the tractor.

The Ferguson System is scientifically sound. It has eliminated the need for lift clutches, cables, trip ropes, coil springs, tongues, axles or transport wheels.

In the case of the Ferguson Plow for instance, penetration is achieved through ingenious use of several interacting factors: the unique Ferguson System of coupling implement and tractor—the natural weight of the implement—the entire plow-base angle of penetration—the "suck" designed into the plowshare—plus all of the other downward forces operating on the plow as it shears, lifts and turns the furrow slice.

FERGUSON IMPLEMENTS cost less to operate

The FERGUSON System automatically saves your IMPLEMENT... your TRACTOR... your TIME... when the implement strikes a hidden underground obstruction

When a Ferguson unit-mounted ground-engaging implement strikes a hidden obstruction, the impact transmitted through the top link releases implement weight from the rear wheels of the tractor. This action automatically transfers weight to the front wheels while the rear wheels become lighter, lose traction, and spin. In addition, suddenly arresting the tractor's forward momentum results in additional release of weight from the rear wheels, producing a "hunching" action onto the front wheels.

SAVES YOUR IMPLEMENT—Ferguson's overload release responds so quickly to sharp impacts that lift on the implement is decreased before serious damage can occur. Almost simultaneously, forward movement of the tractor is halted by loss of traction.

SAVES YOUR TRACTOR — When an implement suddenly strikes an obstruction, there's little chance for harm to your axle, differential, transmission or clutch. Upon impact, automatic overload release relieves implement weight on the rear wheels. Traction is reduced immediately, which prevents excessive strain on axle and gears.

SAVES YOUR TIME—All you do to get back to work is back up the tractor slightly as you raise the implement, drive forward to clear the obstruction, lower the implement and resume your job. You don't have to leave your tractor seat for time-consuming, temper-frazzling heaving or hauling at "lost" implements—replacing shear pins or bolts—rehitching or resetting of adjustments.

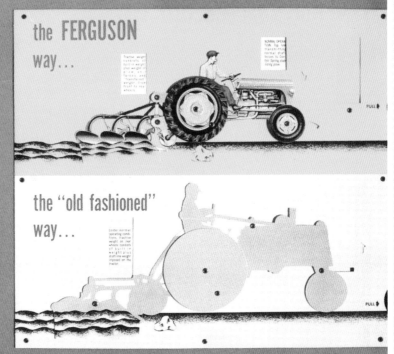

the FERGUSON way...

the "old fashioned" way...

An exclusive feature available only in the FERGUSON tractor

The FERGUSON SYSTEM gives you

FINGER TIP and AUTOMATIC DRAFT CONTROL

of Ground-engaging Implements

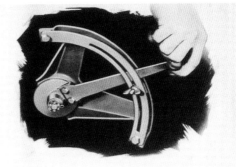

Ferguson's Finger Tip and Automatic Draft Control is not to be confused with "hydraulic lifts" that merely raise and lower implements. The Ferguson hydraulic system gives the operator control of implements both in and out of the soil, maximum flexibility under all working conditions.

The implement is lowered to working depth by the Finger Tip Control Lever. Thereafter, draft is maintained automatically by the built-in hydraulic mechanism of the Ferguson Tractor. To change working depth, or to raise the implement out of the ground, all that is necessary is a mere touch of the Finger Tip Control Lever.

WORKING DEPTH SELECTION

To select draft and working depth, the Finger Tip Control Lever is moved downward until the desired depth is reached. Upward or downward adjustment of the Lever will decrease or increase draft and working depth for various soil conditions.

AUTOMATIC DRAFT CONTROL

Once working depth has been selected by the Finger Tip Control, draft is maintained automatically in varying soils and on uneven ground.

RAISING and LOWERING IMPLEMENTS

To raise implements, the convenient Finger Tip Control Lever is pulled all the way up. The hydraulic mechanism swiftly lifts the implement—holds it there. To lower implements, the Finger Tip Lever is moved downward.

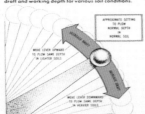

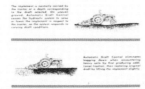

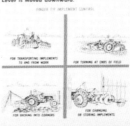

More Convenience...More Flexibility...More Work per Hour

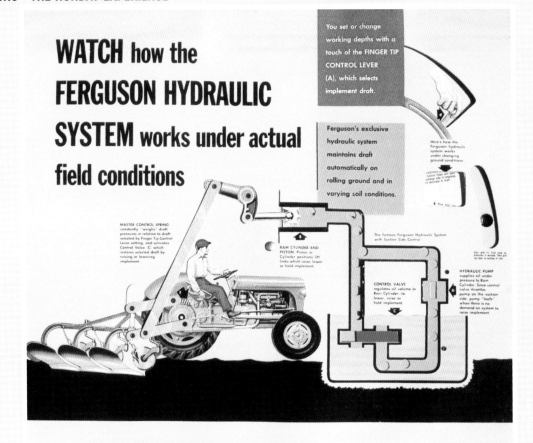

WATCH how the FERGUSON HYDRAULIC SYSTEM works under actual field conditions

You set or change working depths with a touch of the FINGER TIP CONTROL LEVER (A), which selects implement draft.

Ferguson's exclusive hydraulic system maintains draft automatically on rolling ground and in varying soil conditions.

MASTER CONTROL SPRING constantly "weighs" draft pressures in relation to draft selected by Finger Tip Control Lever setting, and activates Control Valve (C) which restores selected draft by raising or lowering implement.

RAM CYLINDER AND PISTON. Piston in Cylinder positions lift links which raise, lower or hold implement.

CONTROL VALVE regulates oil volume in Ram Cylinder to lower, raise or hold implement.

HYDRAULIC PUMP supplies oil under pressure to Ram Cylinder. Since control valve throttles pump on the suction side, pump "loafs" when there is no demand on system to raise implement.

The famous Ferguson Hydraulic System with Suction Side Control

With the FERGUSON System you – *do more work better, at less cost*

The FERGUSON SYSTEM gives you TRACTION without excess built-in weight!

Here's how Ferguson's weight transfer gives added traction

The Ferguson Tractor does not need costly excess weight for heavy draft performance. Instead, the weight of the implement and the soil forces acting on it are transferred to the tractor—adding weight to the rear wheels and giving extra traction as needed. Thus Ferguson gives you not only the maneuverability, speed and economy of a comparatively light tractor, but the traction and lugging power you need for the heavy jobs on the farm.

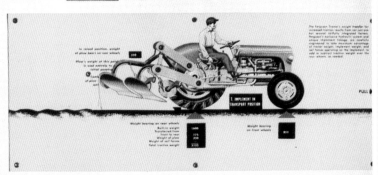

IMPLEMENT in TRANSPORT POSITION

1 With the tractor standing, the built-in weight of the Ferguson Tractor bearing on the rear wheels is about 1600 pounds. When a Ferguson 2-Bottom 14" Moldboard Plow is carried, the load on the rear wheels is increased by weight of the plow plus transferred weight to a total of 2125 pounds. With the plow in transport position, the weight bearing on the tractor's front wheels is 855 pounds.

IMPLEMENT on GROUND

2 During the short period the plow is on the ground before actual penetration, two momentary weight shifts occur simultaneously:
(1) The weight of the plow (350 pounds) is released from the rear wheels to the ground, and becomes a compressive force which helps the plow initially penetrate the soil.
(2) Think for a minute of the rear wheels as supporting a "seesaw". When the weight of the plow is released from the rear end, weight on the front wheels is increased momentarily.

IMPLEMENT WORKING

3 With the tractor moving forward, and when the plow reaches selected working depth, new weight shifts occur which greatly increase traction: (1) During work, both the weight of the plow (350 pounds) and the weight of the downward soil forces acting on the plow (210 pounds) are added to the rear wheels as tractive weight. (2) In addition, again using our "seesaw" example, 280 pounds of weight is shifted from the front to the rear wheels.
Adding all these tractive weight factors together, the rear wheels of the Ferguson tractor under operating load carry as much as 2440 pounds tractive weight. Yet the built-in weight bearing on the rear wheels is only 1600 pounds, and the tractor itself weighs only 2630 pounds!
Therefore, total tractive weight on the rear wheels varies according to the soil forces on the plow. In this way, more traction-producing weight is automatically added to the drive wheels for working in heavier soils.

LIGHTWEIGHT ECONOMY with HEAVYWEIGHT PERFORMANCE

only the WORLD-FAMOUS
FERGUSON SYSTEM
gives you ALL these ADVANTAGES

- **Fast Implement Hookup**
  With Ferguson's fast, easy 3-Point Hookup, changing most implements is a matter of as little as a minute. Many different jobs can be done in a single day by one tractor and one operator.

- **Eyes-ahead Steering**
  Ferguson's *converging lower linkage* allows mounted implements to follow the tractor's front wheels—permits the operator to look ahead, give full attention to changing field conditions.

- **Penetration without Excess Weight**
  Ferguson System ground-engaging implements do not depend on excess weight for penetration. Every pound of implement works—does the job without wasting power and fuel.

- **Finger Tip and Automatic Draft Control**
  Provides constant draft control on uneven ground and in changing soil conditions—as well as effortless raising, lowering and transporting implements.

- **Traction without Excessive Built-in Weight**—Through weight transfer, tractive weight is added to the rear wheels of the Ferguson Tractor as needed. Power-consuming, fuel-stealing dead weight has been eliminated.

- **Automatic Protection Against Hidden Obstructions**—An ingenious hydraulic overload release protects tractor and implement when the implement strikes a hidden obstruction. Without leaving his seat, the operator can raise the implement to clear the obstruction, lower the implement and resume working.

- **Keeps Front End Down**
  Careful integration of tractor and implement through the Ferguson System linkage and hydraulic control mechanism results in a safe close coupled tractor-implement combination which counteracts any tendency of the front end of the tractor to rise dangerously.

- **The Only Hydraulic System with Exclusive Suction Side Control**
  The Ferguson hydraulic control system almost "thinks", acts faster than human mind or hand—gives accurate control in varying field conditions.

...plus many other quality, design and construction features

with FERGUSON'S
CONVERGING LINKAGE
...you drive looking ahead

Your Ferguson integrated implement will always follow the front wheels of the tractor. Ferguson's flexible, ball-joint lower linkage with lines of pull meeting at the center of the front axle eliminates the "pivoting" action around the rear hitch point common to many conventional rear-mounted implements.

Once the implement is properly adjusted for row cultivation as an example, the operator is free to give full attention to the work ahead, watch for surface irregularities or obstructions, bends in the row, plants out of line, or other factors which may affect driving.

On the level—You can cultivate just as straight as you planted—without ever looking backward.

On hillsides—Contour farming presents no problems. Your implement will follow your tractor on curves as well as on straightaways.

Be sure—BE COMFORTABLE with **FERGUSON**

ABOVE A post card from the MF School of Farm Mechanisation in Warwick-shire, England which was originally established in Ferguson days

ABOVE A post card advertising the American built Ferguson 30. These quite frequently still appear for sale

ABOVE A selection of Ferguson Match Books. The three on the left are for the TO 35, TO 30 and TO 20 tractors whilst those on the right are for the Ford Ferguson

BELOW A Ferguson 12 in. ruler. The inches together with a dealer's name appear on the reverse side
BELOW LEFT The inside of a Match Book

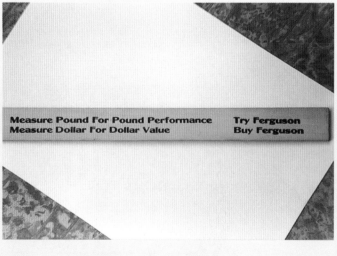

ABOVE A plastic Ferguson key fob which has a holograph on the rear side

ABOVE The two sides of a key fob issued to commemorate the 50th anniversary of the Ferguson system

ABOVE A Ferguson fan made from cardboard. On the reverse is the dealer's name and Ferguson System logo

ABOVE A second type of Ferguson fan

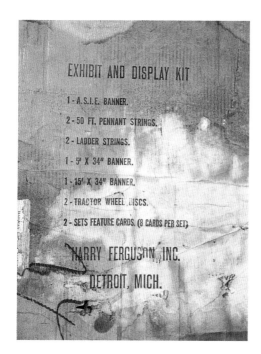

ABOVE Even old packaging material counts as memorabilia! This cardboard box contained the buntings, banners and other items which are now displayed in the museum - see Chapter 8

ABOVE A wheel disc display advertisement which was part of a Ferguson Exhibit and Display pack now displayed in the museum - see Chapter 8

ONE-MINUTE...3-POINT

Converging Implement Linkage

- Link arms converge for maximum implement efficiency and control

POWERFUL

Valve-in-Head Engine

- High-torque lugging power to pull 3 plows in most soils

AUTOMATIC
Implement Protection

- Safety control instantly provides protection to implement . . . tractor . . . operator, when striking hidden obstruction

TRACTION FOR ALL JOBS

Without extra Built-in Weight

- Ferguson System converts soil, implement weight and suction into traction as needed

THIS PAGE Four large display cards for use when the Ferguson tractor was exhibited. These are 14 in. x 10 in. and known as "benefits cards"

The ONE and ONLY
Ferguson System

- Five big advantages — Make farming faster, easier, safer... More profitable

FINGER TIP and
AUTOMATIC Draft Control

- Built-in Hydraulic System does your thinking for you

AUTOMATIC
Steering Alignment

- Radius rods and drag links move together with front wheel change

MORE WORK
per Gallon of Fuel

- Balanced Engineering gives you more work at right speed with less weight

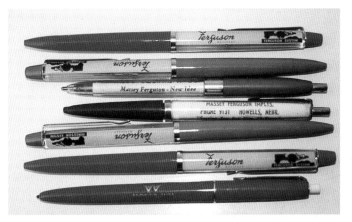

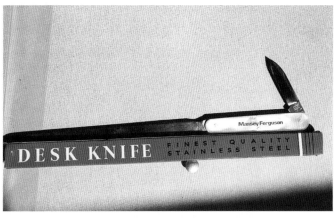

ABOVE LEFT A selection of Ferguson and Massey Ferguson pens

BELOW A Massey Ferguson cigarette lighter

ABOVE RIGHT A Massey Ferguson desk knife

BELOW A commemorative key fob celebrating 125 years of Massey Ferguson history

BELOW A Ferguson "flip" sales book which has details and illustrations of over 100 items of equipment. British and North American versions of these were produced

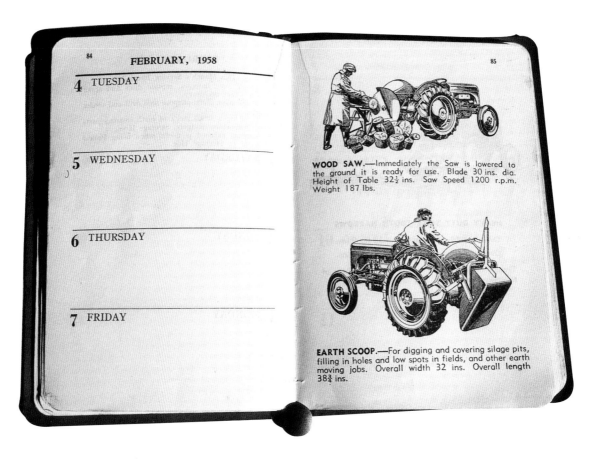

BELOW Harry Ferguson Is honoured in Northern Ireland with a special bank note. This is the latest and second style

ABOVE Inside pages of a Reekie diary. Reekie was a Ferguson agent

CHAPTER 11

Ferguson Literature

Literature relating to Ferguson and his products has become highly collectable in recent years and is constantly rising in price. The most popular are sales literature and instruction manuals, but publications relating to the general history of Ferguson are increasingly sought after. Occasionally astonishing prices are paid. At a sale in 1999 a Ferguson Brown tractor parts list made nearly £1,500 at auction and other pieces of rare literature now make over £100 quite regularly. Some rare examples of Ferguson Brown literature are shown in Chapter 6.

Ferguson sales literature is in many ways quite unique. Whilst presentation styles do vary, the messages given are always straightforward and to the point with almost a total absence of verbiage. Perhaps this reflects the very nature of Harry Ferguson himself who was a no nonsense man through and through, and who knew exactly what his products and ideas were capable of.

Literature collecting is on the increase and provides a valuable insight into Ferguson products and company history. It is a rapidly expanding part of the vintage machinery collectors' movement and presently is providing probably better returns than investment in machinery. But this might change! The most important thing is that it is almost a "no space required" way of being involved in the vintage movement, and some of the beautiful artwork is often more admired by ladies attached to the vintage movement than are tractors and equipment!

A most important part of literature collection is that it is continually revealing new pieces of information about Ferguson company history, the progressive emergence of different products and detail changes to them. More serious literature collectors endeavour to collect every single version of each piece of literature, even though there may only have been very minor changes to the content.

This chapter presents a very brief selection of Ferguson literature from what is a very great range of surviving material. Also included are a few items of equipment made specifically for Ferguson tractors by outside suppliers which achieved quite wide-scale take up. A different selection of material can be found in *The Advertising of Massey-Harris, Ferguson and Massey Ferguson* by John Farnworth.

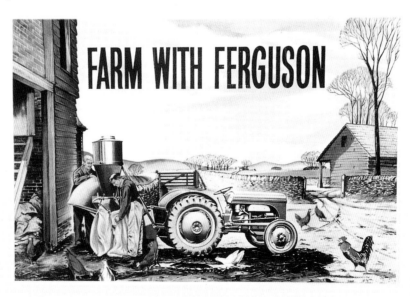

INSTRUCTIONS AND REPAIR PARTS BOOK

FOR

The

Ferguson

Plow

Manufactured by

Ferguson ~ Sherman, Inc.

Evansville, Ind., U. S. A.

A rare instructions and parts book from the earliest days of Ferguson ploughs and before Harry Ferguson ever became involved with tractor production. Ferguson first had Roderick Lean to produce his ploughs but this was a short-lived agreement. Subsequently the Sherman brothers produced them and this was a long-standing relationship. This plough in the Hunday collection is dated March 1923

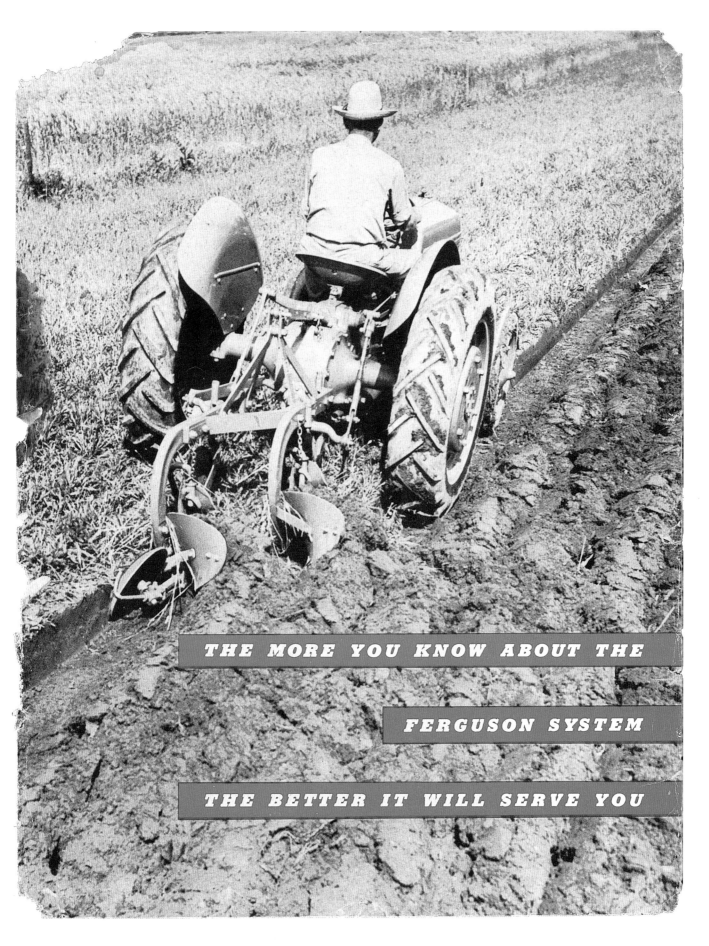

THE MORE YOU KNOW ABOUT THE

FERGUSON SYSTEM

THE BETTER IT WILL SERVE YOU

This 71 page brochure was issued for the Ford Ferguson tractor. It contains a wealth of information about how to obtain the best performance from both tractor and implements. 31 types of implement are listed together with maintenance schedules and lubrication charts

543 - Charles C. Edie

Welcome to Ferguson Park

HARRY FERGUSON, INC. ○ DETROIT, MICHIGAN

This brochure is an introduction to the newly established Ferguson tractor production plant in Detroit, Michigan which was completed in less than 12 months with the first TO tractor coming off the line on October 11th, 1948

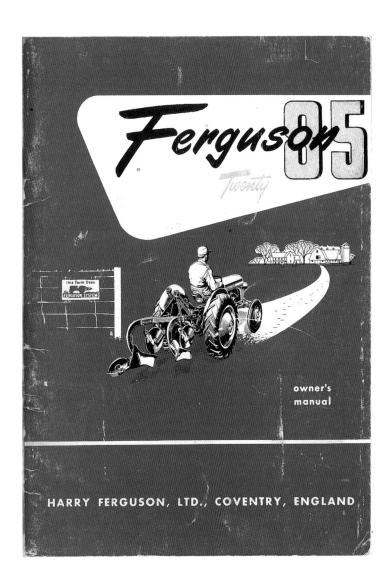

LEFT A 1948 fold out advertising brochure for the TO 20 tractor and RIGHT A 1952 Ferguson twenty-85 owners manual. The twenty-85 was the British built TE tractor with 85 mm Standard engine. This was sold in North America for a period alongside the TO models

Three splendid British Ferguson posters

New
The **FERGUSON** 35
Greater output per man hour
with an even more efficient FERGUSON SYSTEM

Here it is ! The new and more powerful Ferguson 35 — the most advanced tractor ever introduced ! Within one design are incorporated the most advanced use of hydraulics, more engine power, wider range of speeds, better steering and a score of other new features — a firm foundation for increased farming capacity and a greater output per

tractor operator. The Ferguson System tailors together — *for mutual efficiency* — tractor and implement. It eliminates wasted time and gives increased performance — this is not so with other makes. Here is a planned combination which moulds tractor and implement into one complete unit, yet the tractor is at no one time monopolized by an implement — it is free for speedy interchange of front, mid and rear mounted implements. Just read inside about the features of this great tractor !

Available with PETROL, DIESEL, VAPORISING OIL OR LAMP OIL ENGINES

This 18 x 14 in. fold out brochure announces the Ferguson 35 in the UK. The gold and grey livery was to
last only just over a year before it changed to the more familiar red and grey of Massey Ferguson

Go years ahead

The FERGUSON SYSTEM

With FERGUSON

Greater output per man-hour with an even more efficient Ferguson System

A 28 x 19 in. fold out brochure for the "grey-gold" Ferguson 35 tractor. It includes 44 black and white photos of implements and specifications of the four different engines that were offered

Announcing the Ferguson TO 30 tractor to the North American market. A large fold out brochure with cross sectional views of the tractor

A NEW ENGINEERING TRIUMPH
Ferguson 35

Featuring a new standard of control convenience that
lets you FARM MORE . . . WORK LESS . . .

Exclusive Ferguson **4-WAY WORK CONTROL**

The TO 35 tractor was the last of the original style Ferguson tractors to be produced in North America
before the advent of the Ferguson 40 tractor. This tractor saw the introduction of two lever hydraulics to
Ferguson tractors and also ground speed PTO as an addition to the standard engine speed related PTO

FEATURES OF THE
FERGUSON 40 TRACTORS

Product Information Manual

FERGUSON SYSTEM

The Ferguson 40 tractor was only produced in limited numbers for the North American market, but broke with Ferguson tradition by the offering of a standard tractor, high tractor; plus dual and single front wheel tricycle versions

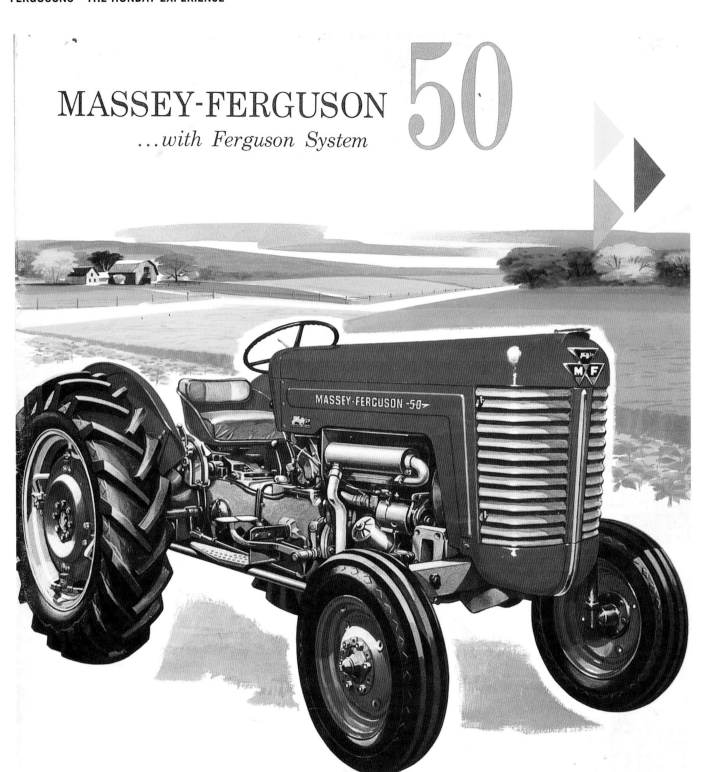

MASSEY-FERGUSON 50
...with Ferguson System

The Massey-Ferguson System of Mechanized Farming

The Massey Ferguson 50 tractor, sold in North America, was a Ferguson 40 in new Massey Ferguson livery. The Ferguson 40 was also marketed in Massey-Harris livery as the Massey-Harris 50 tractor

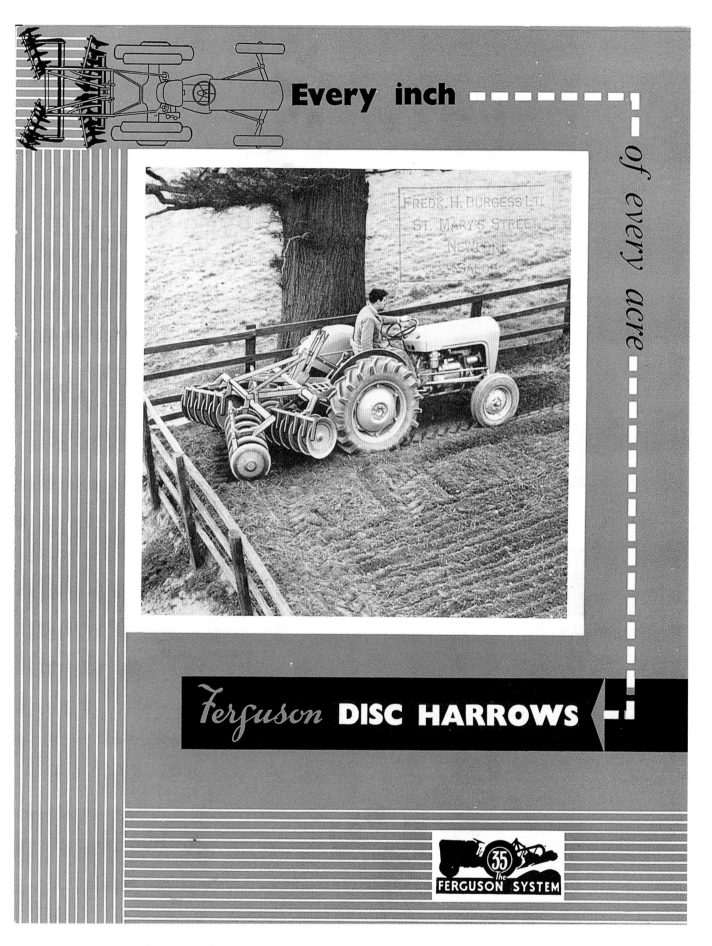

Every inch ─ ─ ─ ─ ─ ─ ─ ─ ─ ─

of every acre

FREDK. H. BURGESS LTD
ST. MARY'S STREET
NEWPORT

Ferguson **DISC HARROWS**

FERGUSON SYSTEM

In this Massey-Harris-Ferguson era British brochure for disc harrows, an old Ferguson message is still being hammered home!

Ferguson
ELECTROMATIC HAMMERMILL

7½d. A TON !
Grinding Oats for Cattle Feed

Hourly output in cwts. and Cost of Grinding per ton	3 h.p.		5 h.p.	
	Cwts. per hour	Cost per ton	Cwts. per hour	Cost per ton
OATS for CATTLE FEED using ¼" Screens	6	10d.	9½	7½d.
WHEAT for POULTRY FEED using 3/32" Screens ...	3¾	1/4d.	7¼	10d.
BARLEY for PIG FEED using 3/32" Screens ...	3	1/11d.	5½	1/4d.

(Electricity calculated at 1d. per unit).

The only Fully Automatic Grinding System

The Ferguson Electromatic Hammermill is a fully automatic mill which cannot fail to cut out the power when grinding is completed. It is ideal on farms with limited power supply and for grinding grain without attention.

Features include:—

★ Full size horizontal grinding chamber with 360° (full circle) screen.

★ 4 times reversible, full size swinging hammers.

★ Direct drive from motor to rotor and internal fan—No losses of power through belts, pulleys, gears, etc.

★ High speed feed impeller and adjustable micro-feed gate ensures steady feed rate.

★ Cannot be clogged by string or straw.

★ Handles mixed beans and corn.

★ Motor totally enclosed is dustproof, ensuring long life, and eliminates fire risk.

★ Available with 3 phase 5 h.p. or single phase 3 h.p. motor.

★ Electromatic Control Panel incorporates Ammeter with automatic protection and Electromatic Power-cut-off.

★ Power is cut off by all-electric "No-load" relay without grain-operated flaps.

★ Multibagger automatically fills six sacks during grinding. Sacks can be individually removed.

★ Also available with small cyclone for single discharge of the meal.

(PATENTS PENDING)

Massey-Harris-Ferguson (SALES) LTD. **Massey-Harris-Ferguson** (EXPORT) LTD.
COVENTRY : ENGLAND

Printed in England   FP523/10M/5/55

The Ferguson Electromatic Hammer Mill was not a widely sold implement and surviving examples are now very rare. An identical machine was also sold by Massey-Harris

Ferguson

COMBINED SPEED REDUCTION AND LIVE P.T.O. UNIT

EIGHT FORWARD SPEEDS AND TWO REVERSE ON YOUR FERGUSON

●

A LIVE POWER TAKE-OFF FOR EXTRA EFFICIENCY

●

READILY FITTED

The unit is fitted between the gearbox and rear axle housing to provide the Ferguson tractor with an alternative set of four extra low forward speeds, together with a second low reverse speed, and to maintain the power take-off in operation whilst disengaging the drive to the tractor rear wheels.   Thus a Ferguson tractor so fitted has a range of eight forward speeds and two reverse whilst acquiring the increasingly recognised advantages of a "live power take-off".   The rapid expansion of P.T.O. driven equipment on all types and sizes of farms cannot but emphasise the outstanding value of this new accessory.

The unit contains a simple, epicyclic train of gears giving a 3 : 1 reduction, the arrangement being chosen for its adaptability and compactness. It is remarkably easy to install and a special mechanical/hydraulic feature prevents all danger of overloading the tractor transmission.   Two levers, interlocked to ensure correct operation, put the unit in or out of work and establish the drive.

Tractor speeds in M.P.H. through all gears over a range of engine speeds with the **reduction unit engaged** are given in the following table:—

Engine R.P.M.	1st	2nd	3rd	4th	Reverse
1000	.55	.77	1.06	2.2	.64
1500	.83	1.15	1.58	3.3	.96
2000	1.11	1.53	2.11	4.4	1.28

Live P.T.O. throughout.

Massey-Harris-Ferguson, COVENTRY, ENGLAND

Ferguson Tractors are manufactured for Massey-Harris-Ferguson, Eastern Hemisphere Division, by the Standard Motor Co. Ltd.

Printed in England

FP585/20,000/6/55

An Epicyclic Reduction Gearbox was offered for TE tractors in the UK. This extended the wheelbase and gave forward speeds as slow as 0.55 mph

Two or three gang Spring Tooth Harrows, and four gang Spike Tooth Harrows being offered for the TE 20 and FE 35 tractors

Weed up to **50** acres in <u>One</u> day
High Speed . . . Low Cost . . . Effective Control

For a really high weed-kill over large acreages it will pay you to couple your Ferguson tractor to the simple, but effective Ferguson Weeder. So quick to attach, so easy to transport from field to field and so thorough in its work, this Ferguson quality made implement is the most economical weeder in existence. No mechanical complications to go wrong but a simple 13 ft. span of 71 delicately sprung tines—spaced every 2¼ in.—which lightly flick the weeds out, leaving them to die on the surface while the crop flourishes in the freshly aerated soil.

Ferguson **WEEDER**

The Ferguson Weeder had the highest work rate of any Ferguson implement and weighed only 264 lb

You can choose from two Ferguson Mid-Mounted Cultivators—both of which can be quickly and easily adapted to fit your crop and field conditions. Effortless finger-tip depth control assures proper shovel penetration. Parallel linkage through which front gangs are controlled provides proper penetration angle of shank or shovel. Available with a wide variety of shovels, sweeps and accessory items, Ferguson Mid-Mounted Cultivators provide efficient destruction of weeds while creating a surface mulch that absorbs water and admits air and light. These are the conditions essential for best plant growth.

Choice of Cultivator Models

TWO

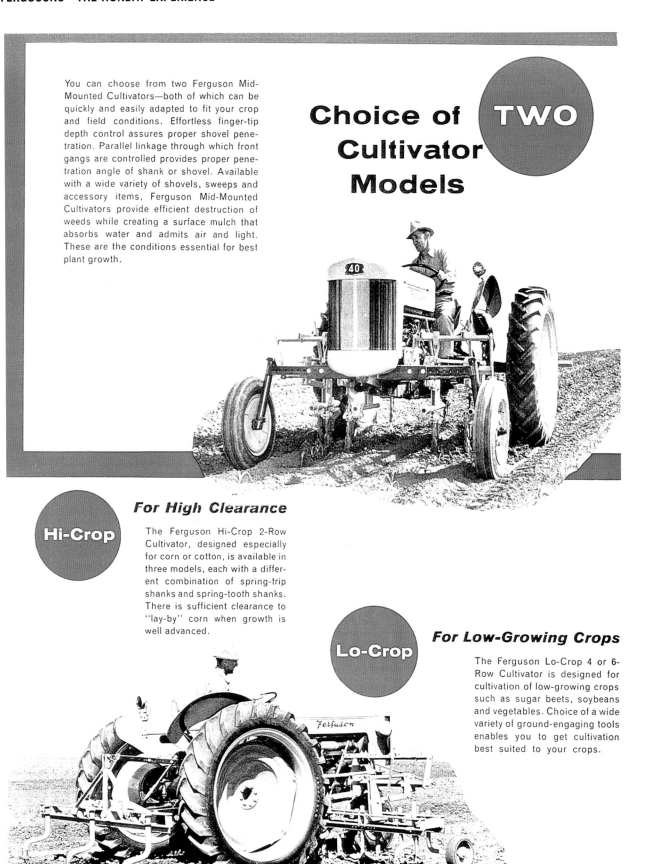

For High Clearance

Hi-Crop

The Ferguson Hi-Crop 2-Row Cultivator, designed especially for corn or cotton, is available in three models, each with a different combination of spring-trip shanks and spring-tooth shanks. There is sufficient clearance to "lay-by" corn when growth is well advanced.

For Low-Growing Crops

Lo-Crop

The Ferguson Lo-Crop 4 or 6-Row Cultivator is designed for cultivation of low-growing crops such as sugar beets, soybeans and vegetables. Choice of a wide variety of ground-engaging tools enables you to get cultivation best suited to your crops.

Rowcrop cultivators for a high Ferguson 40 and a tricycle style Ferguson 40

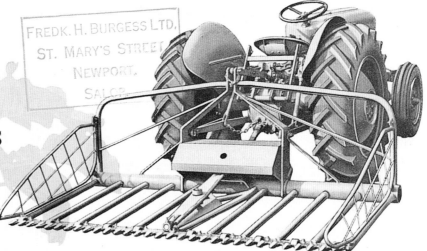

Cuts, loads *and* transports kale

Operated by **ONE** *man —* **ALL** *from the tractor seat* !

Ferguson **KALE CUTRAKE** — **THE 35 FERGUSON SYSTEM**

IT'S PART OF THE **FERGUSON** **SYSTEM** *OF FARM MECHANISATION*

The Kale Cutrake seems to have been produced in small numbers only and mainly for the British market.
Good surviving examples are now hard to find

- **VERSATILE APPLICATION**—Cut hedges, steep grass banks, awkward shaped ditches and under-water weeds at a speedy and economical rate!

- **LIGHT, TOUGH CONSTRUCTION**—Made of tougher-than-steel (but only one third the weight) alloy, the Ferguson Hedgecutter is tough but so light to handle!

- **DUAL PURPOSE POWER**—Pneumatically driven by the famous Hydrovane 25 Compressor, the Ferguson Hedgecutter is an individual attachment—the compressor is free for other year-round work!

IT'S PART OF THE **FERGUSON SYSTEM** OF COMPLETE FARM MECHANIZATION

The Ferguson Hedgecutter utilised compressed air from a Ferguson Compressor. The actual hedge cutter was made from aluminium and light alloy metal and was very light to handle

FERGUSON
SIDE DELIVERY RAKE

Special design for faster work.

Shorter travel and gentle handling of hay.

3 - point mounting for greater control.

Gentle handling of hay permits faster work.

Special self cleaning action.

The unique reel design of the Ferguson Side Delivery Rake eliminates the problem of leaf shattering when working at high speeds. There is no tossing or pitching of the hay into the windrow such as is done with conventional type rakes. Instead there is a continuous lifting of the hay " up and over " into light fluffy windrows which receive a free circulation of air, while, at the same time, the leaves are protected from the direct rays of the sun and the maximum amount of hay protein retained.

The Side Delivery Rake is attached by 3-point linkage and driven by P.T.O. from the tractor. The delivery reel drive is, therefore, both positive and constant. The rake can be raised, like any other Ferguson implement, by finger-tip control for 180° turnrounds and when crossing gullies or other obstructions.

The diagram on the right shows why the Ferguson Side Delivery Rake moves the hay with the minimum loss of leaf, when compared with the conventional type rakes which move the hay twice the distance of the Ferguson Side Delivery Rake.

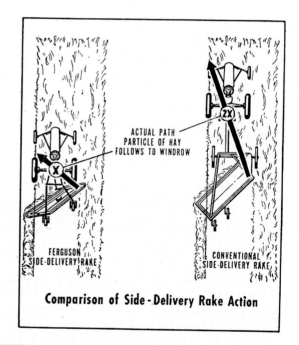

ACTUAL PATH PARTICLE OF HAY FOLLOWS TO WINDROW

FERGUSON SIDE-DELIVERY RAKE

CONVENTIONAL SIDE-DELIVERY RAKE

Comparison of Side - Delivery Rake Action

Massey-Harris-Ferguson (Sales) Ltd.   Massey-Harris-Ferguson (Export) Ltd.
COVENTRY ENGLAND

PRINTED IN ENGLAND   FP481/20,000/5/55

Few Ferguson Side Delivery Rakes were sold on to the British market. They were more common in the drier areas of North America, Australia and South Africa

THE FERGUSON TWO-WHEEL TRAILER

THE FORD TRACTOR WITH FERGUSON SYSTEM IS WORKING A REVOLUTION IN LAND CULTIVATION COSTS

AND NOW

A NEW APPLICATION OF THE FERGUSON SYSTEM WILL WORK A REVOLUTION IN FARM AND INDUSTRIAL HAULAGE

Ferguson soon extended his weight transfer principle from implements to trailers. This 4,000 lb capacity trailer was introduced for Ford Ferguson tractors in North America. The hitch principle was subsequently revised twice on UK trailers with a three ton capacity

FERGUSON *three-ton* FARM WAGON

BUILT FOR TRACTOR POWER
- Recommended for both high speed and heavy hauling
- Adjustable to any standard rack or box
- Saves time with big capacity

THE FERGUSON SYSTEM
of Mechanized Farming

The FERGUSON TRACTOR

A 6,000 lb capacity Ferguson four wheel Farm Wagon being pulled behind a corn picker. No weight transfer here!

Affectionately known as the "Banana Loader" this 10 cwt capacity Ferguson High Lift Loader was very popular with farmers, local authorities and on building sites. The operator was however placed in a very cramped position

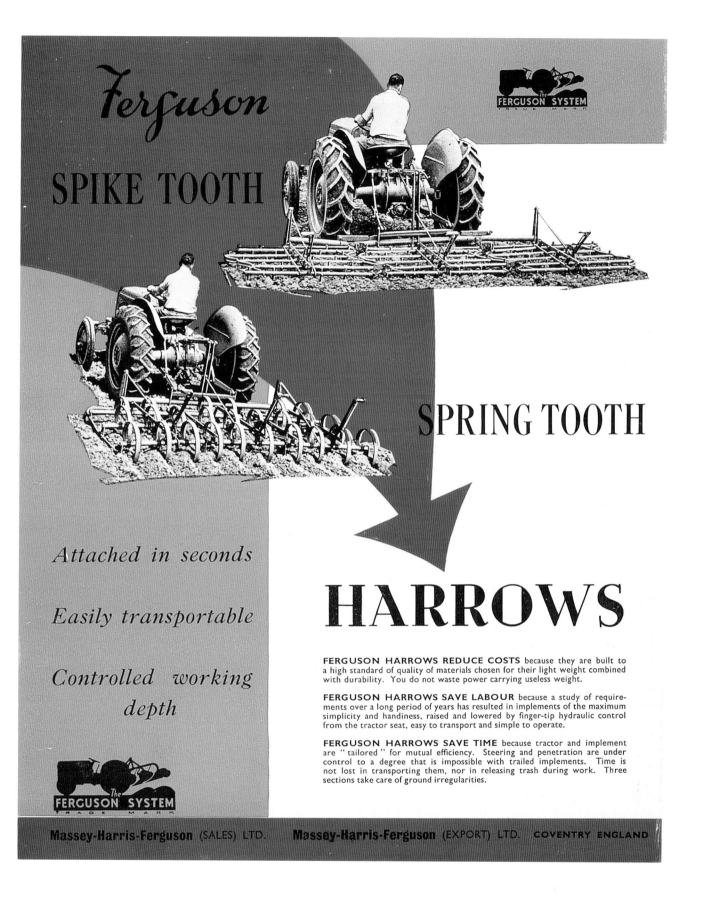

Ferguson

SPIKE TOOTH

SPRING TOOTH

HARROWS

Attached in seconds

Easily transportable

Controlled working depth

FERGUSON HARROWS REDUCE COSTS because they are built to a high standard of quality of materials chosen for their light weight combined with durability. You do not waste power carrying useless weight.

FERGUSON HARROWS SAVE LABOUR because a study of requirements over a long period of years has resulted in implements of the maximum simplicity and handiness, raised and lowered by finger-tip hydraulic control from the tractor seat, easy to transport and simple to operate.

FERGUSON HARROWS SAVE TIME because tractor and implement are " tailored " for mutual efficiency. Steering and penetration are under control to a degree that is impossible with trailed implements. Time is not lost in transporting them, nor in releasing trash during work. Three sections take care of ground irregularities.

Massey-Harris-Ferguson (SALES) LTD.   **Massey-Harris-Ferguson** (EXPORT) LTD.   **COVENTRY ENGLAND**

Three gang Spike and Spring Tooth Harrows. Today the spike tooth types are much more commonly found in the UK

FOUR-SECTION SPIKE TOOTH HARROW
for the Ferguson System

for the Fast Finishing Touches in Seed Bed Preparatio

The entire harrow lifts on the Ferguson Linkage for fast transportation or for clearance of field trash.

Outer sections fold up and lock in place for easy clearance through gates, lanes and—road travel without disassembly.

ACRES . . . IN HOURS

Five to six acres an hour. That's entirely within the working range of every farmer who operates the Ferguson Tractor and the new Ferguson Spike Tooth Harrow—a tillage unit that measures its capacity in terms of *acres* with fewer *rounds* or *trips* across the field.

The Ferguson Spike Tooth Harrow is a high-speed tractor harrow. Increased weight and tension-spring adjustment keeps the Ferguson Harrow hugging the ground, regardless of the rate of tractor speed.

With a weight of over 625 pounds, the Ferguson Spike Tooth is one of the heaviest harrows per foot width manufactured. Tension-spring with five notch adjustment allows the operator to add or decrease the weight of the Spike Tooth for the most effective job on its full 17-feet, 6-inch width of cut.

DESIGNED FOR EFFICIENCY

The Ferguson Spike Tooth Harrow's design for efficiency means *more* than its ability to smooth the soil surface and break up the lumps and clods that put the soil in good tilth for a seedbed . . . or of breaking the ground crusts that follow spring rains . . . or even performing the necessary surface cultivating obligation of killing small weeds.

TILLAGE TIMESAVERS

The Ferguson Spike Tooth Harrow offers many timesaving features.

1. It saves the operator's time with a one-minute, three-point attachment to the Ferguson System.

2. The Ferguson Spike Tooth Harrow saves additional time by allowing the tractor operator to work an entire field, or an entire day, without ever getting off the tractor to clear the harrow sections of surface trash that might otherwise mean clearing by hand. A touch of the Finger Tip Control Lever lifts the entire implement and frees the stalks, roots and stones that soon render most Spike Tooths ineffective.

3. For maximum operating ease and time economy, outer sections fold up and lock in place allowing

In the USA Four Section Spike Tooth Harrows were offered. Their greater width required the use of stay rods to the front axle to prevent lagging of the outer sections when turning or following a contour

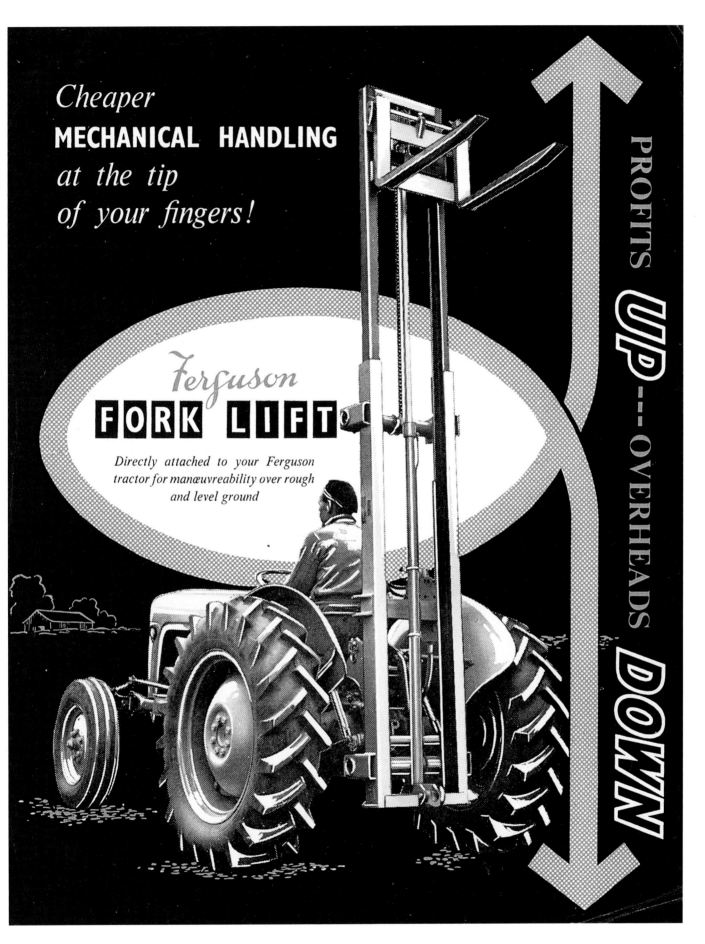

Cheaper **MECHANICAL HANDLING** *at the tip of your fingers!*

Ferguson **FORK LIFT**

Directly attached to your Ferguson tractor for manœuvreability over rough and level ground

PROFITS *UP* --- OVERHEADS *DOWN*

12.5 cwt could be lifted to 10 ft. 7 in. with this Ferguson Fork Lift. This forklift was made under licence by Fewsters Ltd. Stocksfield, and well known to the author, J Moffitt

THE FERGUSON DISC PLOW

WHERE FERGUSON DISC PLOWS EXCEL

- For mixing heavy surface trash with topsoil to conserve soil and water
- For constructing and maintaining soil and moisture-conserving terraces
- For working heavy, sticky or wet soils that do not scour easily
- For plowing stony or root-infested soils
- For penetrating hard-packed soils

THE FERGUSON TRACTOR

THE FERGUSON SYSTEM
of Mechanized Farming

The Ferguson Disc Plow could operate up to 12 in. deep. The three furrow version was created by adding an extra disc to the two disc version. Notched discs were also available for use in heavy trash conditions

FERGUSON REAR-MOUNTED
DYNA-BALANCE MOWER

- Counterbalanced ground-level drive unit
- Built-in lead
- Built-in register
- No knife-head hold-down plates and shims to adjust

... AND MANY OTHER ADVANCED FEATURES

©1955 M·H·F Inc.

The FERGUSON TRACTOR

THE FERGUSON SYSTEM
of Mechanized Farming

The Ferguson Dyna-Balance Mower reduced vibration by doing away with conventional Pitman arm drive. On opening this brochure a cutter bar swings down from the inside, hence the notch in the bottom right corner

A *Time-Money-Labor* SAVE

FOR FARMERS AND CONTRACTORS

FERGUSON BLADE TERRACER

Shown here on a Ford Ferguson in a 1944 brochure, the simple Blade Terracer was a boon for terracing and ditching

FERGUSON
SOIL SCOOP

The
FERGUSON SYSTEM

THE FERGUSON SYSTEM
of Mechanized Farming

This North American Soil Scoop of the Ford Ferguson era had a multitude of uses including building dams for farm ponds, filling gullies, cleaning feedlots, digging irrigation ditches and filling holes in roads to mention but a few. It carries seven cu. ft. and is rear tipping

BOMBARDIER TRACTOR TRACK ATTACHMENT B-TTA-21

OPERATING and ASSEMBLY INSTRUCTIONS

HARRY FERGUSON, INC.   DETROIT, MICH.

Half tracks shown on a Ferguson 30 tractor gave outstanding flotation and traction in snow, ice and muddy conditions

CENGAR SAFETY CAB

— WITH SLIDING CANOPY
FOR FERGUSON TRACTORS

You need a cab on that Tractor —

or you'll be laid up!

Bad weather also loses many valuable producing hours each season when — with such a protection as the Cengar Safety Cab — the Tractor could be working.

BUY FROM YOUR FERGUSON OR MASSEY-HARRIS DEALER

Ferguson never marketed a weather cab for his tractors. Perhaps a surprising and serious omission from Ferguson's long list of accessories and implements? In the UK and elsewhere many manufacturers, like Cengar, were quick to respond to drivers' needs

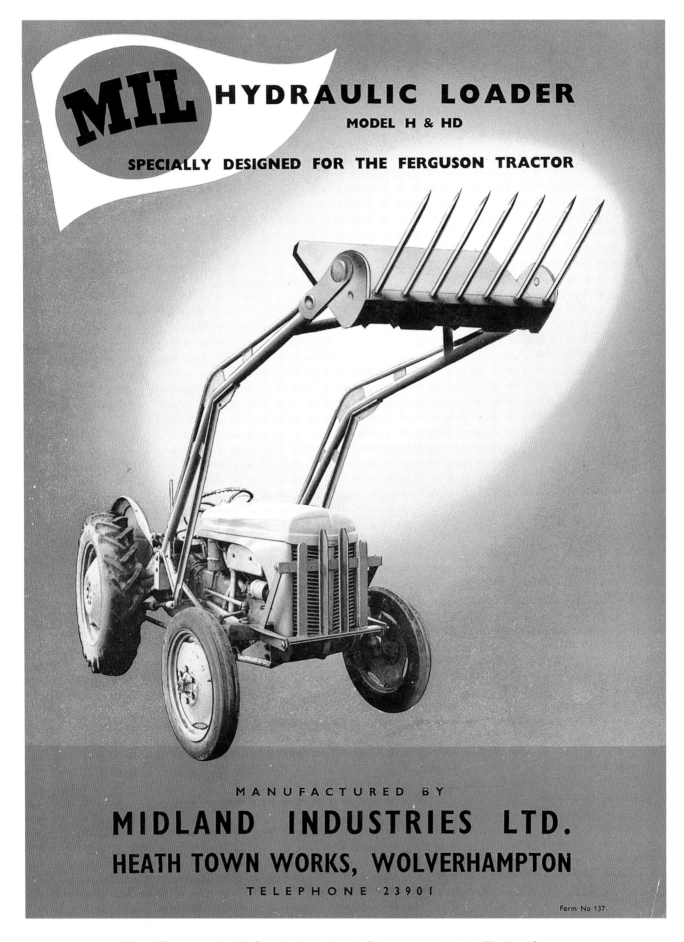

MIL **HYDRAULIC LOADER**
MODEL H & HD

SPECIALLY DESIGNED FOR THE FERGUSON TRACTOR

MANUFACTURED BY

MIDLAND INDUSTRIES LTD.

HEATH TOWN WORKS, WOLVERHAMPTON

TELEPHONE 23901

Form No 137.

Although Ferguson produced their own loaders, other manufacturers were not slow to offer alternative designs. This MIL loader was one of the most common alternative loaders to be fitted to Ferguson tractors in the UK

LOW IN COST...
LOW IN UPKEEP

The New
Everett Trencher
equals

the pick and shovel work of **25** men

FOR INSTALLATION ON FERGUSON, FORD-FERGUSON AND FORD TRACTORS

A 98:1 reduction gearbox was part of the Everett Trencher package which gave a working forward speed as low as 18 in./min. The trencher is PTO driven, weighs 1,450 lb and can dig to 42 in. depth

The Ferguson On-The-Farm Service Unit comprised a dwell-tach tester, volts amp tester, vacuum gauge, compression gauge, timing light, engine and compressor, mechanical tachometer, report charts, spray and grease guns

Never pull from upper link connection

Always set brakes before dismounting, when stopping on a hill or grade

Don't smoke when refueling or inspecting gasoline tank

Keep flames away from filler cap openings

Always open doors before starting tractor engine.

Use caution when removing pressure cap from radiator

Never drive close to deep ditches

Never wear loose clothing around tractor's moving parts

Never put on or remove belt when pulley is in motion

Keep inflammable material away from exhaust pipe to prevent fire.

Drive carefully on the highway observing all traffic rules

Always stop tractor before dismounting

Harry Ferguson was known as a man with a serious mission in life. Humour did however occasionally penetrate the normally straight forward and factual Ferguson literature as shown in these examples of Ferguson safety advisory comic cuts

Your Ferguson Dealer has this Storm Cover and other Accessories

SPARES LIST No. CCE 831B

LUCAS

Quality

EQUIPMENT

&

SPARE PARTS

1956

FERGUSON TRACTORS

(STANDARD ENGINES)

JOSEPH LUCAS (SALES & SERVICE) LTD · BIRMINGHAM 18 · ENGLAND

Compiled and issued by Technical Records Department, Joseph Lucas (Sales & Service) Ltd., Great Hampton Street, Birmingham 18

Lucas were the principal suppliers of electrical components for British built Ferguson tractors

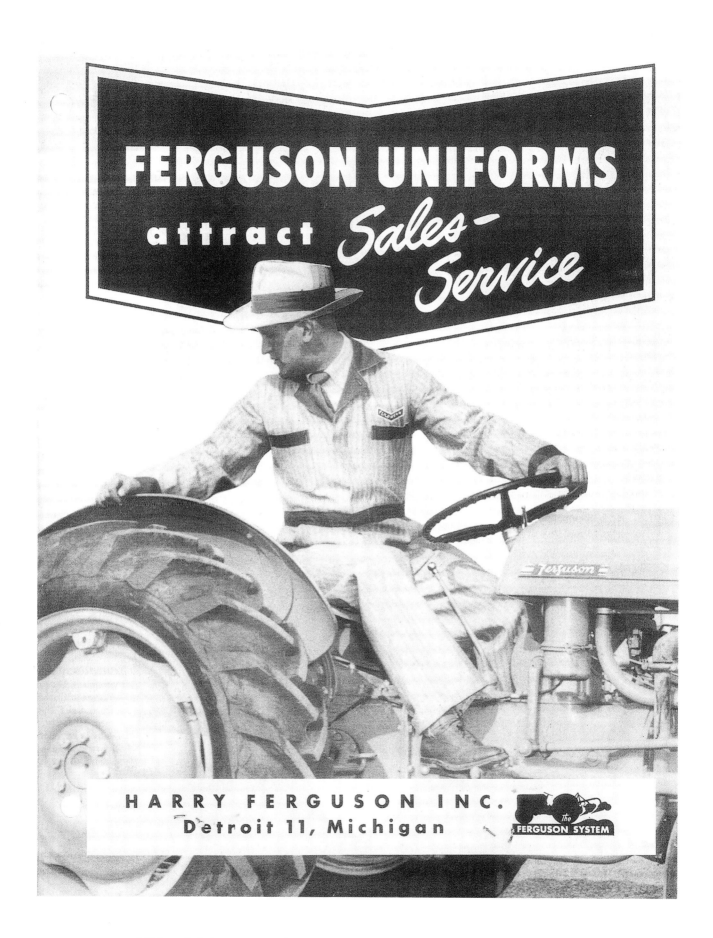

A high standard of turnout was required of USA Ferguson personnel. This brochure lists clothing for all grades of personnel from salesmen to demonstrators and mechanics

SUGGESTED PLANS FOR COMPLETE FERGUSON EXHIBITS

SUGGESTED PLANS FOR COMPLETE FERGUSON EXHIBITS

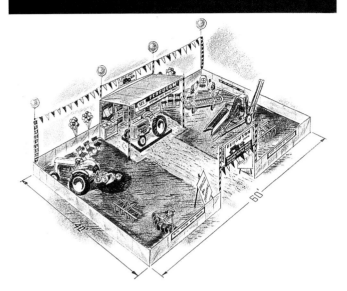

You'll Need These Materials:

Fair Kit
> Two Ropes of 6 Pennants Each
> Jumbo Identification Banners
> Jumbo Posters
> Slogan Streamers
> Ferguson System Posters
> Implement Identification Cards

Exhibit and Display Kit
> Two Strings of Pennants
> Ladder Pennants
> 5' x 34" Banner
> 15' x 34" Banner
> A.S.I.E. Merit Award Banner
> Tractor Wheel Discs
> Tractor Feature Cards

30-inch Balloons
11-inch Balloons
Road Sign
Tent Poles (8 Large, and 6 Small)
Bunting to Enclose Exhibit Space

You'll Need These Materials:

Fair Kit
> Jumbo Identification Banners
> Slogan Streamers
> Tractor Hood Display Flags
> Implement Identification Cards
> Jumbo Posters

Exhibit and Display Kit
> 15-foot Banner
> 5-foot Banner
> Strings of Pennants
> Ladder Pennants
> Tractor Wheel Discs
> Tractor Feature Cards
> A.S.I.E. Merit Award Banner

30-inch Balloons
Tent Poles (4 Large, and 5 Small)
Bunting to Outline Exhibit
Colored Sawdust Trail Inside Exhibit

Such was Ferguson's concern that the company's products always be properly displayed, dealers received advisory leaflets about how to display Ferguson exhibits together with a listing of required materials. Shown here are some 1951 examples

Hitch Your Sales to This Rising S...

PROMOTION ITEMS
NO. 4-1010
NOVEMBER 29, 1955

THE NEW FERGUSON
20-LIGHT MATCH BOOK

Now Ferguson offers you your choice of two sizes of match books ...the 40-light "Billboard" size (see Ad Guide Sheet No. 4-10) and this handy 20-light size. *Both* have advantages and brighten your future your sales. Use these fast-moving, hard-hitting star sales reach more prospects ... at lower costs. Handy, conven ways needed, the 20 or 40 light ads constantly repeat your ge, plant your name and Ferguson's deeply in their mind

These match books offer you:
1. wider circulation
2. increased usage
3. greater flexibility

for as little as **$14.88** per case (2500 books)

GET A NEVER-ENDING STREAM OF PROSPECTS AND CUSTOMERS BY:

1 RESELLING YOUR NEW 20-LITE MATCH BOOKS to drug stores, groceries, jobbers and to Vending Machine operators. These people will split the cost for each case with you, and put your ad into the hands of hundreds of new prospects. Your vending machine operator can put them in the machines at the sales barn, produce houses, etc. You can pin point your circulation ... reach more prospects and get as much as half of your money back too!

2 GIVING THEM AWAY AT FAIRS, SHOWS, MEETINGS. You couldn't personally attend all of the "get-togethers" where your prospects congregate ... so do the next best thing, send your sparkling match book representatives. They're conversation starters that lead you to many additional sales.

SEE BACK PAGE FOR SPECIAL OFFER

Even match books were used to add to Ferguson sales!

HIRE-PURCHASE DOCUMENTS

THE FERGUSON

PAY-AS-YOU-FARM

PLAN

Offered by Massey-Harris-Ferguson (SALES) LIMITED

in association with

The British Wagon Company, Limited

FARM BETTER, FARM FASTER WITH FERGUSON

Massey-Harris-Ferguson (SALES) LIMITED, COVENTRY, ENGLAND

Ferguson offered credit to farmers via the hire purchase mechanism in the UK

FERGUSON SYSTEM
TRADE MARK

Ferguson

TRACTOR
REPAIR TIME SCHEDULE

Massey - Harris - Ferguson
COVENTRY   (SALES) LTD • ENGLAND

Every conceivable repair had a scheduled cost in this 14 page confidential document. Diesel engine
tractors had some different costs compared to the petrol, TVO and lamp oil engines which were all
the same

INFORMATION
VITAL TO YOUR BUSINESS

CONCERNING

Ferguson

FERTILISER ATTACHMENT
FOR POTATO PLANTER

P - RE - 20

These particulars are given
in advance of production and
may be subject to modification

Massey-Harris-Ferguson (SALES) LIMITED
Massey-Harris-Ferguson (EXPORT) LIMITED
COVENTRY . ENGLAND

Quality technical operational advice was provided through an extensive series of "Information Vital To
Your Business booklets"

THE FERGUSON SCHOOL

of

FARM MECHANISATION

STONELEIGH ABBEY
KENILWORTH
WARWICKSHIRE

WORKSHOP SECTION

The Workshop Section provides practical and theoretical training in all aspects of service and full scale overhaul and maintenance of Ferguson tractors. The two standard courses at present are as follows :—

Tractor Workshop ... ... two weeks   Diesel ... ... one week

TRACTOR WORKSHOP COURSE

FIRST WEEK

Principles of Ferguson System.
Introduction to Course—Programme.
Stores—Requisition Procedure.
Dismantle tractor into three major components.
Dismantle engine—using Special Tools.
Lecture on engine components.
Build engine. Valve and ignition timing.
Strip Gearbox—using Special Tools.
Lecture on clutch, steering and gearbox.
Build gearbox, assemble clutch to engine and gearbox.
Lecture on Hydraulic System.
Dismantle and re-assemble Hydraulic Pump and Ram
    Cylinder.

Dismantle Rear Axle and Brakes. Lecture.
Re-build and complete tractor.

SECOND WEEK

Lecture on Fuel System. Carburettors, Governor.
Running adjustments—carburettor, governor, brakes.
Practical Fault Finding.
Lecture on Electrical System.
Practical Fault Finding—using Test Equipment.
Films.
Factory Visits.
Service Policy and Procedure.

15

This 23 page brochure on The Ferguson School of Farm Mechanisation describes in some detail the activities of the Stoneleigh Abbey School in Kenilworth, Warwickshire. Reproduced here is P. 15 which outlines the elements of one of the courses

Now Better Than Ever!

Dearborn HYDRAULICALLY CONTROLLED IMPLEMENTS FOR FASTER FARMING

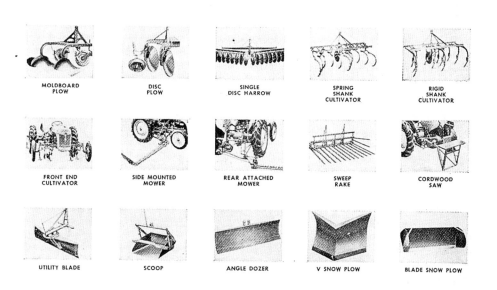

MOLDBOARD PLOW — DISC PLOW — SINGLE DISC HARROW — SPRING SHANK CULTIVATOR — RIGID SHANK CULTIVATOR

FRONT END CULTIVATOR — SIDE MOUNTED MOWER — REAR ATTACHED MOWER — SWEEP RAKE — CORDWOOD SAW

UTILITY BLADE — SCOOP — ANGLE DOZER — V SNOW PLOW — BLADE SNOW PLOW

The production by Ford of the 8N tractor, so similar to the Ford Ferguson and Ferguson tractors, was the cause of the acrimonious lawsuit between Ford and Ferguson

A selection of South African Ferguson literature. Note that Ferguson Industrial Equipment was marketed by a separate company "Industrial Mechanisation". (Courtesy of Rob North)

COPYRIGHT 1946, HARRY FERGUSON, INC., DETROIT, MICH.

Vol. 5   No. 3

Nine Boushee Families Own 24 Ford Tractors Ferguson System

As Ralph Boushee of Emerado, N. Dak., increases his farming operations he keeps on using more Ford Tractors Ferguson System. Mr Boushee now farms 2,800 acres with five of these units. His first one was purchased in 1941.

Mr. Boushee's 1946 crop plan included 1,100 acres of potatoes and 1,500 acres of grain. Although using a number of hired men, his 11-year-old twin sons are his most dependable tractor operators, Mr. Boushee says.

Ralph Boushee is one of nine Boushee families farming in the Emerado and Grand Forks area. All are enthusiastic Ford Tractor Ferguson System users, owning between them a total of 24.

Ferguson System Takes Over from Oxen in Hill Country

Della C. Steele's business has hit rock bottom.

Since 1905 Mr. Steele, who lives near Russellville, Ohio, has trained oxen for farm work in the hilly, rocky land of the area.

"For years," says the 57-year-old trainer, "oxen handled the hill plowing around here. But introduction of the Ford Tractor Ferguson System proved that oxen no longer are needed. Those tractors plow around the hills and in rocky land about nine times faster, so you see what has happened to my business!

"The Ford Tractor Ferguson System is the only tractor outfit I ever saw that keeps the front end right down to the ground when plowing uphill," said Mr. Steele. From now on, his only training work with oxen will be for showing at fairs and similar exhibitions.

TEXAS' GOVERNOR STEVENSON IS "COKE STEVENSON, RANCHER" WHEN OFFICIAL DUTIES PERMIT

Governor Coke R. Stevenson, native of Junction, Texas, and now serving his second term as Governor of the State of Texas, is the owner of approximately 14,000 acres of ranch land located 18 miles west of Junction. The ranch is devoted mainly to sheep and goat raising.

Gov. Stevenson farms approximately 130 acres of tillable land which is planted in corn and small grain. Most of this land is under irrigation from a near-by river. The tillable land is very heavy black loam with a generous proportion of flint rock. The Ford Tractor Ferguson System recently purchased by the Governor is used to farm this 130 acres, in addition to operating a feed grinder and doing various other work about the ranch.

11-Year-Old Replaces 5 Men

Eleven-year-old Robert Fisher of Medford, Oregon, is a busy man at haying time on his father's ranch. With the Ford Tractor Ferguson System and Sweep Rake, Bob is doing the work formerly done by five men, three teams of horses and three wagons in bringing in windrowed hay from the field to the barn.

CHAPTER 12

Ferguson Employees' Experiences

The authors had the privilage of making contact with fourteen people who were prepared to make the considerable effort of recalling their round the world experiences with the Ferguson Organisation. All have written in their own hand, and we owe them a great debt of gratitude.

Ferguson Employees' Experiences

The idea for this chapter really came from a letter which Nigel Liney had originally sent to John Moffitt about his recollections of demonstrating the side mounted combine. The recall of his experiences was felt to be so vivid that the authors decided to try and track down people from around the world who had worked with the Ferguson company and its agents, or who had had very close connections with the Ferguson era.

In the end, the authors have had the privilege to make contact with fourteen such people who had interesting events to recall, frequently accompanied by some treasured photographs. Here we recount their stories from around the world in the order that they were received.

Prototype Combine Tester and Demonstrator, Prototype LTX Tractor Tester

Nigel Liney was involved with the testing of both the prototype side mounted Ferguson combines and the LTX tractor which was planned as a successor to the TE and TO tractor series. Nigel writes:

The Combines

I was in digs in Coventry when I started work with Harry Ferguson in 1950 and later that year a colleague, Michael Blom joined me. It was he who purchased a toy plastic Ferguson tractor and modelled the combine round it, setting it in a model field of grain to give it authenticity. The whole thing looked realistic and on a Thursday, when Harry visited the office, he showed it to him. From this he was told to go ahead and make it.

I was involved in the field testing of the machine and later in demonstrating around the country, ending north of Aberdeen to assess the reaction of farmers. The combine performed well. Our main critics came from the main combine people in those days, Massey Harris. They said you cannot see the cutter bar, but this never gave us a problem. When using a conventional machine you cannot see the knife, only the crop, which if it is blocked could be seen by its hesitation.

Setting off from Fletchampstead for demonstrations in northern England and Scotland. In the lorry cab is the driver Alan Hunt and Nigel Liney is driving the Standard Vanguard pick up

The main problem with the machine was overheating of the tractor engine due to dust blocking the radiator core. The meat safe over the front was not good enough. Dust out of the cylinder cover was a problem as the driver's head was on the same level. You had to stand when driving. The reel drive gave problems if you hooked a low branch, as it had no slip clutch. The result was a broken reel drive gearbox. However a visit to the nearest cycle shop produced the answer as we used Sturmy Archer three speed boxes. The re-thresher was a new idea but could give problems if stones entered, as the pegs at the end of the auger broke off. We used to demonstrate the mounting and dismounting of the machine, which could be done in fifteen minutes to remove and twenty minutes to fit it back again.

Many of the systems used in the machine were incorporated into the MF machines, such as the main crop elevator beaters fitted to the MF 760, the re-thresher on the MF 760 and 4/500 machine. The open augers on the tables fitted to the combines were made in Eschwege in Germany, and France. The opposed action of the grain pan and shaker shoe was universally used on all MF machines. When we tested these machines, the Massey Harris 730 combine fitted with the Austin A40 engine was being evaluated at the same time, the result being a decision taken not to produce the Ferguson.

France sent over their version of the

mounted combine, but this was a very different machine as they cut the tractor in half. The driver sat on the rear half of the tractor, at the front of the combine, while the engine was fitted crosswise at the rear. This of course defeated the whole object of an easily removed tractor and although we had one in Coventry it was sent back to France and we heard nothing more of it.

ABOVE RIGHT A demonstration in Scotland with Alan Hunt driving and Arnold Shepherd on the bagger unit

ABOVE Relaxing between spells of demonstrating. Nigel Liney left and Arnold Shepherd on the right. The low ratio gearbox is clearly visible. The tractor appears to be a British built TE type Ferguson

Many of the problems were probably overcome in later machines, as I remember numbers ten and eleven being produced.

The man who was on the bagging platform could have quite a problem if he was not fast enough in fitting a new bag as the grain could spill over if not done quickly. However the three spout bagger overcame this and later the tanker model made life easier.

ABOVE On test in the Cotswolds. The driver of the US built TO tractor is R Dowdswell and there is a French engineer on the bagging unit

ABOVE A tanker type version of the combine on test in the Cotswolds. The tractor is clearly a US built TO type and does not appear to be fitted with a low ratio gearbox

The LTX (Large Tractor Experimental)

In 1950 the first of the LTX range was built with an in house make 50-60 hp petrol engine. This unit was fitted with a three furrow plough and driven out of the workshop and into the field we used for basic tests and demonstrations for visiting export customers by Harry himself. After his short test and appraisal he gave the go-ahead for it to be tested for 1,000 hrs non stop ploughing/cultivating. This meant we worked it night and day in shifts on some of the heaviest ground in Warwickshire, no matter what the weather and no cabs in those days.

The first time we had it in the field the wheel grip was such that it pulled the treads off the tyres we were using. This was not through wheelslip but simply was caused by the extra grip supplied by the new hydraulic system on the tractor. Once new tyres were fitted of a different make, testing carried on. After 1,000 hrs the LTX was taken back to engineering, stripped, nothing found to be wrong and put back to work again.

While testing it was found that the front end was light as it needed double front weights to keep it down. Also the power was not enough for its capabilities, so the next version being worked on with a totally new type of 70 hp diesel engine, and designed in house by a talented Polish gentleman named Sekowski and Bill Harrow, was increased in length by nine inches. This machine was then put through its paces and proved to be unbeatable. (The intention was to increase the hp in stages up to 100 hp.

Modifications such as to the steering had to be made, as one had to keep your thumbs out of the wheel while discing or risk injury! I asked the designer to try himself with a warning. Unfortunately he hung onto the wheel and was considerably shaken when he found himself on the bonnet facing backwards. The steering was soon changed after this.

Many times the LTX proved itself superior and the opposition used to watch us from afar with field glasses. There was an instance where one of our people was ploughing with a four furrow plough in a field where a TE 20 with a winch had bogged down near a pond. The winch rope had been left out in the field and the driver of the LTX did not notice. The rope fouled the last furrow, but the driver did not notice until he reached the headland, where he found the bogged tractor had been pulled out and was following the LTX!

Ploughs of various widths and number of bodies were tested from three furrow deep digger up to five furrow ten, twelve and 14 inch models. Large tillers, discs and trailers were easily handled.

All of us who used this tractor would agree that it was the greatest mistake to shelve the project even after proving to Massey-Harris that the LTX could pull five furrows on heavy ground up hill against anything they could produce, which was very little in those days.

A tragic end to a superb product.

Implement Tester and Demonstrator, and Ceylon's "Mr Tractor"

Peter Warren recalls:

The start of it all

I must confess that before ever driving a Ferguson tractor I had driven a standard Fordson, but later a Ford Ferguson. The transfer to Fergusons was like giving up a rattletrap! I joined Avon Tractors, the Ferguson dealers in the Vale of Evesham, in 1945 and worked for them until the following year when I joined the RAF. Six months later in a turn of fate I was invalided out. I needed work so applied to Ferguson. Being of such ex-serviceman status seemed to help and I soon had an interview at the Ferguson Bottswood offices with Trevor Knox and John Chambers. John Chambers, who was responsible for product engineering, was to become my boss and I was to work a lot with his right hand man, Alex Patterson.

At Avon Tractors I had gained experience of some Ferguson implements and was assigned to the implement testing section of the Ferguson organisation. The experience gained in this role was to serve me well as my career developed, and indeed still now in partial retirement as a consultant to Smallholder tractors, also of Evesham, who use Massey Ferguson backends and other components to make their 45 hp simple design Smallholder tractor for which we have high hopes of considerable overseas exports. Indeed my career progressed through the

Ferguson era to that of both Massey-Harris-Ferguson and Massey Ferguson. After a spell of field testing implements at Ferguson, I moved to their demonstration team, again equally valuable experience.

Ferguson discipline

Harry Ferguson imposed an almost military discipline on his implement testing and demonstration teams whether the tractors and implements were at work, or simply parked up for the night. He was meticulous in the extreme, but the demand for this certainly meant that he created a crisp and precise performance wherever Ferguson equipment was placed on trial or show.

If you were a tester or demonstrator woe betide you if the lynch pins were not fitted back in their retaining clamps after use, and it was a grave offence to move a tractor with the link arms in the lowered position – they always had to be raised. After each day's work tractors had to be washed and dried. For any prolonged period out of work they had to be covered with a Ferguson cover.
Tractors had to be parked in dead straight lines – and I mean dead straight! Perhaps I can emphasise how straight they had to be by the fact that all gear levers had to be seen to be in line and at the rear all the top links had also to appear in line.

Testing and demonstrating

Much of my early work was concerned with evaluating the wear qualities of implement tines, plough shares and mouldboards. Harry Ferguson, when he could, would follow field testers around their sites in his Bentley car. We worked out of the Fletchampstead site generally doing all our testing within a ten mile radius. However for any road tests, usually matters of brake evaluation, we might go as far out as Edge Hill.

Whilst working with ploughs I dropped one on my foot and broke my big toe. It was the best stroke of luck in my life as I was temporarily assigned to office work where I met the girl who was to become my wife - she worked in the statistics section.
I was involved with testing the original trailer hitch, and later

BELOW Some of the ladies of the Fletchampstead offices

its revised design – the pick up hitch - which was to become so popular. The original design was difficult to hitch because of the need to reverse up and against the trailer to engage the coupling. The problem was that usually the trailer brakes were inadequate to hold it against the tractor during the coupling process. Not too many of the first hitch type were sold even though the original idea for hitching two wheel trailers in a manner whereby they transferred considerable weight to the tractor back wheels had been evolved during Ford Ferguson days in the USA. The real breakthrough in this concept came with the revised design whereby the lower links actually lifted the trailer into a locked transport position. Road testing with the original three ton trailer and hitch was often with a full load.

only part discharged load back to Fletchampstead to pick up a fork. Sleeping policemen (speed humps) were a feature of the compound even in those long off days. Luck would have it that at some speed Jimmy hit one of these and the jolt jumped the spreader into gear, cleared the offending brick and much of the load discharged on the tarmac beneath the Ferguson directors' canteen! It was a weakness of the Ferguson spreaders that the control lever was prone to slip and engage gear when not required.

On another occasion we were demonstrating loaders and spreaders at an NFU sponsored demonstration in Scotland. We had fitted it in with a series of countrywide muck spreading demonstrations. Many other manufacturers were present and

Full load was achieved by hand loading 120 56lb steel weights on to the trailer platform! When we knew that this would be the first job of the next day it was always a challenge to be last to arrive at work in order to avoid loading duty.

I was also involved with much testing of the manure loaders, potato spinners and ploughs. We had many laughs on the muck loader and muck spreader evaluations. I must place it on record that I found the "Banana" loader something of a dinosaur of an implement to use – so cramped in the "cockpit", and two levers, an accelerator and gear lever all to be handled! However I liked the first loader – the L-UE-20 which was mounted on the front axle. When loading in the old farmyards there was always a risk of picking up a brick and these sometimes jammed the spreader beater bars. On one occasion this fate befell fellow demonstrator Jimmy Edwards who hadn't brought a muck fork out with him as we normally did. So he had to drive the

THIS PAGE Muck spreader and loader testing where we had to watch for the bricks!

I was seriously concerned about how I could make the Ferguson loader-spreader combination stand out from the crowd. Fortunately I was struck by a rare stroke of genius and decided to perform the whole event in a crisp pressed black suit and sparklingly polished black shoes. The reasoning was that only with the Ferguson rig was it possible to undertake the whole operation repeatedly without ever dismounting from the tractor seat – thanks of course to the pick up hitch. Indeed we did make our mark on the event.

One final story on the muck spreaders. I was called out to a dealer area where a particular batch of spreaders were not performing well at all. They were skidding and there was insufficient power being generated from the land drive wheels. I got everyone out of sight and reversed the tyres – they had been fitted the wrong way round! They performed well after this and I was asked what they had needed. "Just a small adjustment" was my response.

Harry Ferguson would issue "challenges" to other manufacturers. This was aimed at getting the opposition out in the open to prove that his Ferguson System was better than any of their products. Of course no other manufacturer had such a range of matched implements that could remotely compete with Ferguson System efficiency and none of the big manufacturers such as Ford or David Brown would respond to the challenges. However one company that did respond occasionally was the BMB company which made the small President tractor up in Lancashire. They felt that the sheer exposure to Ferguson and resultant publicity would be good for them!

For a very short period of time I was involved with the development of the prototype LTX 60 tractor. Unfortunately this was dropped and gave way to the 65 tractor. My memories of it are few, but it was a powerful and well-balanced tractor which would pull the tread off its 4 ply rear tyres when working on heavy clay.

Yes Prime Minister

Mr Winston Churchill used Ferguson equipment on his Chartwell estate. He requested that Fergusons come and clear quite an extensive area of heavy scrub around the perimeter of his fields. At Ferguson we felt there was an opportunity for some good publicity – especially for the Ferguson winch. But it was not to be. Churchill had not told us that in the scrub were some massive elm and oak tree stumps which had resulted from the felling of trees for the war effort. There was no way a Ferguson winch would tackle these and we had to resort to hand labour using the famous low geared, hand operated "Monkey" which will pull over the Eiffel tower given time. For some we resorted to dynamite! I make no apologies for showing here one of the most widely used photos from Ferguson archives – that of Mr Churchill on this occasion. The picture shows me using the tiller to clear out brambles, Mr Churchill, Captain Soames and Mr Eden, and of course Mr Churchill's poodle Rufie II. In the event Mr Churchill only allowed this one photo to be taken of the operation and this is it! The whole operation took three months and included the pulling out of barbed wire security fences that had protected the great man. The work came to involve the use of a subsoiler, winch, tiller and plough.

TOP The winch clutch could on occasions stick on – the strict advice was that one always had to be seated with foot ready to depress the main tractor clutch

MIDDLE Hand winching when the Ferguson couldn't!

BOTTOM That single, much used photo

Training

Whilst at Ferguson, I also had the good fortune to be involved in the start up of Ferguson training facilities. The world famous training school was first established at Packington Hall and then moved to Stoneleigh Abbey and thence on to Stareton.

Photo calls

Good fortune has decreed that I will go down in posterity in the Ferguson literature archives. I feature heavily in the very practical Ferguson

Mouldboard plough manual (the more or less A4 size booklet). We had great fun getting together the pictures of perfect ploughing. I am also featured in some of the colourful Ferguson implement advertising literature. Perhaps my favourite is the one entitled "Ferguson Pays Hands Down On Any Size of Farm" in which is seen a hand supporting a Ferguson tractor – the hand is mine. Another favourite is the "Facts About Farming Ferguson" on which I am the tractor driver.

Overseas calling

One morning I was called to the office of Trevor Knox to be advised that there was a problem with Ferguson distribution in Ceylon! I went out on a supposedly short assignment and ended up staying for ten years. During this time I held a variety of positions for distributors Brown and Co. ultimately ending up as General Manager of their agricultural division. We ended up selling 5,000 tractors in ten years, the grey Fergusons proving ideal for small rice paddy fields and benefiting from the failure of heavier less manoeuvrable tractors such as Fordson Majors and tricycle type Farmalls.

I set up a training school there exactly on the lines prescribed by Harry Ferguson. The main principles adopted were:

- Before anyone could purchase a tractor the driver had to be trained for four days.
- No warranty would be issued for the tractor without a trained driver.
- Any new driver had to be trained or the warranty would become invalid.
- 12 months service was built in to the price of the tractor, the customer only having to pay for oil without which the warranty was invalidated.

I also introduced for the first time HP financing to Sinhalese farmers which was taken up with enthusiasm as it helped them in their tax manoeuvres with the government of the day!

Using the meticulous presentational discipline I had gained from working with Ferguson in the UK, an important part of my work was the establishment of well planned showrooms for Brown and Co. and their dealers, and also the staging of prestigious demonstrations around the whole of Ceylon.

My period in Ceylon saw the introduction of the Ferguson 35 grey/gold tractor for which I have not too much respect! - then the red 35s and 65s. The first 65s went in to sugar cane estates.

Brown and Co. were also the Standard Motor car distributors and through this I became involved with the Ceylon Monsoon Rally. I regularly drove a Standard Triumph with my wife as navigator. It was in this role that the newspaper reports came to identify me as Mr Tractor!

Recollections of Harry Ferguson

OPPOSITE TOP LEFT Some early trainees at Stoneleigh Abbey. Here are a group of lady students from Studley college. Dick Chambers in the front row and Peter Warren at the rear left

OPPOSITE TOP RIGHT Peter Warren in the ploughing manual.

OPPOSITE BOTTOM Early days in Ceylon with a Massey-Harris tractor alongside a Ferguson

BELOW Brown and Co. main showroom

BOTTOM LEFT Time off for Peter "Mr Tractor" Warren in the Monsoon rally

BOTTOM RIGHT Despite the failings of the grey-gold Ferguson 35, a challenge cup for the best demonstrator team could still be won

ABOVE LEFT Introducing the grey-gold 35 in the Massey-Harris-Ferguson era

BELOW A specially designed trade stand for the Kurunegla dealer

ABOVE RIGHT Public display advertising was frowned upon in Ceylon, but this was overcome by Brown and Co. providing free road signposts with additional Ferguson information!

Continuing success into the MF era

ABOVE Changeover era – A Ferguson 20 and Ferguson 35 jointly displayed

BELOW The first MF 65 tractors on the island went to the sugar cane estates

OPPOSITE MIDDLE RIGHT The Sinhalese municipalities were good customers for tractors and trailers adapted for refuse collection

OPPOSITE BOTTOM Peter Warren demonstrating between the coconut palms

RIGHT The Sinhalese Minister of Agriculture receiving a tractor from Peter Warren and donated under a British Aid scheme at Galle Face Green

BELOW Early success

Sir Jeremy Chance, Bt. writes:

Those who remember seeing him demonstrating his tractors will agree that among his many talents Harry Ferguson was a consummate showman. Typical was the occasion in 1948 when he drove a TE 20 tractor into and out of Claridges Hotel in London for a press conference. And in 1953 when, so it is said, he suggested the toss of a coin to settle a difference of $1 million in negotiations with Massey-Harris – a toss that he lost.

My first sight and recollection of Harry Ferguson was in the grounds of Stoneleigh Abbey, near Coventry, where he demon-strated the ability of the TE 20 with mounted implements to operate in small fields and awkward corners, in this instance a roped off square of ground. The occasion, in the summer of 1948, was a visit by the Oxford University Plough Club of which I was an undergraduate member. Over lunch he used his model tractor to show how, if the mounted plough were to hit an obstruction, damage was avoided by the hydraulic release valve causing loss of traction and the tractor to stop instantly. He also spoke to us of his crusade to reduce the cost of food production and prices by means of more efficient mechanisation – his Price Reducing Campaign.

It was chiefly this visit to Stoneleigh and the Banner Lane factory and the cause that Mr Ferguson espoused that encouraged me to apply for and accept two years later a traineeship with the Company. So I was back at Stoneleigh for my basic practical training at the former riding school there and in the nearby Deer Park. (It was later that the Training School was moved from the Abbey to be established and expanded in the former Deer Park army camp.)

Also on this Stoneleigh course was Harry Ferguson's daughter Elizabeth. It was she, by that time Mrs Anthony (Tony) Sheldon, who, some twenty-five years later, did the honours at the School's quarter century celebrations, I being in charge of it at that time.

Harry Ferguson was a great stickler to orderliness. At the Stoneleigh Riding School I remember that after the day's work the tractors and implements had to be washed-down and parked 'dressed by the right' in a straight line. This routine was instilled in us by Dick Chambers, then in charge of the School.

I was sharply reminded of these standards in the following year when one morning I happened to pass the great man in a corridor of the Fletchampstead Highway offices at Coventry. I was dressed in grey flannels and tweed jacket on my way to some outside assignment. I thought he looked at me rather sharply. Soon after I was summoned to the MD's office to be told by him that the Chairman expected his staff to be properly dressed with suit and tie at all times.

The Price Reducing Campaign was very much in evidence during the early 1950s, certainly for those of us who were concerned with the Company's PR and promotion work at that time. My chief and mentor was Noel Newsome who, during the war, had been Foreign Editor of the Daily Telegraph and had broadcast as the 'The Man in the Street' on the BBC world news programme. He, together with Tony Lees, formerly with the 'Farmer & Stock-breeder' magazine, and with Harry Ferguson himself, were the main mouthpieces for the Scheme. Tony Lees wrote the series of papers that set out its aims and rationale.

Mr and Mrs Ferguson were hospitable and caring towards their staff in spite of their relative remoteness from all but the most senior. I remember one summer a garden party at their Abbotts-wood home to which they had invited practically everyone, a possibility when the staff totalled around 450 people.

The amalgamation in 1953 of the Massey-Harris and Ferguson companies revolutionised what, in the case of Ferguson, had been solely a research, development and distribution company – no manufacturing. It was a surprise and puzzle to most of us when so soon afterwards he resigned as Chairman to concentrate on four-wheel drive and transmission systems for the motor industry. His new company, Harry Ferguson Research, later to move to Baginton, near Coventry Airport, had drawing offices and workshops at the rear of the Massey-Harris-Ferguson offices on Fletchampstead Highway. This, in retrospect, was a curious arrangement and caused a good deal of disturbance in the rest of the building until sound-proof partitions were erected.

So, by the mid 1950s, the magnetism and yet quixotic inspira-tion of the Harry Ferguson genius had withdrawn from our work-ing lives. We were vaguely aware of his personal idiosyncrasies which continued to trouble relationships with his associates. We knew that he resisted any change to the colour of his 'little grey Fergies' as the tractor range was developed. It was even suggested that he did not support the development of larger, higher horsepower machines. Yet we learned later that even before the merger with Massey-Harris his engineers were working on an enlarged version of the TE range; and that not long before his death in 1960 at his Abbottswood home there were prototypes of new tractors incorporating torque converter trans-missions.

Bringing the Ferguson System to Japan in 1954

Alexander von Behr ("Sandy Behr") writes:

Setting the scene

The BOAC Argonaut droned on southwards, bound for Rangoon on New Year's Eve of 1953. Our four Rolls Royce Merlin engines, perfected in wartime Spitfires, howled like banshee concrete mixers through the four hour flight from Calcutta. In the first-class lounge at the extreme rear of the plane (as far as possible from those deafening Merlins) BOAC stewards were opening bottles of Veuve Clicquot champagne, orange labels glinting unmistakably, so that half a dozen of us could drink in the New Year at 17,000 feet. All Harry Ferguson's young gentle-men flew first-class in those distant days. Without perceptible embarrassment, everyone joined hands, and we sang Auld Lang Syne around the central table. Although I could not have suspected the outcome at that moment, it was a fitting way for me to start an uninterrupted series of HF, MHF, and MF jobs, across the South of Asia: taking me from Japan to Singapore, thence to India for five years, and back to Singapore. That proc-ess would only end, in November of 1965, when I returned to Coventry, with a young wife and two little boys, as an unwilling, unqualified and sorely underpaid General Marketing Planning Manager for Massey-Ferguson Export Ltd. In retrospect, it was not surprising that the considerable professional success I had accumulated during the eleven years prior to 1965 suffered frustration and near-reversal during the lingering aftermath of Harry Ferguson's traumatic sell-out to Massey-Harris, from which so much had been expected by so many people.

Back to my tale. On 13 July, 1953, six months before that night flight to Rangoon, Paul Spencer, HF Export Sales Manager, a man of discernment, energy and decision, had called me into his office. "I want you to go out to Japan, Sandy, and open up the market there for us," he said, with his usual crispness. I managed somehow to remain on my feet, upper lip stiffening. The horrors and atrocities of the war with Japan were fresh in everyone's memory. Was I to be pitted against these terrifying little demons, so shortly after joining Harry Ferguson Ltd. in October of the previous year? Common sense prevailed, and I pulled myself together. With a shaky air of confidence I assured Paul that this was a marvellous idea, and that I was eager to get on my way. After all, I was fully armed with the practical techniques and the martial philosophies I had acquired during nine months of strenuous training at Ferguson's world famous Training Centre, in Stoneleigh Abbey. I could talk for hours about the benefits of the Ferguson System, and I could demonstrate them with every machine that carried the Ferguson name. I could take each piece of equipment apart, repair the faults, and put everything together again, as was to be necessary several times in the near future. I had been sworn in as one of Harry Ferguson's giant-killers, and it was up to me to show some gratitude for this dramatic chance to win my spurs in battle. The logic seemed excellent - but it didn't silence the alarm bell that continued ringing until I finally understood, a year later, the true extent of Japanese warmth and friendship.

There followed several more months of specific training and intensive field experience in Europe, including a one-man visit to represent HF on the wrong side of the Iron Curtain, at the September 1953 Leipzig Fair – a story in itself. My departure to Japan was frequently postponed because of the complications resulting from the dramatic merger with Massey-Harris, and the difficulties the new, combined management faced in deciding whether or when to merge the two competitive machinery lines, with their valuable but conflicting brand names. Although Massey-Harris was already active in Japan, there seemed to be no reason why the Ferguson System should not be swiftly introduced there in parallel, as an independent venture. By September of 1953, a date for my departure had been set, and my two TEF 20 diesel tractors, with 26 implements and a packing case full of carefully chosen spare parts, began to show up in the Export Company tractor and implement Programming Schedules: moving closer each week to the Banner Lane assembly lines and the docks.

Christmas festivities had ended for me with my departure, on 27th December, 1953, for Heathrow and the Far East. The first leg of the journey was by BEA Elizabethan to Paris (just time, between take-off and landing, for a splendid lobster lunch) to spend a couple of days meeting the formidably cosmopolitan John Beith from the Massey-Harris side, and the Bouillant-Linet family: Papa and two extremely active sons, who jointly owned and ran the Ferguson distributorship for France, and who masterminded a wild welcoming party for me at The Lido.

Then on to Rangoon, Hong Kong and Manila, with new friends to welcome me at every stop. That safari was to end in Japan, where I would spend the next eighteen months in unsupervised isolation: apart from a brief visit by a Canadian superior from Massey-Harris, whose rigid addiction to a diet of steak and coffee disconcerted our Japanese hosts. My calling cards, engraved in copper-plate, on the instructions of the management, assured me that I was now Far Eastern Representative, Harry Ferguson Export Ltd, of no fixed abode. In a couple of hours time we would start our slow descent towards Burma, for my first commercial mission. I tried to settle down for some much needed sleep; wondering already how I was to tackle my Rangoon objective, and hoping that nobody would penetrate my new and rather patchy disguise.

Rangoon

Far below, the tiny lights of jungle fires sparkled and winked up at us from the Akyab peninsula, as we began our slow letdown to Rangoon airport. Although I had slept at the KLM Hotel in Karachi during a programmed BOAC stopover, and I had stretched my legs on the tarmac at Calcutta, those wintry halts were insufficient preparation for the steamy odours and the wet heat of Burma at two o'clock in the morning. Ken Kwoh, my target for the day, had come to meet me, and we began to talk about the growing success of the grey Ferguson tractors in Burma; for Ken ran the national Ferguson Distributorship. But the real objective of my visit, after a shower, a brief sleep, and a large English breakfast, would be to settle down and try to figure out a way of using Ken's contacts in mainland China to sell Ferguson tractors there in the sort of quantities which could have a measurable effect on the largest agricultural country in the world.

Ken and his partner, C. F. Tao, were excellent hosts, and we spent several hours reaching common ground, as a basis for launching an attempt at a joint commercial initiative into the mainland. I duly reported my findings back to Coventry headquarters, but I never heard whether my diplomacy bore any commercial fruit, and I suspect these events were overtaken by Paul Spencer's single-handed personal success in obtaining an order from the Chinese government for several hundred tractors and implements, worth £1.5 million, later in the year. Paul Spencer, retired and still hale at 87, told me over the 'phone in February, 1998, that the tractors were shipped to Tainan Island, and were paid for by means of a large barter deal.

Interlude in the Philippines

In order to see something of the Massey-Harris view of life, before plunging into unknown Japan, I spent a week in the Philippines: studying and trying out a wide range of Massey-Harris machines, in the sweltering rice fields, with Jimmy Chan and John Sylvester, the two Canadians who were the cops on the M-H Far East beat. So far, the Ferguson crusade had not reached Manila, although I was to catch up with it during my second tour of residence (in Singapore) ten years later. Massey-Harris affairs in the Philippines were entirely controlled by a large and highly intelligent Filipino of 100% Chinese extraction, John Sycip, who owned and managed a big general engineering business at his large premises, including a Massey-Harris distributorship. It seemed to me that he controlled my two new friends pretty closely, as well. The nature of Big John's relations with officialdom, and with potential customers, demanded delicate co-ordination of effort and reward. This was my first practical lesson in Eastern commercial diplomacy.

Landfall Japan

The lush atmosphere of the Philippines, tropical, menacing and extremely hot, was in profound contrast with the icy, snow-bound, concrete jungle of Tokyo. As I found out, nothing could be more striking than the behavioural contrasts between the Japanese and the Filipino neighbours: who still despised, without knowledge or question, their former enemies and occupiers. My passage through the inward formalities at Haneda airport in Yokohama, ten miles south of Tokyo, was noisy and somehow threatening. Finally I pushed through the arrival doors in the wake of a heavily loaded porter, looking for help. To my relief and delight, three small Japanese men, wrapped in identical dark blue overcoats and woollen mufflers, welcomed me with deep bows, and introduced themselves as the senior echelon of Machinery Section B, led by Ueyenishi Masao: which would be responsible, within Tozai Koeki Kaisha (eventually to become the leading element in a reconstituted Mitsubishi Ltd) for importing and distributing Ferguson tractors and implements in Japan. Little did I suspect, at that deeply remembered moment, how much I would grow to like and respect them all: especially Fujii Yukichi, who spoke good English and was to be my "Minder" until maybe, one day, I might be able to move about alone. In fact, I reached that stage of familiarity with language and customs in six months, and began to enjoy travelling about by myself.

Dinner in Tokyo

I was to learn subsequently that it is even more important in Japan than elsewhere to start any kind of social gathering with a measure of alcohol, in order to dispel as quickly as possible those severe national inhibitions which might otherwise impair communication, and which are shared to some extent by Anglo-Saxons. I also learnt that the interval between formal medication and informal oblivion in Japan could sometimes be surprisingly short. I soon realised that my three new friends were determined to get to know me as quickly as possible. Thirty minutes after our arrival at the Nikkatsu Hotel we found ourselves in the impressive hotel restaurant each studying a large menu intently. To my consternation, each of my three hosts slowly chose exactly the same menu as I did, starting (unwisely in their cases) with a lethal Dry Martini cocktail: causing immediately the embarrassing redness of complexion with which strong alcohol afflicts almost all Orientals.

The details of our first discussions around that table are lost in the sands of memory, apart from one question which I shall never forget. Towards the end of the meal, Fujii San, who must have known already that he would have to spend many months shepherding me around Japan, yielded to an unbearable curiosity, (stimulated no doubt by cocktail and subsequent beer) and asked me very seriously "Please most kindly inform me, Mr Behr, are other representatives from your esteemed company as large and as young as you are?". This earnest enquiry, enunciated with great care, silenced all conversation while I searched desperately for a suitable reply.

I already knew, from my preparatory briefings, that grey hairs and lengthy experience are rightly revered in Japan. These three executives, and especially Ueyenishi San, the Section Manager, would be depending on me, alone, for all the specialised advice that they would need in order to achieve the demanding business objectives imposed on them from on high: namely, to secure country-wide success for the Ferguson System, or face disgrace. They had been reared from earliest childhood in a culture in which it was the entirely honourable custom to reward failure with death: frequently self-inflicted, as a parting mark of esteem. Who, after all, was this clumsy 27-year-old Gaijin barbarian, an inelegant 6' 3" tall, and unpleasantly pink of skin, on whom they must now depend for their professional success? Furthermore, the Lord High Executioner would undoubtedly require a personal report in his large office the following

morning. I sensed all this, and somehow managed to string together a number of platitudes which might have the effect of saving everyone's face. It seemed to me that my companions heaved profound sighs of relief when I explained that Harry Ferguson Ltd was actually managed and staffed by a large team of elderly dwarfs, amongst whom I was the glaring exception, except in the matter of my extraordinary familiarity with Ferguson equipment, shared by all. I discovered long afterwards, when Fujii's question had become a fondly remembered joke, that I had indeed succeeded in dispelling their very reasonable doubts.

It was only some three years later that I finally saw a copy of the letter Paul Spencer had sent to Tokyo in 1953, giving our newly appointed distributor the glad news that "one of our most experienced and competent Representatives will accompany the tractors and implements you have purchased and will stay with you for as long as is necessary to establish the Ferguson System in Japan". In point of hard fact, I was perhaps the least qualified amongst my HF contemporaries to carry out those demanding duties. But most fortunately I didn't know it: and neither did the Japanese, although my comparative youthfulness had aroused their prudent suspicions.

The Japan Job

Tanabe Bunichiro the Managing Director of TKK, who welcomed me with a little speech, became a good friend and eventually rose to be the President of Mitsubishi, in 1976. I remember especially Tanaka Tetsuo, whose skilful commercial diplomacy, fanned by Paul Spencer, had resulted in an Agreement for the importation and subsequent distribution of HF equipment in Japan and Okinawa, through Tokyu Motors, the Standard Motor Company Distributor. I looked at Tanaka San with some interest, for he had a fierce and cunning appearance, and had spent some years in prison for war crimes committed while a senior officer in the army. He became a good and reliable friend, nevertheless, and was always extremely kind to me, providing excellent advice when really tough problems occasionally arose. We agreed that a long process of field demonstrations would be necessary in order to convince the all-powerful agricultural co-operatives, and the various arms of the Ministry of Agriculture, that our small tractors were indeed suitable in every way for farming in Japan. This decision had the happy result of taking me and my equipment from one end of rural Japan to the other: a privilege extended to few foreigners. In those distant days I had the opportunity to recreate for myself many of the simple pleasures of Samurai life: without the bloodshed, and all at Massey-Harris-Ferguson's expense.

What about the Tractors?

The best news waiting for me on arrival at my new and comfortable office in the Old Mitsubishi Building, not far from General

LEFT In the city centre snow, a dignified entrance to the demonstration area by Sandy Behr on a TEF 20

BOTTOM LEFT Arranging a demonstration in Sapporo city centre, Hokkaido in April 1954. Sandy Behr making final adjustments to a two furrow plough

BOTTOM RIGHT Showing off a Multi Purpose seed drill in snow in Sapporo city centre

MacArthur's former Headquarters and the Imperial Palace, was that the two TEF 20 diesel tractors, with 26 implements, had just arrived at Yokohama, and would soon be cleared through Customs: a process which has always been excessively complicated in Japan; hampered efficiently by the grim intentions of a Trade Ministry determined to protect local industry, whatever the product you're trying to clear. Not for nothing were TKK designated as "importers". In those days, only the largest companies, staffed by experts in the Byzantine intricacies of goods clearance, could hope to defeat the Japanese Customs within a reasonable period of time. It was to general surprise and delight, therefore, that the first consignment was opened up, under the roof of Tokyo Motors' workshop at Setegaya, as soon as 21st January, and we quickly had the four wheels safely attached to the first unit.

The assembly job was protracted by the necessity for me to explain every step, and many technical digressions, to Fujii San; who had to take notes for a new English vocabulary, and then translate everything for the future benefit of the mechanics who were helping me. Fortunately a charming and gifted Japanese, Oyama, had already arrived at Ferguson's Education Centre, in Warwickshire, and would receive a thorough training there before returning to Japan, to share my duties. It was necessary to protect Oyama San eventually from the dangers of excessive specialisation, for he could not afford to waste his lifetime career progression, within the global Mitsubishi organisation, concentrating on tractors or putting his expensive training to its intended use for the rest of his life. And indeed, the whole complement of "Ferguson" Managers and technicians revolved in this way every 2-3 years: moving all over the world in accordance with the peremptory demands of succession within the Mitsubishi Corporation.

Putting our Equipment to Work

By Saturday afternoon, 23rd January, 1954, and to my enormous relief as midwife and mechanic, both tractors were running sweetly. We could begin to think about operator courses, and the all-important first major demonstration to the great and the good of the Japanese agricultural establishment, at Zama, under the lee of Mount Fujii, about 40 miles south-west of Tokyo. But by now, snow had fallen in record quantities all over Honshu, the Japanese mainland, and so all we could do was to plan theoretically for the time when the weather, and the condition of the soil, would allow us to start in earnest the work for which I had come all this way.

The logistical problems were often bizarre. We discovered one day that the Ferguson patents might be rendered void if we did not take urgent action to publish them anew, after the arrival of the tractors, so I was plunged into protracted legal discussions. It was extremely difficult to discover a suitable diesel-engine lubricating oil without voiding the engine guarantees given by the Standard Motor Company. In those distant days there was

ABOVE The first big Ferguson demonstration event was at Zama near Tokyo in February 1954. Here Sandy Behr shows off the manoeuvrability and adjustments of a Spike Tooth Harrow

LEFT Well in advance of the seasons, Sandy Behr demonstrates a Ferguson mower in February 1954 at Zama near Tokyo

no Japanese motor car industry, and it was therefore difficult indeed to get any of the day-to-day bits and pieces which are always needed in order to make good shipment shortages. I had been unwisely discouraged from bringing any tools with me, because of a misguided belief that "that kind of thing is bound to be available once you get there". We had great difficulty in locating and connecting up a diesel-pump test bench, although Nissan and Daihatsu diesel trucks were in use by then. However, all these problems were overcome, and I had the very real pleasure, on 28th January, of watching my newly trained drivers putting the tractors through their paces in the yard at Setagaya. It only remained to assemble the many implements that had accompanied the tractors, give everything a lick of paint, and get ready for field training at Zama, once the weather improved. It was critically important to get hours on the tractors and on their new drivers. We worked long and hard in the winter sunshine, and my first task on reaching our practice fields each morning was to stick a dozen bottles of good Sapporo beer in the snow on the north side of a suitable hedge.

Another three weeks were to pass before we could put on the all-important demonstration to the Japanese Ministerial representatives, who would be our adoption customers. Their general approval, formalised by a few token purchases for government agricultural stations, would have to be obtained before we could reasonably expect to make any commercial sales to suspicious farmers in the Northern Island of Hokkaido, where it was believed that our real market would be discovered. Those three weeks bought me the time I would need to train the nucleus of a Japanese technical team; to start learning Japanese intensively, and to assimilate all the Japanese customs which would eventually enable me to allay the suspicions voiced at that first dinner at the Nikkatsu Hotel. I also practised my own equipment handling skills, as I had decided that I must astonish our prospective customers with a demonstration of the fastest possible exchange, and field operation, of at least a dozen implements. All these objectives were accomplished on schedule, and successive groups of expert onlookers were suitably amazed at the rapidity with which Harry Ferguson's beautifully engineered implements could be exchanged with each other.

Such was the dedication and energy of the Mitsubishi men that we very seldom encountered difficulties. I insisted on continuous "fail-safe' preventive maintenance for the two tractors, with frequent oil changes, as a result of which we never suffered a breakdown, or a breakage in operation. My chief problem was to act also as an impartial company Representative for the Massey-Harris franchise, a double act that puzzled both distribution teams sorely, as I switched disguises from time to time to disappear and attend to the needs of an obvious competitor. Massey-Harris had been established in Japan well before Ferguson, and there was a growing population of tractors: chiefly versions of the M-H Pony. The M-H Distributor felt, with some justice, that I was an upstart enemy, and I had to muster hitherto unsuspected reserves of diplomatic skill to carry out this strange head-office assignment: ensuring especially that confidential buying contacts were not 'betrayed to the other side'. The existence of such an insane regime in the field (it had not been sorted out by the time I left Japan) was yet another indication of the problems

ABOVE Sandy Behr in May 1955 with his faithful "minder" Fuji Yukichi appreciating the turnover mechanism of a single furrow reversible plough

BELOW February 1954 in Zama again sees Sandy Behr with a three disc plough demonstrating to Japanese government crop experts

ABOVE This Paddy Puddler was made by Harry Ferguson's Indian operation and exported to Japan. Here it is seen in Hoyshu in May 1955

created by a merger that had been settled by the toss of a coin.

Apart from trips to explore sales opportunities in South Korea and Taiwan, I remained uninterruptedly in Japan until April of 1955, by which time I could hand over a small but promising business, staffed by well-trained mechanics and operators, to my good friend Kato San, the Managing Director of Tokyu Motors, the Main Dealer for Japan. I sailed south to my new HQ in Singapore, and the rest of the Far East was added to Japan, South Korea and Taiwan to give me a far larger beat, though I was still single-handed at the time I left for India, at the end of 1955.

Over the ensuing years, Japan became an important market for M-F equipment of all kinds, and tractor sales once or twice approached 3,000 units a year. As with so many other products pioneered in the West, farm tractors were eventually manufactured in Japan and MF sales dwindled. One of my last missions, as a director of the world-wide MF Export Company in Switzerland, was to source from Japan, for sale in M-F livery, an excellent locally designed tractor, similar in many ways to the diesel engined TEF 20. In 1953, of course, 'expert' opinion was that the Japanese would never succeed in making cars, let alone tractors. Indeed I was once asked by the Managing Director of a major Mitsubishi engineering plant whether such a venture, which they were then contemplating doubtfully, could ever succeed. After a moment's reflection I gave my approval, and the rest is history.

My Brother-in-Law – Harry Ferguson's Butler

A chance meeting in the Douglas Arms Hotel, Bethesda between John Farnworth and Dennis Griffith revealed that Dennis had once supplied a 10 lb. salmon fresh from the River Ogwen for Harry Ferguson's table. How the salmon had been acquired is another story! - but the meeting led to an introduction to Mrs Margaret Sansom whose brother in law was Harry Ferguson's butler at his Abbotswood Estate home.

Mrs Sansom recalls:

My brother in law, George Joyce, had worked as a butler for several aristocratic families and after leaving Michael Astor he was to take up his position in 1952 with Mr and Mrs Harry Ferguson, a position which he held until some years after Harry Ferguson's death. He and his family lived in one of the Abbotswood lodges and we used to go and stay with them on occasions, and our son used to spend his summers with them. My husband and I were fortunate enough to meet with Mr and Mrs Ferguson on several occasions and we were always pondering what gift we could take along for them. It was difficult to think what a millionaire might appreciate. However on one occasion, Dennis Griffith, a friend of my husband's, thought of a fresh salmon from one of our local Welsh rivers. It proved to be a splendid idea and was received with profuse compliments by the great engineer. George no doubt ended up supervising the cooking of this celebrated fish. He had a large household team under his command which variously included cook, housemaid, footman and parlour maid. I cannot recall how many of each type of personnel. Abbotswood was a superbly kept estate. I well remember the beautiful and extensive gardens which were tended by several gardeners. The estate as I recall comprised several farms. Each year the Fergusons would open up their gardens to the Nursing Association. I well recall the kindness of Mrs Ferguson – I still treasure a Christmas card from her, which has pasted in it a photograph of the gardens. Mr Ferguson fascinated me with his attention to detail in the garden – he could regularly be seen walking the lawns and pulling out offending weeds, which he carried off in a basket. He was a small man and somehow looked typically American – perhaps that is why he succeeded so well in business over there!

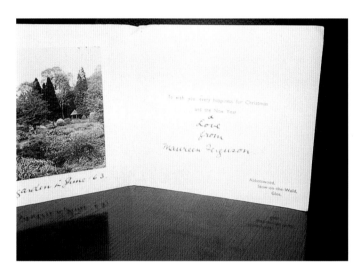

ABOVE Christmas greetings from Mrs Maureen Ferguson

When George left the service of the Fergusons he was fortunate enough to receive a couple of mementoes which I have to this day. These are a box of giant matches which Harry Ferguson used for lighting his fire and one of his Royal Worcester morning teacup and saucers.

ABOVE Larger than life matches used to light Harry Ferguson's home fire

A Pommy takes on Australia

Frank Davey writes:

Herewith the thoughts of a Salesman or as I prefer to call myself, a Company Representative.

Demob, Fordson success and redundant

After demob from the RAF I, in common with thousands of others, set about looking for a job, this made all the harder because of my age, I didn't get out until a couple of years after VE day and all the best jobs had been snapped up. I eventually landed a job with a Ford agent in north London, selling Fordson tractors. After a lot of hard work I became quite successful selling both tractors and all sorts of new implements that were coming available. Then one day I walked into the office. "Don't take your coat off, you're not stopping." Due to the steel shortage the company were having a 30% staff cut. Last in, first out. I had £30,000 worth of outstanding orders to my name. No compensation, not even a week's wages.

No dole, no job, therefore emigrate

From there on life was quite desperate; no dole, no job. Eventually, about 1952, I got a job as a driving instructor in London. Pay four shillings per hour's lesson, no client, no money; working often 16 hours a day to get in eight or ten lessons. I decided to emigrate on the £10 scheme and in November 1953 arrived in Freemantle one Sunday afternoon.

I had a few addresses, one of which sounded hopeful. British Tractor and Machinery Co., sole importers of Fergusons for Western Australia. Tuesday morning I went in unannounced to see them. I was greeted very well by the management, invited to have a mug of tea whilst at the same time being told there were definitely no vacancies. The longer I was there, the more impressed I was with the company and decided to pull out all the stops. They kept on saying no jobs available. Then I spotted in a far corner a brush and a pile of rubbish on the floor.

"Don't you need someone to clean up that floor?" "You wouldn't do that, would you?"

Pommies

At the time there were a lot of "whingeing Pommies" mostly trying to impress how important they were. There was a very bitter anti-Pommy feeling. Pommy had a bad name because they were supposed to be always whingeing and saying how they did things better at home. Pommy Bastards was a normal greeting. In practice, how it worked was this:

They would tell you very strong anti Pommy jokes designed to cause the maximum embarrassment and annoyance. If you got annoyed you were a Pom. If you treated it as a joke and had a good laugh, you were a new Aussie. I never ever experienced any trouble in all my years on the road.

I got the job as a sweeper-upper. From then I became a Goffer (go for this, go for that) and made a lot of friends in the works and started to get my feet under the table. Then one very special day, one of the six reps handed in his notice. He was starting up on his own. In short, I got the job as rep for the lower great south of Western Australia.

A rep at last

I was subjected to a very intense tractor and implement training - we had our own test ground, more like a giant soft sand pit. Unless you were very highly skilled in handling a Fergie you would easily get bogged down and much to the amusement of the lads have to be pulled out. The aim was simple. You had to learn to handle any implement better than any farmer that you came across.

The great day arrived when I was sent off into the Bush to call on the various agents. To the very great credit of my Managing Director I was sent off with instructions that were to stay with me for all my working life – "Go and be useful to someone."

1000 tractors in 1000 days

As a result, instead of calling on an agent as a "smart arse from Head Office", I was able to call, go out to see a prospective "cocky" with their rep, sell a tractor and implements and give the sales order to the agent so they would get the credit. With any successes I had I always passed on the order papers without my name on it. As a result I was regarded as an unpaid aid to their Sales staff. Thus British Tractor and Implement Co. prospered. One thousand tractors were sold in the first one thousand days of business. Years later I began to wonder if I was telling "porkys".

However I have a copy of the complete records, as supplied by Banner Lane, of the name of every ship and date of arrival in Freemantle – the numbers tallied!

Special sales talk

My approach to sales was perhaps a little different to some of the others in opposition. Firstly I had one great advantage; I had spent several years as a Farm Pupil in different parts of the home country from boyhood. This meant that there is hardly any job, hard, horrible, unpleasant, or very enjoyable that I haven't been trained to do, starting with the war-time Fordson Major "War Ag" tractor. As a result I had an immediate 'rapport' with any farmer that I met. Pigs, cows, sheep etc.

Secondly, I had a poor memory for figures! As a result, I never quoted hp or any technical data to my farmers. Instead I related it to what the tractor would do for him. How it would save him hard-jakker.

I made a point of not knowing prices – I always made out I had to look up the price list. That way I was only interested in what the Ferguson would do for him, how much profit it would make for him.

I used to delight in when I was addressing a meeting to have a heckler call out "How much is a Ferguson compared with the opposition?" "I am sorry I don't know their prices but I imagine our tractor/implement prices are much more". This moved interest away from a price war to consideration of the real value of the Ferguson System.

Every day seemed to bring something new. It was 250 miles from Perth to my main agent in Albany. I suppose on average I used to travel about 800 to 1,000 miles each week. Odd things come to mind. One day I was travelling for several hours on a long straight strip of dirt road. I hadn't seen another car for hours when there was the sound of a light aircraft passing overhead. A few miles ahead I saw a man standing in the middle of the road. It turned out to be the pilot who asked me where such and such a homestead was. I directed him to the homestead only a few miles away. He thanked me and went back to his aircraft. Only when I was again on my way did the humour of it occur to me. Not often do you get the chance of telling a pilot where to go!

The wild bunch

Just after I started I was asked to go to a very remote saw mill settlement. I was warned they were a bit of a wild bunch who liked to eat salesmen for breakfast. It was just like a Western movie. Only a collection of wooden huts and tents, the square only seemed to have one real building with any life in it – the pub.

ABOVE Showing off tractors and implements at the Mount Barker Show in 1954

So in I went – more than a bit worried - just like the films of western pubs. I pushed open the doors and there was complete silence just like when the Marshal arrived. There seemed to be real hate in their eyes as they eyed me up and down. I clearly was not welcome. I had nowhere to run! So I thought I had better defuse the situation somehow. I walked up to the bar and in a whisper that all could hear I said "Landlord, do you sell Pommy Bastards Beer?"

With that, there was a roar of laughter. "Have one with me," several shouted. My visit turned out to be a great success. Apparently they had had a bad time a few days earlier when a Pommy had tried to tell them how to run their mill.

The hospitality of the struggling cockeys in the outback is quite amazing. Unlike in most places where the salesman is about as popular as a pork chop in a synagogue, in the bush you had to have a damn good excuse why you had to leave. Once I arrived at dinner time when the shearers were all round the table (a thing I always tried to avoid). While I was talking to the owner, a plate was passed round the table with nothing said and each man slid off a little bit from his plate and it was put in front of me to share their meal. Now that is real hospitality. I was close to tears.

So many memories...

Circus in the bush

Bush demos were always fun, you never knew what was around the corner!
We at head office had what was known as a "Circus". This consisted of a flat top truck on which we had two tractors, one with a front end loader and crane attachment, and twenty implements packed on in a big heap, and a Fergie tractor on the back. Not forgetting of course the driver who was a highly skilled demonstrator. This "circus" was shared by the six of us and it went all over Western Australia.
I had my demonstrations very carefully worked out. I would

get whatever crowd that I could muster by various means to assemble at an arranged exact time. They would arrive with no sign of anything going on. Then out of the bush would arrive the circus.

ABOVE Grey/gold Ferguson 35 proves its worth with a four furrow plough
LEFT Demonstrating the "butterfly" single furrow reversible plough moving at quite a pace in 1953

First the trailer dropped, then off came the tractor with the front loader and crane. All the implements were then taken off one by one and arranged in a semi-circle. At the same time the other tractor would be demonstrating the first implement. I would allow three minutes per implement and so in about an hour and a half they had seen everything. They hardly knew where to look first. After the "circus" they were invited to have a go themselves.

There was of course a great deal of "leg pulling" about this little "toy" tractor. I never lost an opportunity to show a farmer how one of the personal difficulties that he experienced on his own farm could be helped by the Ferguson System.

Challenging and sinking Ford
Of course, many of the demonstrations were in direct opposition to the Ford equipment of the day. Neither side would offer any quarter when it came to "pulling a fast one" to gain some advantage, often appearing to be bitter enemies. What people didn't know was that we would often have a beer together after the events!

On one never to be forgotten day we were demonstrating ploughing alongside Fordsons and Internationals on one of those fertile natural swamps that were used at the time for growing tobacco and early potatoes. These swamps were very unusual though I seemed to take them very much for granted at the time. There were areas of 5-10 acres of brackish water on which vegetation had deposited for thousands of years forming a floating crust of 8-10 ft. deep. The plough would turn up black

"potting mould" material so rich that it would grow anything. This day I had successfully done a bit of ploughing when we stopped for lunch. I drove off the swamp on to hard ground. After lunch there was just a hole where the Fordson had been! We got some poles but we never did find it in twenty feet of water. It had dropped to the bottom of the lake.

The Ferguson System for soldier settlers
A lot of my customers were Soldier Settlement Farms. They had returned from the war and were given financial and material government grants to develop virgin plots of land – usually 1,000 acres per family. They were given weekly wages on a decreasing scale over several years until they became self sufficient. Then they were required to start paying the mortgage. However the land development was the important thing and paying back the mortgage secondary. Thus millions of acres were opened up. There was nothing more satisfactory than to call on one of these desperately struggling one horse farms and sell him a tractor, and then to watch him progress and later to be able to sell him a second and possibly a third tractor as he started to make money for the first time in his life as a result of the Ferguson System.

The favourite implements
Various implements found various uses as follows:

1. Nearly every tractor sold included a tiller for pulling out "mallee" roots. This was one of the first implements which farmers had seen to be protected from breaking by the three point linkage.

2. And then there was the subsoiler! It was not used for subsoiling but stripped of its disc and used solely to rip up rabbit warrens!

3. Blade terracers were widely used on the dirt roads to smooth out the corrugations.

4. Then there was the 1/3 cu. yd. earth scoop, modified to limit its drop to a few inches and driven like mad in, out, and around. The soil would be tipped on the bank and the dropped material subsequently driven over later to compress the walls of a rising dam or catchment. Two lads pioneered this method and were able to dig a dam cheaper than other contractors using Allis Chalmers heavy bulldozers!

LEFT Close inspection of Tractor and Grader Blade at a demonstration

Homesteading
The priorities of opening up new land were dropping a well shaft, building a dam, building a barn, then and only then building a homestead of asbestos and corrugated iron.

Teamwork for dam building – no task too large for Fergusons

Close up of the soil scoop with tractor fitted with dual wheels

Mud makes for weight transfer

These dams were always thick mud at the bottom. So naturally I would put a Fergie tractor and trailer in the mud. I would then invite a member of the audience to drive out the empty tractor and loader. It was almost impossible to manage to get out because of the wheel slip.

Then I would load the trailer with mud, hitch up again to the tractor, and then drive out with ease thereby showing off how the transfer of weight from trailer to tractor dramatically aided traction. Provided I had set everything up right, this was very impressive and many sales resulted.

One day deep in the outback we were demonstrating the welding kit attached to the PTO. All went well. Then we left the equipment overnight covered by canvas. Next morning the generator wirings were full of scorpions! – nasty potential killers.

From Ferguson to MF and home

I continued with Ferguson until we lost the franchise to Massey Ferguson Sunshine H.V. McKay. I was pressured into joining MF as District Supervisor.

My first job was to sign up agents for MF. Very heavy hard sell tactics from the USA were adopted as company policy. They went down like lead balloons and a lot of ground was lost. The policy was later modified when it was found not to work.

My wife needed specialised surgery and we returned to UK. In retrospect not a good move. There was no better medical treatment available to help her. We left our hearts in Western Australia. Arrived November 1953, left November 1959.

LEFT The side rake was a popular implement in Australia and seems to have been equally useful on wet material or hay

BELOW A rare shot of Massey-Harris 701 baler in Ferguson livery during the Massey-Harris-Ferguson era

South Africa's 10,000th and 20,000th Ferguson tractors

Rob North recalls from an album made of these events by an enthusiastic dealer of the day.

The 10,000th

Unfortunately the exact date of the arrival of the 10,000th Ferguson in South Africa is unknown. The voyage of this tractor from Banner Lane to Durban Docks, and then 6,000 miles around South Africa as part of a National Veld Trust Soil Conservation Campaign were carefully recorded in black and white photographs. The tractor was finally delivered to a farmer, Mr Eric B Allen who had won a competition for it. He lived near George

ABOVE The Album in which the 20,000th tractor story was reported for posterity

BELOW The 10,000th tractor for South Africa being packed at Coventry

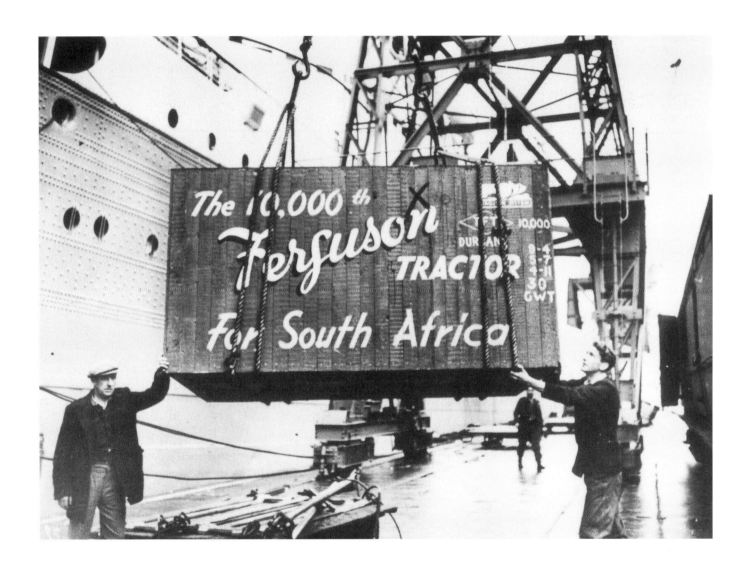

ABOVE Lifting the 10,000th aboard

LEFT The 10,000th arrives in Durban, S. Africa. Capt. H A Deller of the "Cape Town Castle" hands it over to Mr D L Vorderman

BELOW The reception party at the official landing of the 10,000th

ABOVE The 10,000th is loaded onto a Ferguson (early type 3 ton) trailer pulled by an earlier Ferguson

BELOW Loaded and ready for dispatch to the assembly plant

ABOVE Tractor assembled and plough mounted prior to the handing over ceremony on the dockside

BELOW Mr E W Gowne, chairman of the Ferguson Dealers Association of South Africa and South West Africa addressing the assembly

ABOVE The winner of the 10,000th – Mr Eric B Allen of George, Cape Province

RIGHT The route of the 6,000 mile tractor trek around South Africa

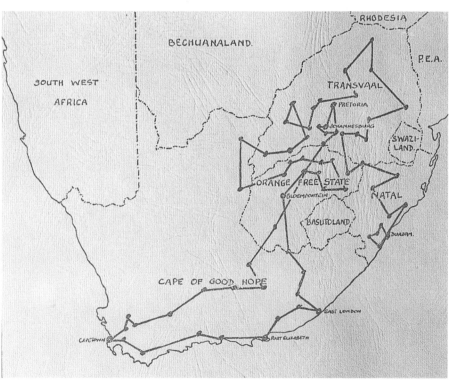

in Cape Province. A selection of the photographs recalling this epic journey is shown here.

The 20,000th

The arrival of the 20,000th tractor was a similar epic, but for this we have the date and some introductory story.

The 20,000th Ferguson Tractor to be imported into the Union of South Africa was landed from the "Edinburgh Castle" at Durban Docks on March 19th 1956. It had been hoped that this

ABOVE LEFT The arrival of the 20,000th in Durban. Captain Christie of the "Edinburgh Castle" hands the unit over to Mr D L Vorderman. 19th March, 1956

BELOW The reception party at the handing over of the 20,000th aboard the "Edinburgh"

ABOVE RIGHT Lowering the 20,000th on to the quayside. The special case was painted in the colours of the Union flag

auspicious occasion would have been celebrated three to four years previously, but unfortunately it was delayed owing to import control restrictions.

It was felt that this milestone in the history of the Ferguson

Organisation in South Africa should be celebrated in a suitable manner and it was decided that no better means could be found than by assisting in the education of the youth of the country. To achieve this an approach was made to the Union Department of Agriculture who indicated their willingness to accept the "20,000th", together with a comprehensive range of implements, all of which would be used in their various facilities for the promotion of agricultural research and education. It was also decided to offer to the department, who gladly accepted, a

ABOVE The 20,000th loaded ready for transport to the assembly plant

LEFT The assembly plant was in fact the Playhouse Restaurant

series of four bursaries which would be instituted annually, each of which would operate for a period of four years. It was agreed that these bursaries should be given to promising students who otherwise would not have the means to carry on to a

university for higher education and the attainment of a degree in agriculture. The Department of Agriculture, together with the Public Service Commission, agreed to select the bursary student for each of the ensuing years.

The special presentation display panel

The 20,000th being presented to the guests

Mounted on a stand prior to the presentation

Mr M S Du Toit, director of Technical Services, accepts on behalf of the Union Department of Agriculture, the 20,000th from Mr D L Vorderman

Other photos of interest

Here are a few more photographs of interest which recall more of the Ferguson era in South Africa.

TOP The Royal Show Stand at Pietermaritzburg in 1956. The entrance was formed by connecting two front end loader frames to form a bridge for a third TED. These were the days when farmers actually bought at shows!

ABOVE LEFT The inscribed plate which was mounted on the tractor dashboard

ABOVE RIGHT Konstant E Bruinette accepting his bursary from Mr D L Vorderman

LEFT The original Ferguson importers for South Africa were Tractors and Farm Tools Ltd who also acted for Massey Ferguson after the Ferguson and Massey-Harris merger

I was Harry Ferguson's son-in-law.

Tony (A.J.) Sheldon writes:

I was asked by Harry and Maureen Ferguson to stay a long weekend at Abbottswood, their house in Gloucestershire in order to partner their daughter, Elizabeth Mary Ferguson at a dance. She had recently been doing a tour of Denmark, representing the Ferguson company and so knew all about tractors. We got on very well together and eventually we became engaged in 1950 and finally married on the 8th December, 1950 having been married at St. Michael's, Chester Square and Harry providing the most wonderful reception at Claridges Hotel afterwards with a honeymoon touring Morocco organised by Jacques Bouillant-Linet the French distributor, a very colourful character.

I had a job that I didn't like very much at that time and was eventually asked by Harry to join him as his Personal Assistant at Abbottswood. When one arrived as a guest, it was always very beautifully organised as an English country house with the butler and the footman and silver for tea. Harry very much liked his "cup o' tea." I was required to read the newspapers, drive the cars, talk, go for walks and generally be useful. He had great discomfort sitting and had a special chair seat made which he carried about with him, but he very often needed to lie sideways on the sofa. The local doctor, Michael King from Stow-on-the-Wold was very good at helping him but couldn't cure his problem.

This was the time when Standard Motor Company were in full production of the Fergie tractor which of course was going all over the world and had an extremely efficient distributor organisation. Very little profit was taken on the tractor but more profit was taken on the implements which were provided by subcontract to all the distributors and this was organised by the offices in Coventry under the managing directorship of Alan Whatwood.

The one thing you had to be in the Ferguson organisation was on time and not late. If you were late you missed your appointment. Even the Chairman of GKN who had driven down from Birmingham was not seen as he was several minutes late. As I followed on later I tried to keep this policy in place. As Harry explained, it was very rude to keep other people waiting and I thoroughly agreed with him. He had his daily walks round the estate and of course also round the garden which was world famous. Mrs Ferguson was the gardener but there was also a head gardener and eleven other assistant gardeners as well. At this time the Ford lawsuit was going on in America but basically the lawyers dealt with that matter. But there would be visits by them to England every now and then. The policy behind the Ferguson companies was to get everything made to the highest possible standard and quality, taking the least profit and the Ferguson organisation throughout the world was in full swing at this time.

Harry then began to turn his attention to motor cars and became involved with Tony Rolt, Freddie Dixon and Count Teramala who had invented a torque converter. A research and design centre was set up at Coventry and the basic principles of four wheel drive and anti skid braking, and common sense ideas were applied to the design of a motor car, for example low centre of gravity. The Dixon Rolt team included Claude Hill, a design engineer and together they all designed a flat four engine, a low centre of gravity vehicle and as lightweight as possible by giving it an aluminium body. In fact the first design of this car was horizontally opposed, vertical fall placed at the back end of the car. On the first day it came down to Abbottswood for testing on the back drive, Harry lost control on the corner as the weight was basically in the back end of the vehicle so this design was immediately scrapped. Also extensive testing was taking place with the torque convertor of Count Taramala but this never managed to produce the mpg required.

We were driving into Coventry at least once a week to cope with the problems that would arise up there and Harry began to realise that due to his ill health he couldn't cope with the tractor situation and the car and so set about trying to find a partner. This eventually arrived in the form of Massey Harris and after a deal of negotiation, a deal was arranged but at the critical moment a million dollars separated the two parties from agreement and Harry said, "well, let's toss for it." And so he took out a half crown and called "heads" and lost the deal over the million dollars but the join up still took place. The directors of the Massey-Harris company had the half crown engraved in a silver cigar box of magnificent proportions. Smoking cigars was one pleasure that he had in his life. With the money obtained from this join up he was able to pursue his motor car ideas and it appears that it is only just happening that the motor car companies are thinking of making four wheel drive cars in 1999.

In order to publish the merits of four wheel drive and anti skid brakes a racing car was built which eventually Stirling Moss drove and won the Gold Cup at Oulton Park. This car then retired eventually to a museum at Donington and there is a possibility now that it may be resuscitated again to drive but not to go racing.

I must emphasise that it was a very happy family with Harry, Maureen, Betty and myself and especially when the grandchildren came along, he delighted in taking them for walks round the park and across the river etc. We by now had a house which was about five miles away in a village called Evenload

Footnote: The company called Harry Ferguson Ltd. exists to the present day and has licensed the patents involved in the viscous coupling and torque splitter. The first four wheel drive and Anti Skid Braking car in the world was the Jensen FF. This used a ball and ramp mechanical clutch system which was subsequently replaced by the viscous coupling. The company is still involved with four wheel drive and Anti Skid Braking. Some fifteen million viscous coupling units have been made by Japanese, European and American companies using Ferguson patents.

Massey Ferguson in South Africa

An extract from an article written by J P A Maitre, Hon Vice President, The Association of Massey Ferguson Dealers in South Africa.

Massey-Harris' presence in South Africa began in the 1880s. The commercial house R.M. Ross and Co. of Cape Town became distributors for the reapers and binders. Subsequently other distributors were appointed, although Ross & Co. remained as chief agents.

In 1925 Massey-Harris decided to open a branch office at Durban. In December M-H formed its first local company, M-H

(South Africa) (Pty) Ltd.   Subsequently depots were opened in Johannesburg and East London.   When Ross and Co. went out of existence in 1931, M-H succeeded them in the Cape.   Further branches were opened at Salisbury and Nakuru, Kenya.

During the second world war, supply of imports dwindled ominously, this caused Lt. Col. K. Rood, who was then chairman of the Union Steel Corporation, to embark on the local manufacturing of implements.   S.A F.I.M. (South African Farm Implement Manufacturers) was created at the end of 1939 and soon became the largest local manufacturer of implements.   The venture was backed financially by Federale Volksbeleggings and Champion Ltd of Bloemfontein.

SAFIM specialised in the manufacture of animal drawn implements, but lacked the expertise to manufacture tractor-drawn implements.   Col. Rood approached M-H with the result that MH acquired a 20% share in SAFIM which at the time was managed by Dr. Kusc.

M-H bought part of Federale shareholding, eventually gaining control of SAFIM with a 52% shareholding in 1952.   In 1960 control of Champions was acquired and M-H owned the bulk of SAFIM.

In 1947 the late Mr Justin McCarthy, Chairman of the McCarthy Rodway Group, together with Mr D.L. Vodermann successfully applied for the national representation of Ferguson Tractors in South Africa.   There were some eighty applicants for the franchise.

A company called Tractors and Farm Tools (TAFT in short) was subsequently floated and listed on the Johannesburg Stock Exchange in 1949 with an issued share capital of £300,000.   McCarthy Rodway were the largest shareholders with 25% of the equity. There were some three hundred shareholders in all.   The Directors were J.B. McCarthy (Chairman), L.A. Brazier, F.V. Evans, J.P.W. Howden and P.J. McCarthy.

The management team known to the writer were as follows: D.L. Vodermann (USA), General Manager; J.R. McCarthy C.A. (S.A.), Secretary and Financial Manager; Boet van Niekerk, Manager; Ben Johnson, Sales Manager; Dick Southey, Ian Gillies, Piet Stoffberg & others, District Managers; B.Badenhorst, Training Manager; Arie Weeda, Engineering Specialist; Angus Bowness, Service Manager; Rex Alexander, Spares Manager, and Jim O'Niel, Farm manager.

The small grey petrol and paraffin tractors were an immediate success with the South African Farming Community and sales were only limited by the availability of import permits in the early years (1948 to 1954).   Sales averaged about two hundred units a month in the period to 1954 but increased substantially when the diesel version was introduced, followed in 1956 by the FE 35 models in paraffin and diesel versions.

A model farm school was created true to the Harry Ferguson mould. The farm Lincoln in the Richmond district of Natal was purchased, new buildings designed to incorporate lecture rooms, dining room, lounge, bedrooms to accommodate the students, etc. were built. The training received was excellent and all of us who attended courses at Lincoln knew just about all there was to know about the Ferguson System. We were far better trained than our competitors.

After the merger of Massey Harris and Harry Ferguson, separate representation continued.   However as TAFT was a success

history, and in line with MF policy of moving towards one product line, the entire franchise was consolidated under the TAFT banner in 1957.

On the 1st of November 1957 Malcomess were given the franchise for harvesting equipment and trailed implements followed by the Landini tractor franchise after MF acquired Landini of Fabrica Italy.

The introduction of the MF35X and the MF65 tractors had a further impact on sales and MF became market leaders.

In 1960, in line with MF intention of handling their own distribution, Messrs. Varity, Shiner, Mawhinney and Reeth from MF Toronto visited South Africa.   Tractor and Farm Tools was purchased on a friendly take over basis for R 2,000,000.   The distribution agreement for harvesting and trailed implements with Malcomess was terminated and the MF head office was located at SAFIM Vereeniging under the management of Dr L.B. Knoll.

The consolidation of the various businesses under one roof initially resulted in chaos.   However order was quickly restored, greater efficiency achieved and the MF tractor and implement range remained market leaders.   In 1963 almost one out of every two tractors sold in South Africa was a Massey Ferguson.

The executives at Massey Ferguson S .A. Ltd were as follows: Dr L.B. Knoll, Managing Director; Dick Harris (USA), Director of Marketing; Ben Johnson, Sales Manager; Floris Brandt, Comptroler, Jan le Grange, Director Planning & Procurement; Bill Drennan, Publicity, Advertising and Public Relation; Geoff Metcalfe (UK), Service Manager and Lawne Schroeder, Manager, Cape Town Branch. plus a team of district managers made up of some outstanding people.   The writer worked closely with Les Pearce and the late Peter Stoffberg.

By Ferguson up the Sani Pass

The province of Natal has as its eastern border, the mountainous Kingdom of Lesotho (formerly Basutoland).   The only route into this country from Natal is from Himeville via the notorious Sani Pass.   Built originally as a bridle path for pack animals and later modified to accommodate four- wheel drive vehicles, one climbs an incredible 4,300 feet in approximately nine miles to reach the top at 9,340 feet.

Against this backdrop, the following story is told by Aubrey Burgess of Harare, Zimbabwe.

I used to work for the Ferguson dealer in Pietermaritzburg from 1950 to 1954.   In 1953 we were approached by a Catholic Mission in Mokhotlong, Basutoland, to supply them with a new Fergie, various implements and a two-wheeled hydraulic tipping trailer.

Once the transaction was completed, plans had to be made to get the equipment to the Mountain Kingdom.   The tractor presented no problem and could be driven over the Sani Pass, but the implements and the two-wheeled trailer had to be dismantled, railed to Ladysmith for final transportation to Mokhothong by, I think, a double winged twin engine De Haviland.   The final hurdle was how to get our servicemen to the Mission and back.

LEFT In the 1960s the trip over the Sani Pass was repeated with an FE 35

To the rescue came one of our customers and an old school chum of mine from Merchiston Prep and Maritzburg College, David Arnold, complete with an orange-coloured Willys Jeep.

The task of driving the tractor was given to our tried and trusted workshop assistant, Jack Dhlamini, and he duly set off at the crack of dawn to the first rendezvous, Himeville. Our serviceman, Cheeky Calder, with David Arnold set off in pursuit later that day. Early the next morning, Jack started his trip up the pass on the Fergie with David and Cheeky bringing up the rear. When Jack had reached the halfway stage up the pass, he stopped, switched off the ignition and walked back to the Jeep to confront Cheeky Calder. He said, "Sir, I do not want to go any further". When Cheeky inquired why this was so, Jack's response was "Because, Sir, there is too much Ntakati (evil spirits) up here. Cheeky tried to get him to change his mind but failed in the process. Jack set off down the pass and would meet them in Himeville. He just wanted to get away from here. (Although not yet at the steepest part, Jack nevertheless felt threatened by the sheer immensity of the vertical mountain slopes now rising right above him and felt that this must be a place of evil spirits - Ntakati).

Cheeky did not have a problem in negotiating the sharp bends on the pass because with the small turning circle of the tractor, assisted by the independent brakes, he could turn the Fergy on a tickey (thrupence). The big problem was the Jeep. The vehicle had a poor turning circle and the spare wheel, attached to the left-hand side of the body, limited the degree of manoeuvrability round the bends. They removed the spare wheel which did help, but on some of the bends they had to go through seven or eight movements to get around the hairpin. In some of the movements, the wheels were perilously close to the edge of the cliff where a drop of some 2,000 feet awaited them. Finally, the summit was reached and they set off for Mokhotlong some 36 miles distant. To reach this village, a further pass had to be negotiated at 10,500 feet. Truly this is the 'Roof of Africa'. On arrival, Cheeky carried out the installation of the tractor, supervised the re-assembly of the implements and trailer, gave a demonstration of how everything operated and then handed the equipment over to the Mission Station staff. A job well done.

The return trip down the pass was a little less traumatic but the bends still had to be negotiated with extreme care using the seven to eight movements manoeuvre to get around them.

A good few hours later they reached Himeville, collected Jack Dhlamini and returned to Pietermaritzburg to somewhat of a hero's welcome.

About a week or two later, a story was published in the local Natal Witness newspaper, giving details of the trip by David and Cheeky, and stating that "history had been made". They were the first people to have driven a vehicle over the Sani Pass.

Some South African Stories

Gus Macleod-Henderson writes:

1. When Ferguson tractors were demonstrated in areas like the Orange Free State and Transvaal, the farmers would take one look at this small grey tractor and say that it couldn't pull anything. One sharp demonstrator suggested that the Ferguson be hooked back to back with the likes of a John Deere, Case, Farmall, Allis etc. The Ferguson would have its linkage drawbar connected to the other tractor's fixed drawbar. The clever demonstrator would then unobtrusively raise his hydraulic linkage enough to lift the other tractor's rear wheels almost off the ground. With the opposition having no traction, it was easy for the Ferguson to win the contest.

2. Another sales technique used the effect of the Ferguson's faster field speed to advantage. The salesman would arrive on the farm and watch the farmer ploughing with his trailed plough and large tractor. He would then bet the farmer that he could beat him with the Ferguson in two rounds of the field. The farmer would scoff at this challenge, but a short while later the lorry carrying the Ferguson and plough would conveniently arrive and unload. The salesman would set it up and move into the field, usually catching up the farmer after one round. This was due to the Ferguson's ability to turn much faster and tighter with a three point implement. Selling the Ferguson after this was easy.

3. In sugar farming areas, the Ferguson was used to plough straight down some incredibly steep slopes. This worked OK until the advent of the plough shear bolt. If these broke, the plough bottoms no longer retarded the tractor which then accelerated downwards.

4. My neighbour used to cart eight tons of cane per load up steep hills which when wet, would need oxen to help out. He managed two trips daily to the mill 18 km distant. The Ferguson would 'dance' up these steep hills on its back wheels only.

5. A Greytown farmer bought his first Ferguson TED in 1952. After a thorough installation by the dealer, the driver went off to work. On his return he noticed that the PTO shaft was exposed - the cap must have fallen off. After trying by hand to push the shaft into the rear of the tractor, he decided that a 14 lb hammer might be more effective to knock the offending shaft out of sight. One can imagine what damage was done to the tractor and consequently to himself by the farmer when he found out.

6. A diesel TEF was sold to a farmer in SW Africa who lived 500 km from the dealer. After going through the whole installation with the new owner, the dealer left and returned to base. On arrival, the telephone was jangling. The farmer was on the line wanting to know how to turn the engine off - turning the key had no effect. The dealer had omitted to tell him that he should pull a knob with a 'C' marked on it - this looked like the choke knob on a TED!

7. New disc plough demonstration on a farm. The tractor was filled with petrol but the cap was missing. A spark caused a fire which spread between my legs and the family jewels were now at stake (no pun!). Time to bale out quickly. Having been used to later FE 35s, I put my left foot down onto what I expected to be a stable foot board, only to find ground. I thus cartwheeled out of the seat and landed in front of the rear wheel which then ran over my leg. (no damage only to pride. Jewellery OK!). The plough was fortunately raised at the time, but I had to run after the tractor to stop it.

8. When a Ferguson tractor and a Ferguson plough were set properly, it was possible to climb off the tractor and let it continue on its merry way, ploughing a straight furrow. Many a sceptical farmer said that we had radio control or something equivalent.

9. A most unusual application of a Ferguson was a conversion to a crane for cane bundle loading. The tractor was mounted on a chassis, the cable was mounted onto a rear wheel rim and depending on the weight of the bundle, a particular gear was chosen. Reverse or neutral with the brakes was used for lowering. Many Fergusons were used this way before the advent of hydraulic cranes.

Mack Shone's Experience of the Ferguson System

Mack Shone writes:

When the Ferguson TE20 range of tractors was first introduced in South Africa in 1948, our local paper "The Frontier Post and Times" carried an article advising of a demonstration to be held on a farm in the Aliwal North District. The demo was to be held by James W Weir of East London as no local dealer had been appointed as yet. My father and I read about the revolutionary new "Ferguson System" and decided to go to the demo. As it happened, we were at the station railing off our wool clip to East London when we noticed three small, grey tractors being off-loaded from a truck further down the platform. Off we went to have a look and Dad's first words were "But these are just toys!" Anyway, they were driven off down the street with

that very distinctive exhaust note - all had downswept exhaust systems. One tractor had a 938 tiller on behind; another a two-furrow mouldboard plough, and the third a single tine ripper and it was fascinating to see these implements being lifted up off the ground by the hydraulic three-point linkage system. The tractors were all TEA models operating on petrol which was, at that time, about two shillings a gallon - equivalent to six cents a litre!

Anyway, we went to the demo which was well attended by local farmers and the general opinion amongst the farmers was that they were too small for large scale farming operations. However, by the time the demo was over, quite a number of the farmers had changed their minds! My father went to the Rep. who was doing the demo and said "I have a piece of ground on my farm that is overgrown with Buffalo kweek grass and if this tractor and tiller can get this grass out, I'll buy them." So two days later the tractor and implement was brought over by the Rep. who was shown the offending area of the field. He had to use first gear to start off as the grass was very thick and matted but eventually was able to use second gear and, by cultivating at right angles to the first cut, was able to loosen and remove most of the grass. The net result was that Dad placed an order for a tractor and tiller with nine tines and not seven of the demo model. All for an inclusive price of £587.10.00d and this included belt pulley, a set of tools, drawbar and stays, spark plug tyre pump and a canvas cover for the tractor.

The following year the threshing contractor arrived to thresh our wheat which he had done for many seasons previously. We used to send three spans of oxen to fetch the outfit - one for the thresher, one for the steam engine and a third for the elevator Later on, he replaced the steam engine with a Farmall "M" tractor and it was driving the thresher (a 4'6" drum Ramsomes Sims & Jefferies), when a crankshaft bearing went and the threshing came to a grinding halt. This could have resulted in up to a week's delay so I offered him the use of the Fergy. The contractor laughed and said "If that tractor can drive that machine, I'll thresh your wheat for nothing!" So I fitted the belt pulley and lined up the driving belt. It was quite difficult to get the machine turning but once up to speed, the Ferguson handled it quite comfortably and the threshing was finished that same evening. The contractor couldn't believe his eyes and was quite prepared to honour his bet and we eventually settled on half the price!

We traded the TEA in for a TED in 1954 and when the farm was sold up in 1964, the TED had just done over 9,000 hours. The only major expense was a set of tyres, a new water pump, generator and starter overhaul, kingpins and bushes, tie-rod ends and, of course, a couple of batteries. A really versatile little workhorse (all 23HP of them!) and its a great pity that they no longer manufacture them."

I Supervised the Build of the First 12 TE 20 Tractors

Alex Patterson recalls:

I joined Harry Ferguson Motors Ltd as an apprentice at 17 years of age. The apprenticeship was for a six year period as a motor mechanic.

In those days you had to pay the employer £100 for the privilege of being an apprentice!! The pay was 61p a week. I worked on Austin cars, but really preferred the Rileys as a quality machine.

During the war the work on cars stopped and was replaced by war production. Harry Ferguson Motors did some contract work for Bofors guns, Stirling bombers and Churchill tanks. We made a range of components on the premises. I became responsible for assembling and installing production machinery.

There were 120 men in the workshops. Work was interesting and you built up knowledge during apprenticeship. Promotion came early before the end of my apprenticeship period. I was keen on something more interesting.

Harry Ferguson's key engineers Archie Greer and Will Sands asked me to join them in the tractor research team. I was delighted.

I had already become familiar with the tractor by doing demonstrations and test driving.

In 1945 I was dispatched to England for three weeks to assist demonstrations to the British government and Board of Trade.

Trevor Knox, Harry Ferguson's man in the UK was given the brief to find a suitable factory in the UK to produce the Ferguson System tractor. Various sites proved unsuitable. The Standard Motor Co. had a van facility in Kendal. This was inspected but proved too small and remote. Trevor Knox got word that there was a factory in Coventry that might be suitable. He was dispatched in Harry Ferguson's Rolls Royce to make a good impression on Sir John Black. So it was that Banner Lane became the chosen factory and work started.

I supervised the building of the first batch of 12 TE tractors.

I remember one specific incident that had the great brains of Harry Ferguson's team working full time. No. 1 tractor had noisy tappets and nothing could cure it. Harry, Archie and Willy and some oil company experts all had a go at the problem.

After a couple of weeks I tried squirting some oil down the push rods and the noise stopped. I did not know why it did, but I informed the "team". The solution was to grind a little flat at the end of the push rod to give an oil cushion. This stopped the noise.

I remember another instance later of problem solving by trial and error. We had a problem with a sticking control valve which reduced the efficiency of the hydraulics and affected the control lever movement. This had been a problem for some time and all sorts of tolerances had been tried but to no avail. One day during the testing I tried oscillating the "stuck" valve - it freed itself. I tried it a number of times and it worked. That is how the oscillating valve mechanism was developed and cured the problem. Simple once you have found the obvious answer!!!

The No. 1 tractor of the first 12 built was kept by Harry Ferguson at Abbotswood as the "Master Tractor" and it was in use until Harry's death in 1960.

Working for Harry Ferguson was not easy. He was a hard task master, tolerated little in the way of breaking rules – and rules there were a plenty!!!

Dress code was very strict – suits only, no sports gear. Always a smart shirt and tie. Cost me twice as much as it could have with a more relaxed view on the subject.

One day I was summoned to Abbotswood. It was a Saturday i.e. day off. I turned up in a casual jacket and he took one look at me and said "Alex you don't look right"... I defended myself by saying it was my day off....Saturday. I did not impress much!!!

Another hard rule to follow sometimes was the cleaning off of demonstration/test equipment after performance. Regardless of the weather or time, it had to be done before "hometime" or the next day could be painful if Harry found out.

The "Notebook Rule" is well known from various anecdotes written already. Everybody was given a notebook and each day had one page of actions that had to be done. Harry would insist on seeing the state of the notebook at any time....

He liked to state that he carried his notebook and adhered to the rule, and if he could do it running the entire company then "you" could do it with only a fraction to worry about.

Abbotswood was Harry's pride and joy. He kept it trim and beautiful with the help of tractor No. 1 and some implements. He tried a number of mower types to keep the grass trimmed to half an inch height. Difficult with a cutter bar. He even tried sheep. That did not work out as they left crap and wool all over the place, very untidy. That was out.

Another obsession was noise. Tractors had to be quiet. He did not like diesel engine due to noise and smell....

Rolls Royce was the ultimate noiseless vehicle, tractors should aspire to that...........

I maintained close contact with Harry after he left Massey-Harris-Ferguson to concentrate on the car business. Although he had no say or influence he still contacted me to discuss various design aspects and try and influence my thinking.

A great man with a passion for his baby – the TE 20 tractor concept.

An International Instructor

Roy Harriman writes:

Disillusioned, so join Ferguson

After graduating in agriculture at Seale Hayne College in 1945 I joined the War Agricultural Executive Committee, firstly as Land Drainage Officer and later as Agricultural Advisor in Staffordshire.

I became disenchanted with the official approach to marginal lands farmers "increase production or be dispossessed" at that time, in the efforts to grow more food – a lot of the farms were nothing but slag heaps.

In the post war years I felt there would be greater scope in commercial agriculture. Early in 1950 I wrote to Harry Ferguson in search of an opportunity having had a lot of hands on experience in holidays with relatives lucky enough to be allocated a Ford/Ferguson tractor with a basic range of directly mounted implements. In those days in the winter months the Ford/Ferguson tractor was not comfortable without a platform and no fender protection like the Fordson.

From my enquiry I received an invitation from Noel Newsome – the then P.R. Director at Harry Ferguson to visit him at the offices on Fletchampstead Highway. On arriving there I was told that Mr Newsome was ill but he would see me at his home – a panelled room apartment at Stoneleigh Abbey to where the Harry Ferguson School of Mechanisation had just moved from Packington. Mr Newsome could not move – he had gout! – notwithstanding I felt the interview had gone well. This proved to be the case when I was offered a job on the education side with the carrot of becoming an overseas representative in due course.

Initially I was trained in all aspects of the Ferguson System being a member of each fortnightly course for dealers and their staff, farmers and young farmers – courses for the latter were always held at week ends commencing Friday evening and finishing Sunday afternoon with members residing in Stoneleigh Abbey.

To Turkey, Study "The Bible"

After some weeks of Field Courses and Tractor Courses I became an assistant Instructor. At this time pressure was on from Overseas Distributors for instructors to go to them in their environment to undertake courses and my appraisal (if there were staff appraisals at that time) indicated that I would be suitable to train our Turkish Distributor, dealers and staff in Turkey. At this time there were around four hundred Ferguson tractors in the country and I was to go for three months to train staff at the four main dealer headquarters namely in Adana, Izmir, Ankara and Istanbul.

It was a concentrated effort to train as many people as possible – a salary of £7.50 a week plus all expenses including first class air fare, and £20 per week on top as an overseas allowance. It also brought its problems – hitherto I had specialised in field operations – ploughing, cultivating and the like at the Stoneleigh School – it came as a shock to find that few students wished to know how to plough – every rural dweller in Turkey knew how to scratch the soil!

No – their main aim was to learn something about the tractor – engine, gearbox, transmission, hydraulics etc. – with this knowledge they had something of value and could then branch out in their own location – no one could find a job as a field technician.

As instructor I had to burn the midnight oil most nights with "The Bible", a comprehensive Harry Ferguson Service manual, to make sure I knew how to tune the engine and set the hydraulics etc. etc.

In the introduction to the manual the first paragraph reads: "It is with the intention of placing the most detailed information in the hands of those people who will be responsible for carrying out service to the Ferguson Tractor that this publication is prepared."

Overseas Itinerary

I returned to the UK and was absorbed into Stoneleigh – in addition to field work and instructing, time was spent in the commercial department at head office learning about payment terms, letters of credit and the like, time was also spent on the assemble line at Banner Lane.

In the spring of 1951 I went off again to Turkey – still on a training mission but on a more permanent basis liasing with the Harry Ferguson Middle East office in Nicosia to where it had recently moved from Cairo. In addition to responsibilities in Turkey I was asked to visit Iran, Aden, Somalia and Ethiopia where the Ferguson System was being established, from my Istanbul base.

I well remember arriving in Tehran on July 6th 1951 – the day after the arrival of Averell Harriman – the roving ambassador for President Truman of the USA – who had flown in to try and resolve the oil crisis. There was a lot of unrest and anti British feeling with the unilateral nationalisation of the Anglo Iranian Oil Company. Left wing elements were also creating riots in the streets despite the curfew.

The authorities at Tehran airport bemused and questioning about two Harrimans arriving on consecutive days – especially after the ugly scenes of the previous day. I eventually arrived at the Park Hotel and on checking in I was handed a cablegramme (ticker tape pasted on a message paper) – it was from Coventry requesting me to proceed to Khartoum in the Sudan to arrange demonstrations!!!!

At this moment I was approached by a well-dressed Iranian gentleman who asked for my passport from the concierge and went away. I wrote a reply – something along the following lines:- "impossible to proceed Khartoum to arrange demonstrations have just arrived Tehran – Harriman". The next day, after more riots and hangings in the city the same Iranian was waiting for me in the foyer —he approached and asked why I did not send the message through diplomatic channels – I went through the whole explanation again – I was an agriculturalist working for a tractor manufacturer and had come to arrange tractor demonstrations – he seemed satisfied and went away. I subsequently discovered that the message was never sent!

The Iranian authorities refused to renew my visa later in the year and I returned to Istanbul via the Nicosia office – what a haven Cyprus was lodged in the Ledera Palace Hotel in Nicosia.

Down in the Aden Protectorate we had a fleet of tractors operating at the Abyan Board – a Colonial Office development some sixty miles along the sea shore (no tarmac road) from Aden – I spent many happy weeks with the expatriate staff training operators on this cotton project.

The Politics of African Farming – A Ferguson Frontier

Next stop was Hargeisa ex British Somalia – here in addition to training with the Department of Agriculture I was asked to help out in a political problem in the North West of the country. Here there was a productive agricultural plain, part of which had been ceded temporarily from Ethiopia some years previously. It was now time to give this area back to Ethiopia and the local Somalis were actually up in arms – spears, swords, old Italian rifles etc. It was decided that the new frontier line could be marked out with a deep furrow so I was asked to do this with the TE 20 and plough. A detachment of Ascari tribesmen with Military Attache and District Officers were present and their first job was to order and cajole all the Somalis to put their weapons in the back of the Land Rover – this they did with great reluctance on being challenged by the Ascaris. The next step was for the District Officers to mark the new boundary with stakes every 100 yards or so over a distance of about two miles. I drove the tractor to commence the furrow and the natives, not wishing this productive land to go back to Ethiopia, became very agitated and threatened to attack the tractor (and operator!). The Ascaris brought the situation under control and it was decided I should have an armed guard of four Ascaris, two walking each side of the tractor with fixed bayonets as the new boundary furrow was drawn – regrettable that this area has become a region of armed dispute in recent years.

Next stop Addis Ababa – here I had to look at His Majesty's (Haille Selassie) estates which were spread throughout the Kingdom, with a view to mechanisation. They were indeed in a bad way, orange groves overgrown and the like. We set off with the distributor – two Land Rovers and a Borgward four wheel drive truck which carried tractor and implements. This trip took about three weeks, mainly under canvas (cleaner than some of the village houses) and I think I saw nearly every African game animal. At the end I believe the Palace placed an order for half a dozen tractors.

On my return to Istanbul I became an Overseas Representative although I still carried out demonstrations and courses – by this time I could identify every nut and bolt of the TE 20!

Massey-Harris Takes Over

The take over of Harry Ferguson by Massey-Harris meant that we had to rationalise distribution with the aim of placing the joint franchise with one distributor. This created its problems. In the main the Middle East took over the joint franchise but we had a major problem in Turkey. Here Massey-Harris enjoyed the services of the State Agricultural Machinery Company who had and were doing significant business. It was not until 1958 that the decision was taken in the face of possible denationalisation, and the fact that the government body would not agree to provide exclusivity, that our future lay with the private sector Harry Ferguson distributors.

My Experience of Harry Ferguson

I met Harry Ferguson on a number of occasions when he visited Stoneleigh Abbey or when I was visiting head office on Fletchampstead Highway – I don't think he ever remembered my name.

To me he was a bundle of nervous energy often wrapped up in his own thoughts, a stickler for detail and precision – he could be charming one moment and abruptly incisive the next, and a master at explaining in a no nonsense manner his methods and ideals.

He did not seem to be at all concerned in what geographical area one had been demonstrating his Ferguson System – if there were problems or difficulties he could always bare these down to a question of operator efficiency involving lack of maintenance – this was easy to say but difficult to achieve in the developing world.

Two problems I faced all the time – one was the regular and at least daily replenishment of clean oil in the engine air cleaner in the terribly dusty conditions – this was not really overcome until

twenty years later with the introduction of the dry air cleaner – one could just not get operators to change oil which was a messy business anyway. The second difficulty was the lack of detergent lubricating oil at this time in the developing world – this prevented carbon build up around piston rings in Lamp Oil engine model tractors – this was overcome by representations to the oil companies who quickly made this type of oil available.

I personally never received a "ticking off" from H.F. – despite the fact that on occasions I would visit head office without my black leather covered flip-over note book – he would often ask for this element of dress to be produced and heaven help you if you had some scribbled note on the first page (such a note should have been dealt with and the page removed before going out of the office!)

One or two of my colleagues did have their moments – the tractor tool box contained one spanner and one spanner only – this was about ten inches long and ruled off in inches and the only spanner needed to set any implement in the Ferguson System. A colleague visiting head office one day was in the workshop at the rear looking for such a spanner, could not find one and picked up an adjustable spanner. He was walking back with this along a corridor – H.F. came along in the opposite direction, saw what he had in his hand and snatched it and threw it with some force clattering down the corridor through the workshop where it came to rest with a bang against the corrugated iron wall – there was an embarrassing silence and H.F. said with some feeling something like "Never let me catch you using such an imprecise tool again!"

H.F. had an office overlooking the Highway – over the road was a cinema and a few shops including a hairdresser. A colleague one day sauntered over the road to the hairdresser, unfortunately for him H.F. was in the office meditating and saw this. He called the concierge – a liveried gentleman in the foyer with the message to send the "young man" to his office when he returned. So a clean cut young man was shown to the inner sanctum. He was well and truly "dressed down" for having his haircut in the firm's time – this must have hit a nerve for the young man retaliated indicating he spent all his hours promoting the Ferguson System and felt the company should be prepared to forego thirty minutes for a haircut. It was reported that the response to this was "GET OUT".

There was one occasion when H.F. was at a loss for words. He was in the toilets one day washing his hands with his usual thoroughness and he saw a "young man" enter, do what he had to do, and proceed to go out. H.F said "Young man, don't you wash your hands before going back to your desk?" To which the chap replied "Oh but I am not going back to my desk, I am going to lunch!"

I happened to be back in the UK when HF won his famous case against Henry Ford. To mark this victory H.F. invited all his employees to a magnificent garden party one Sunday afternoon at his residence in Abbotswood – a good time was had by all.

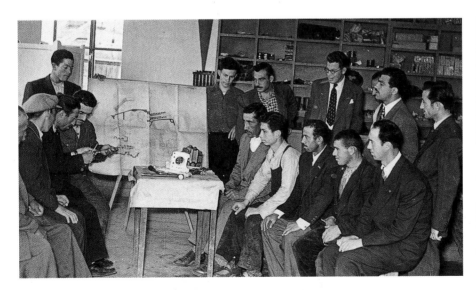

TOP Field course in Anatolia 1951

LEFT Service Course in Anatolia 1952 "The Hydralic Pump"

ABOVE Field Courses in Anatolia 1952

ABOVE Field course in Iran 1951

LEFT Threshing in Iran 1951. A tall order for the Fergie, but it coped proving the threshing machine was evenly fed

Excellence Live On

by RM Weyman, Engineering Director - AGCO COVENTRY

The laws of physics and mechanics do not change they just get re-applied, and this must surely be the case with agricultural tractor design, post Harry Ferguson. From those early trials in 1917 when the tractor-implement interface was being explored and from which the "Duplex" hitch emerged, came an understanding of the mechanics and primary forces involved. From this fundamental work, a tractor-implement design solution evolved, which dramatically improved operator safety, as the tractor no longer turned over backwards when the plough hit buried obstructions. The concept of weight transfer from the implement and the soil forces to the tractor rear axle could now be fully and safely exploited. Combining the tractor and implement into one unit with a "virtual hitch point", and exploiting the benefits of weight transfer allowed Ferguson to realise further objectives, those of reduced overall weight and improved tractor efficiency.

From the Duplex hitch, Ferguson's ideas developed via the Black tractor in 1933 to the Ferguson Brown tractor in 1936. This was the first fully commercialised, hydraulically operated three point linkage design that many of us would recognise today. This is a design so fundamentally correct that it is estimated to be in use on over 80% of the world's tractors today, regardless of their make or place of manufacture. From the Ferguson Brown to the present day, history is well documented and involves a number of manufacturers that owe their existence and development in this industry to this early work by Ferguson.

From a Massey Ferguson perspective, the origins of today's products, for example the MF240 that is being produced in Coventry and other worldwide locations, can be clearly seen. The geometric relationships between the lower links, the top link, the linkage cross shaft and the famous Ferguson "Scotch Yoke Pump" are remarkably similar to those early machines, which Ferguson had designed. Their operating principles are identical.

Even the application of electronics to tractors has not changed the fundamental operating principles of the plough-tractor combination. When Massey Ferguson pioneered the use of sophisticated electronic control on the MF 3000 series tractors in 1988, the basic three-point linkage geometry and method of operation did not change. Clearly a demonstration that the design concept is fundamentally correct and needed no further refinement to harness modern technology.

Ferguson's influence was not just confined to tractor design, he firmly believed in supporting the whole mechanised farming process. Harry Ferguson pioneered the idea of a full line of implements to work with the tractor, and today, what company does not support a full line of associated implements? Getting the best out of these products requires training and once again Ferguson pioneered an approach which lives on to this day.

Massey Ferguson runs a very comprehensive training school at Stoneleigh, a venue Harry Ferguson would remember well, whose sole aim is to train in the proficient use and maintenance of Massey Ferguson tractors and associated implements. In 1999, 3,000 students, equipment dealers and farmers from all over the world passed through this training school and as a result the world's farming process is a little more efficient.

Harry Ferguson's influence has been widespread, not just in agricultural mechanisation although it is in this area I believe he will be best remembered. His pioneering work and its applications to world farming has not been surpassed and is evident all around us, even today, his excellence lives on.

Appendix
Further Reading and Interest Clubs

Books:

Ferguson Implements and Accessories. John Farnworth. Publisher Farming Press

Massey Legacy Vol. 1. John Farnworth. Publisher Farming Press

Massey Legacy Vol. 2. John Farnworth. Publisher Farming Press

The Advertising of Massey-Harris, Ferguson and Massey Ferguson. John Farnworth. Publisher Farming Press

Harry Ferguson, A Brief History of His Life and Tractors. Massey Ferguson Tractors Ltd.

Harry Ferguson and I. Michael Winter

Harry Ferguson. Bill Martin. Ulster Folk and Transport Museum

Harry Ferguson – A Tribute. Duncan Russell. Royal Norfolk Agricultural Society

The Ferguson Legacy. John Farnworth. In Journal of the Royal Agricultural Society. 1996

Ferguson: The Story Continues. Max Smith. AGCO

Harry Ferguson, Inventor and Pioneer. Colin Fraser. Publisher Old Pond

The Fergie "20" Family. Allan T Condie Publications

A Worldwide Guide to Massey-Harris , Ferguson and early Massey Ferguson tractors. John Farnworth.
(Under publication with Japonica Press).

A Worldwide Guide to Massey Ferguson Industrial Equipment. (Under publication with Japonica Press).

Interest Clubs (Club activities + magazines)

Friends of Ferguson Heritage. PO Box 62. Banner Lane, Coventry, CV4 9GF. UK

The Ferguson Club. The Secretary, 21 Greystown Avenue, Upper Malone Road, Belfast, BT9 6UG
N. Ireland, U.K

Twin-Power Association Inc., Massey-Harris-Ferguson Collectors. C/o Beverly Hughes, RR #3, Ilderton,
Ontario, NOM 2AO, Canada

Wild Harvest Massey Collector's News. (inlcudes MF and Ferguson) PO Box 529, Denver, IA 50622, U.S.A.

Magazine only

Wild Harvest, c/o Keith Oltrogge, PO Box 529, Denver, Iowa 50622, USA

Index

Page references in **bold type** are to illustrations or to the captions of illustrations.

Look out for these additional books from Japonica Press

"The Ford Tractor Story - Part One Dearborn to Dagenham 1917- 1964" - Stuart Gibbard

A detailed account of Ford Tractor production. Includes a section on the American Tractor line and many rare and previously unseen photographs. Written by award winning tractor book author Stuart Gibbard.
ISBN 09533737 0 3

"The Ford Tractor Story – Part Two Basildon to New Holland, 1964 – 1999" - Stuart Gibbard

This companion volume to Stuart Gibbard's highly acclaimed first part of The Ford Tractor Story concentrates on the time during which Fords's agricultural business grew into an organisation of global proportions, eventually taking over both the New Holland and Versatile farm equipment companies.
ISBN 09533737 1 1

"The Big Book of John Deere Tractors" - Don Macmillan

The Big Book of John Deere Tractors is the **Ultimate Encyclopaedia** of John Deere Tractors from around the world. This is a book that the enthusiasts will refer to again and again. A model by model historical reference to John Deere tractors-including European models-from they're beginning until today.
ISBN 09533737 2 X

"The Big Book of Caterpillar"- Robert Pripps & Andrew Morland

Contains the complete history of this world famous company it includes steam, gas and diesel farm tractors and logging crawlers from the 1860s to the present. It includes Cat predecessor companies, Holt, Daniel Best, and C.L.Best as well as discussion of products from associated companies such as Russell Grader, Letourneau and Trackson.
ISBN 09533737 3 8

"Ultimate Tractor Power – Articulated Tractors of the World Volume 1" - Peter D. Simpson.

Volume l covers from A to L and includes ACO, AGCO, Big Bud, Deutz, Ford, Kharkov to name but a few, also included is a section on prototypes and one offs. Close contact with the manufacturer has enabled the author to include company history and specifications not covered previously. **ISBN 09533737 4 6**

Volume ll Publication early 2001 will cover the remainder of the alphabet and also examine special conversions of these big tractors from wheels to rubber tracks. Also more one off's built on the farm, with a section on four-wheeled drive articulated scale model tractors and collecting tractor sales literature.

"A Worldwide Guide to Massey Harris, Ferguson & Early Massey Ferguson Tractors" - John Farnworth

Identifies over 300 models of tractors aided by photographs of key model types. Both agricultural and industrial models of the period are included.

Tractors not commonly associated with Massey Ferguson history are also covered. These include Landini tractors manufactured immediately after the take-over by MF, Ford Fergusons and the very early Sawyer Massey steam and Gasoline engine tractors. These are increasingly becoming recognised as part of Massey Ferguson history and lineage.
ISBN 09533737 6 2

"Vintage Allis Chalmers Tractors" -Chester Peterson Junior & Lynn K.Grooms Covers all Allis-Chalmers models from 1924 on, including the Monarch and Advance –Rumely models, Peterson and Groom also discuss Allis-Chalmers' various acquisitions and mergers, plus the current ownership by FiatAgri of Italy.
ISBN 09533737 7 0

Check with your local bookseller or order directly from Japonica Press
Telephone: 01377 270209 ~ Website:www.classic-tractors.co.uk

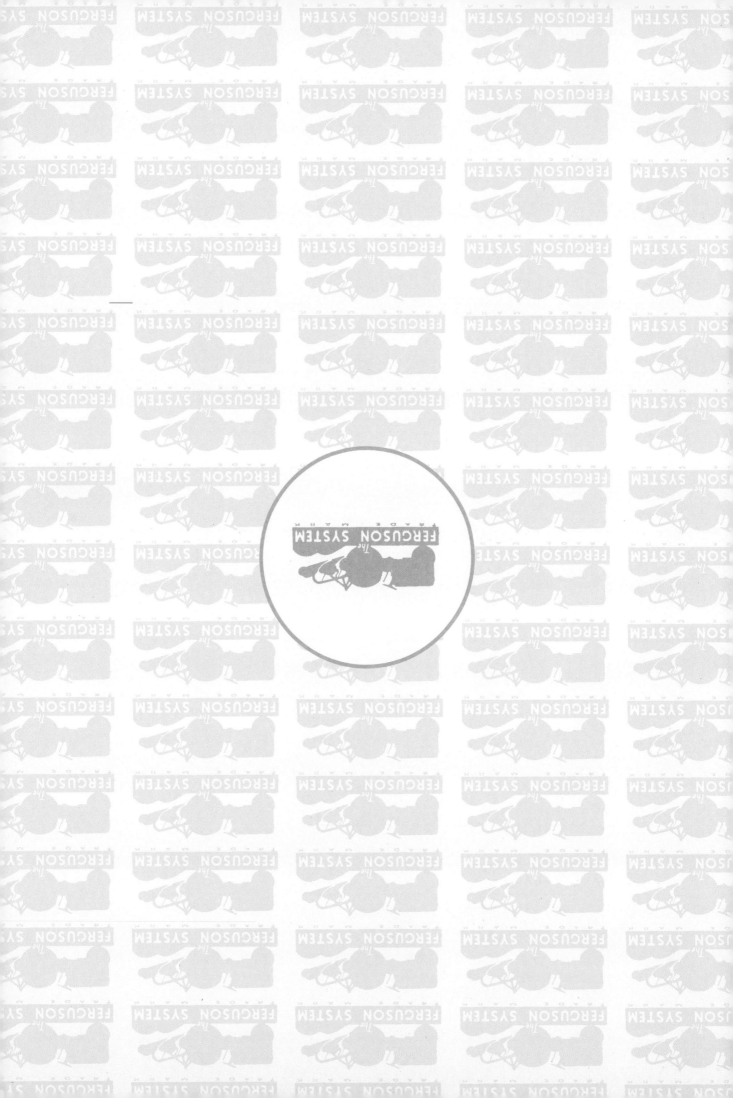